Frances Uglow.

SONGS FROM THE PSALMS

FULL MUSIC EDITION

Edited by Michael Perry and David Peacock
with
Christopher Norton and Chris Rolinson

Jubilate

in association with CPAS

Hodder & Stoughton
LONDON SYDNEY AUCKLAND TORONTO

Also from Jubilate Hymns, published by Hodder and Stoughton:

Hymns for Today's Church
Carols for Today
Church Family Worship
Psalms for Today
Psalms for Today/Songs from the Psalms
Combined Words edition

Copyright Information
Every effort to trace copyright-holders and to obtain permission has been made; the publishers would welcome details of any errors or omissions. Corrections will be incorporated into future reprints. This title is available in the USA from Hope Publishing Company, Carol Stream, Illinois 60188, USA.

British Library Cataloguing in Publication Data

Perry, Michael, *1942–*
Songs from the psalms – music ed.
I. Title II. Peacock, David
223.2052

ISBN 0 340 52243 7 hbk
0 340 52939 3 pbk

 Printed in Great Britain for Hodder and Stoughton Limited, Mill Road, Dunton Green, Sevenoaks, Kent by Richard Clay Limited, Bungay, Suffolk. Liturgical Psalms set by Rowland Phototypesetting Limited, Bury St Edmunds, Suffolk. Music and all other text set by Barnes Music Engraving Limited, East Sussex. Hodder and Stoughton Editorial Office: 47, Bedford Square, London WC1B 3DP.

CONTENTS

PREFACE

'Sing to the God of our salvation!'

The psalms have come down to us as a treasure-store of spiritual encouragement. In them the grace of God is revealed and through them we are able to express our wonder and adoration. They inspire both art and music, they give us words for celebration, and they match our moods of joy and sadness.

Individual psalms are very different: some speak of kings and victories, others offer sensitive words to those who are at the end of their resources. Some are designed for large congregations celebrating, with the aid of drama, the great acts of God in the history of salvation; others are vehicles of individual piety. The psalms are God's provision for worship. We must not neglect such gracious gifts. *Songs from the Psalms* challenges us once again to find a central place in our worship for this resource from the word of God.

Musicians approaching *Songs from the Psalms* will find a whole range of informal material drawing on the current psalm worship repertoire: Iona, St Thomas More Centre, Taizé, etc. Here too, are contrasting formats: response-style, solo songs, music group items, antiphons. We have also set metrical text to informal music of a high standard. New settings have been composed with an immediacy that enables occasional use. There is in *Songs from the Psalms* both the adventurous and the traditional.

Songs from the Psalms affords an opportunity to praise God with words from the Scriptures and in a contemporary idiom – and to draw worshippers' attention to the greater resources of the book of Psalms itself.

We acknowledge the work of song-writers who have found inspiration in setting the Scriptures to music. We owe special thanks to Michael Baughen, Chairman of Jubilate Hymns and Bishop of Chester, who began this series with *Psalm Praise* – a pioneering book which opened the door to the psalms for many, and encouraged a new generation of musicians to attempt lively settings.

We offer this volume along with the sister collection *Psalms for Today* to English-speaking Christians – for their delight, and for the praise of our glorious God.

MICHAEL PERRY and DAVID PEACOCK

USING *SONGS FROM THE PSALMS*

* It will be understood that many of the keyboard arrangements give only an outline of the accompaniment. Consequently, enterprising keyboard players will want to improvise and elaborate upon the given arrangements, in a style appropriate to the nature of the song.

* The chords given in *Songs from the Psalms* have been chosen with the average guitarist in mind. With many of the arrangements, capo markings are given to make the songs more accessible. '**Capo 5(C)**' means place the capo at the fifth fret and play the chords in brackets, which will be found to be in the key of **C**, rather than **F**.

* For chords marked '. . . **sus**' assume they are sustained 4th chords.

* '**N.C.**' indicates no chords are to be played.

* For chords marked '. . **aug**' play the equivalent augmented chord. For example '**Caug**' = C aug. 5th.

* A guitarist may find it easier to dispense with the 'extras' of a chord – for example, instead of **C9** play C; instead of **Csus** play C; instead of **Cm7** play Cm.

* Bass notes are given where appropriate. Bass players are encouraged to follow these where possible.

* On some items, certain chords are in bold type. By playing these chords only, the average guitarist will be able to accompany the songs with greater ease. However, these chords are not consistent with the keyboard harmony and are more suited to 'guitar-only' accompaniment.

1A If we love the word of God

Dartmeet

Words: from Psalm 1
Michael Perry
Music: David Peacock

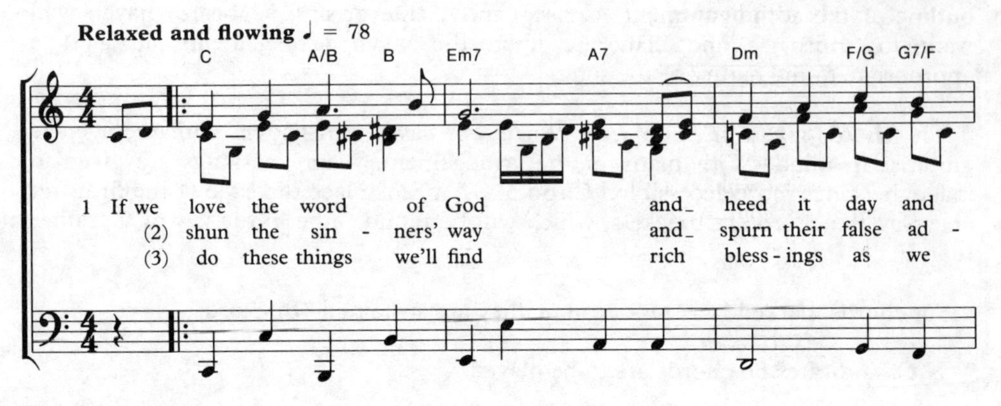

Relaxed and flowing ♩ = 78
C A/B B Em7 A7 Dm F/G G7/F
1 If we love the word of God and_ heed it day and
(2) shun the sin - ners' way and_ spurn their false ad -
(3) do these things we'll find rich bless - ings as we

Em Am Dm7 F/G Am7 Em/F♯ B7 Em A7
night; if we make God's truth our law, God's
- vice; if we turn from God - less lies and_
go; then we'll flour - ish like a tree where

1.2. 3.
Dm7 Gsus G G7 Dm F/G G C
coun - sel our de - light: 2 If we
e - vils that en - tice: 3 If we
liv - ing wa - ters_ flow.

Alternative tune: Fullness, *Psalms for Today* 1A

When we walk with God

Words: from Psalm 1
Michael Perry
Music: Chris Rolinson
Moderately with bounce
C Gsus G Dm7 G C C7 F/A C7/G F F♯dim C/G G7 C
1 When we walk with God, we are blessed: not the wicked and their schemes, nor the evil and their dreams – when we walk with God, (yes) we are blessed.
2 When we trust in God, we are blessed: when his law is our delight, and we heed it day and night – when we trust in
3 When we feed on God, we are blessed: like a growing tree in place by the flowing streams of grace – when we feed on
4 When we walk with God, we are blessed: for the Lord is at our side as our strength, our hope, our guide – when we walk with

1E Bless-ed is the man

From Psalm 1
Words and music: Michael Baughen
Music arranged Jim Thornton
Descant: Noël Tredinnick

With confidence
Capo 3(D)
1 Bless-ed is the man, the man who does not walk in the coun-sel of the un-god-ly– bless-ed is that man; he who re-jects the way, re-jects the way of sin and who turns a-way from scoff-ing– bless-ed is that man: but his de-light by day and night is the
2 He is like a tree– a tree that flou-rish-es be-ing plant-ed by the water– bless-ed is that man. He will bring forth fruit– his leaf will wi-ther not, for in all he does he pros-pers– bless-ed is that man: for his de-light by day and night is the

1.
2.
F7 (D7) B♭ (G) Gm (Em) F (D) C7 (A7) F (D) F (D)
law of God al - migh - ty.
law of God al - migh - - ty.
DESCANT
F (D) C7 (A7) Dm (Bm) Gm (Em) C7 (A7) F (D) F7 (D7)
3 The un - god - ly are not so for they are like the chaff__ which the
3 The un - god - ly are not so for they are like the_ chaff which the
B♭ (G) C7 (A7) F (D) Dm (Bm) C7 (A7) F (D) Gm7 (Em7) G7 (E7) C (A)
wind blows a - way__ the un - god - ly are not so;____ the un -
wind blows clean a - way – the un - god - ly are not so; the un -
F (D) C7 (A7) Dm (Bm) Gm (Em) C7 (A7) F (D) F7 (D7)
- god - ly will not stand up - on the judge - ment day__ nor be -
- god - ly will not stand up - on the judge - ment day nor be -

1
B♭ (G) C7 (A7) F (D) Dm (Bm) Gm (Em) C7 (A7) F (D) C7 (A7)
-long to God's own peo - ple — the un - god - ly will not stand: but
-long to God's own peo - ple — the un - god - ly will not stand: but
F (D) Gm7 (Em7) C7 (A7) F (D) Gm7 (Em7) C7 (A7)
God knows the way of right - eous men and un -
God knows the way of right - eous men and un -
F7 (D7) B♭ (G) Gm (Em) F (D) C7 (A7) F (D)
-god - ly ways will per - ish.
-god - ly ways will per - ish.

F (D) C7 (A7) Dm (Bm) Gm (Em) C7 (A7) F (D) F7 (D7)
Bless - ed is the man, the man who does not walk__ in the
Bless - ed is the man, the man who does not__ walk in the
B♭ (G) C7 (A7) F (D) Dm (Bm) Gm (Em) C7 (A7) F (D)
coun - sel of the un - god - ly – bless - ed is that man!
coun - sel of the un - god - ly – bless - ed is that man!
Instrumental variant of descant from 1
8va

1F God is with the righteous

Words: from Psalm 1
Michael Perry
Music: American traditional melody
arranged Chris Rolinson
Happily
Introduction
Verse
1 God is with the right-eous – they shall not be moved;
2 God con-demns the wick - ed – they shall be re-moved;
3 Hap-py when we hear him – we shall not be moved;
God is with the right-eous – they shall not be moved: just like a tree grow-ing by the
God con-demns the wick - ed – they shall be re-moved: just like the chaff blow-ing in the
hap-py when we hear him – we shall not be moved: just like a tree grow-ing by the
ri - ver-side they shall not be moved.
wind all day they shall be re - moved.
ri - ver-side we shall not be moved.
Chorus
WOMEN
MEN
They shall not – they shall not be moved;
They shall be – they shall be re-moved;
We shall not – we shall not be moved;
WOMEN
MEN
ALL
they shall not – they shall not be moved: just like a tree grow-ing by the
they shall be – they shall be re-moved: just like the chaff blow-ing in the
we shall not – we shall not be moved: just like a tree grow-ing by the

to repeat in F
Key change to G
ri - ver-side they shall not be moved! moved! 7 If we fol-low Je-sus –
wind all day they shall be re-moved!
ri - ver-side we shall not be moved!
we shall not be moved; If we fol-low Je - sus – we shall not be moved; just like a
tree grow-ing by the ri - ver-side we shall not be moved.
Chorus
WOMEN
We shall not –
MEN
we shall not be moved;
WOMEN
we shall not –
MEN
we shall not be moved:
ALL
just like a
tree grow-ing by the ri - ver - side we shall not be moved!

4 Happy when we love him . . .

5 Happy when we serve him . . .

6 When we read the Bible . . .

7 If we follow Jesus . . .

3B O Lord, how many are my foes

Words: from Psalm 3
adapted from the New International Version
by Ian White
Music: Ian White
arranged David Peacock

Dramatically
Gm7
SOLO
1 O Lord, how ma - ny are my foes, how ma - ny rise a -
C
Gm7
- gainst me; how ma-ny say of me that 'God will not de -
C
F/G
G
Flowing
- liv - er him'!
ALL
2 But you are a
C
G
v.2
shield a - round me, Lord, my glo - rious
(3) sleep – but I
(4) Lord, de - liv - er me, for I have

F
F/G
C
F/G
G
One, who lifts up my head. To the
wake a-gain, sus-tained by the Lord. I will not
seen you deal with your e - ne - mies. From the
C
G
Lord I cry a - loud, and
fear ten thou-sand men drawn
Lord de - liv-erance comes: may your
vv 2.3.
Am
Dm7/G
C
F/G
G
from his ho - ly hill he ans - wers me. 3 I lie down in
up a - gainst me on ev - ery side. 4 A - rise, O
v 4.
Am
Dm7/G
C
bless - ing be on all your peo - ple.

4B O righteous Lord

Words: from Psalm 4
Margaret Wilson
Music: Christopher Norton
Calmly
Capo 3(Am) Cm (Am)
Cm/B♭
A♭9 (F)
E♭6/G (C)
1 O right - eous Lord who set me right,
2 They turn a - way from you, my God;
3 Ma - ny de - mand a clear - cut sign:
p
Fm7 (Dm7)
Cm/E♭ (Am)
Dm7 (Bm7)
Gaug (Eaug)
who broke all bonds and led me out
they look for truth in cle - ver lies,
'O that God's hand might bring us good!'
Cm9 (Am9)
Cm9/B♭
F/A (D)
from black des - pair to bound - less hope:
no hon - our give to your great name:
Yet to my heart you bring more joy

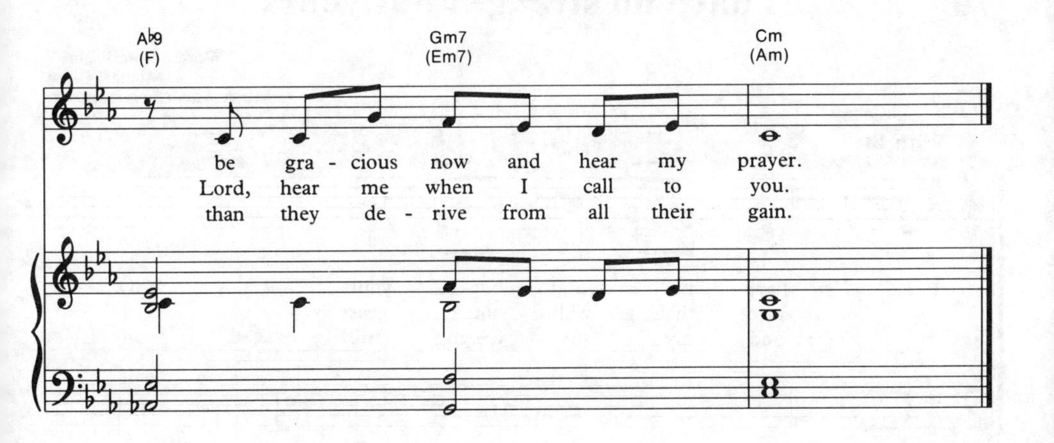
A♭9
(F)
Gm7
(Em7)
Cm
(Am)
be gra - cious now and hear my prayer.
Lord, hear me when I call to you.
than they de - rive from all their gain.

4 Lord, teach them how you sought us out,
and set your sign upon our hearts;
teach them to rest in silent trust,
shine on them with your glorious light.

5 O Lord, my Lord, who gave me joy
surpassing all that wealth can bring:
in peace I lie, in peace I sleep,
safe in your care, safe in your care.

Optional instrumental part

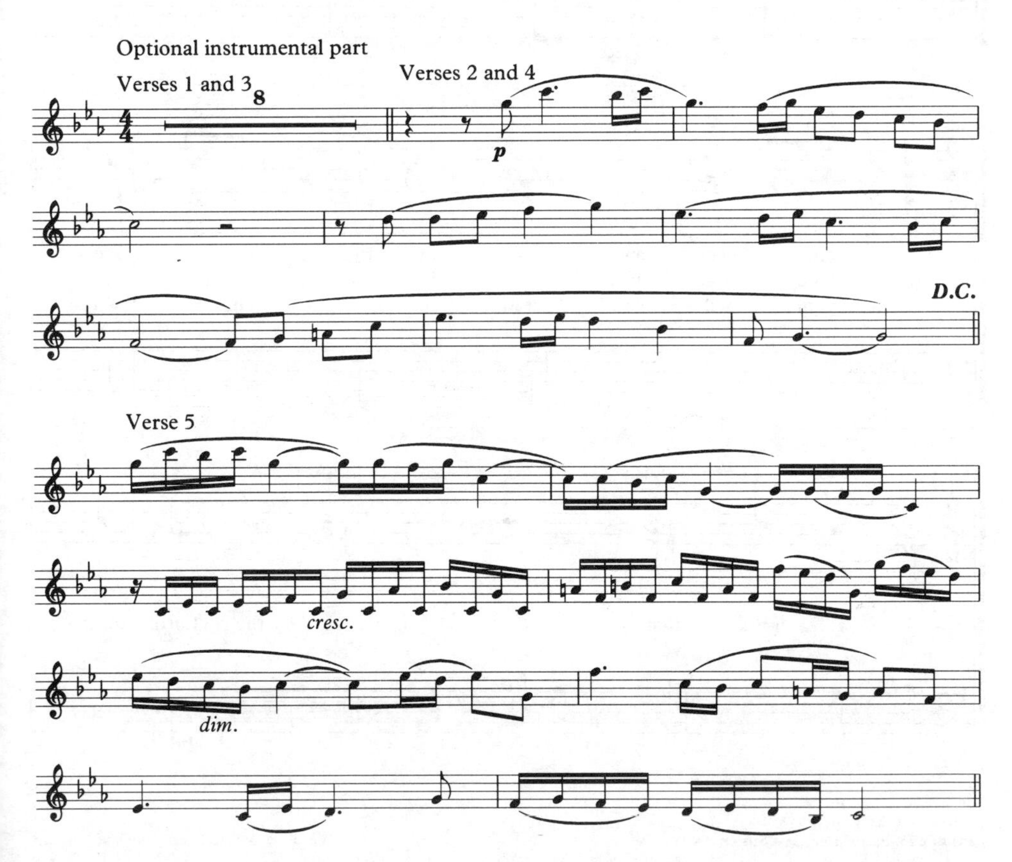
Verses 1 and 3
8
Verses 2 and 4
p
D.C.
Verse 5
cresc.
dim.

7B I have no strength but yours

Words: from Psalm 7
Michael Perry
Music: Chris Rolinson

With life
C
F/C
C
1 I___ have no___ strength but___ yours, O
(2) love that___ will not___ cease I
(3) God, my___ sov - ereign_ still, my
F
F/G
C
Em7
God, my hid - ing - place; you snatch me from the
owe my life, my all; and just - ly if I
shield, my joy, my crown: you hon - our those who
F
C
Dm7
G
li - on's___ claws and save me by___ your___ grace.
break God's_ peace then pun - ish - ment___ will___ fall.
do your___ will, you tread the e - vil___ down.
A♭
E♭
I will give thanks to the Lord most

F
C
A♭
high; I will sing praise
E♭
F
C
to his right - eous name. I will give
Gm7
B♭
C
Am
thanks to the Lord, I will sing
B♭
Gm7
C
Fine
F/G
D.𝄋 al Fine
praise to his name.
2 To
3 My

8D

How majestic is your name

From Psalm 8
Words and music: Michael W Smith

Joyously
mf
D G Em7 D/F♯
D A A9/C♯ D G Em7 D/F♯
D A A9/C♯ D
O Lord, our Lord, how ma -
G Em7 D/F♯ D A A9/C♯ D
- jes - tic is your name in all the earth; O
D G Em7 D/F♯ D
Lord, our Lord, how ma - jes - tic is your name in all the

A A9/C♯ D G Em7 A G/B A7/C♯
earth; O Lord, we praise your
D G Em7 A G/B A7/C♯
name; O Lord, we mag-ni-fy your
D C♯ F♯m E A A/G D/F♯ G
name. Prince of peace, migh-ty God, O Lord God al-
to repeat
Asus A D G Em7 D/F♯
-migh - ty!
last time
Asus A D G Em7 D/F♯ D
migh - ty!

8E

Sovereign Lord

Words: from Psalm 8
Michael Perry
Music: Chris Rolinson

Forcefully
Introduction
E
A/B
B
E
A/B
B

E
A
E
Bsus
B
1 Sov-ereign Lord, in all the earth
2 When I lift my eyes I see
3 Yet you prove to us your love
4 Sing a-loud our saviour's worth –

E
A
E
Bsus
B
G#7
how ma-jes - tic is your name! In - fant
all the stars you set in place: who am
and ex-alt us ve - ry high, mak - ing
mer - cy, truth, and love pro - claim: Sov-ereign

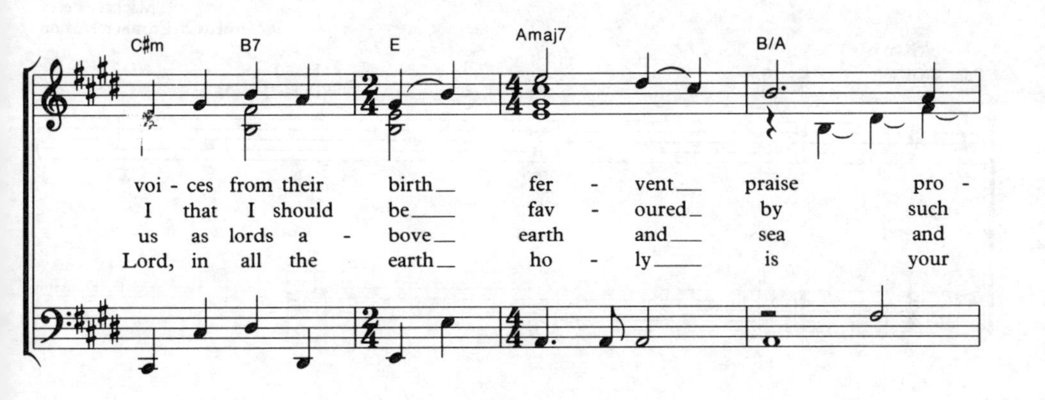
C♯m
B7
E
Amaj7
B/A
voi - ces from their birth fer - vent praise pro -
I that I should be fav - oured by such
us as lords a - bove earth and sea and
Lord, in all the earth ho - ly is your

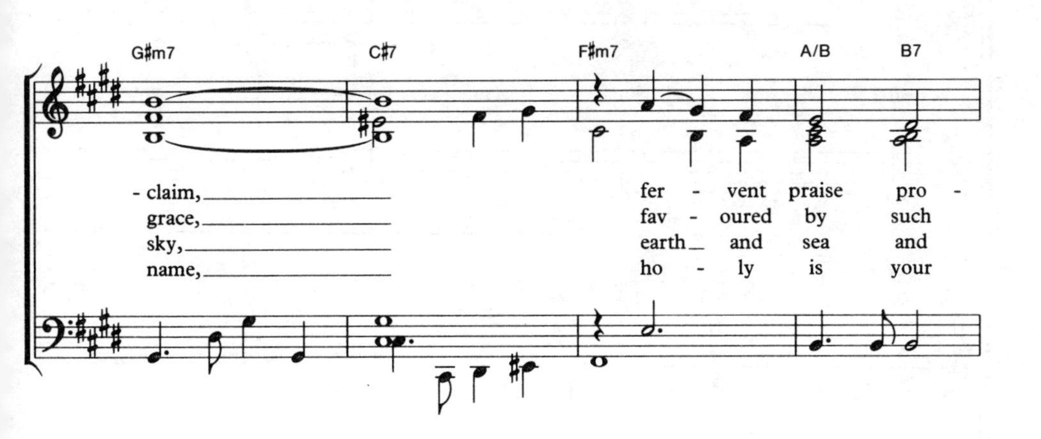
G♯m7
C♯7
F♯m7
A/B
B7
- claim, fer - vent praise pro -
grace, fav - oured by such
sky, earth and sea and
name, ho - ly is your

1.2.3.
E
A/B
B
4.
C
A
E
- claim.
grace?
sky.
name!

9 I praise you, Lord

Words: from Psalm 9
Michael Perry
Music: Christopher Norton

Simply
Capo 3(D)
F (D)
Gm/F (Em)
Fmaj7 (Dmaj7)
mp
I praise you, Lord, with all my
Gm/F (Em)
F (D)
Gm/F (Em)
heart, re - joic - ing in your
1.
2.
F/C (D)
C7 (A7)
F (D)
F (D)
Fine
won - ders! I - ders!
Verses
B♭ (G)
F (D)
B♭ (G)
GROUP A
GROUP B
1 Your jus - tice is per - fect, your jus - tice is
2 You gov - ern the peo - ples, you gov - ern the

Alternative tune: Confitebor tibi, *Psalms for Today* 9

F
(D)
Gm7
(Em7)
F/A
(D)
GROUP A
GROUP B
per - fect, your judge - ments are true, your
peo - ples, you help the op - pressed, you
B♭
(G)
F/C
(D)
B♭
(G)
F
(D)
GROUP A
GROUP B
judge - ments are true; the wick - ed have fall - en, the
help the op - pressed; and no - one who seeks you, and
B♭
(G)
F
(D)
B♭
(G)
GROUP A
wick - ed have fall - en, their names are for -
no - one who seeks you is ev - er for -
F
(D)
Gm7
(Em7)
B♭/C
(G)
D.𝄋 al Fine
GROUP B
ALL
- got - ten, their names are for - got - ten. I
- sak - en, is ev - er for - sak - en. I

The call-and-response verses may be sung in a variety of combinations
e.g. solo/congregation, men/ladies, group A/group B.

13B Forgotten for eternity

Cokewith
Words: from Psalm 13
Michael Saward
Music: David Wilson
Instrumental part: Noël Tredinnick
Steadily and with feeling
Capo 3(G)
Bbmaj7 (Gmaj7) Eb/Bb (C) Bbmaj7 (Gmaj7) Eb/Bb (C) Bbmaj7 (Gmaj7) Ebmaj7/Bb (Cmaj7)
1 For - got-ten for e - ter - ni - ty
2 Res - tore to me se - re - ni - ty
Bbmaj7 (Gmaj7) Eb/Bb (C) Bbmaj7 (Gmaj7) Ebmaj7/Bb (Cmaj7) Bbmaj7 (Gmaj7) Bbmaj7/A
is that to be my des - ti - ny? Your
and, in your gra-cious cha - ri - ty, lest
Gm (Em) Cm/G (Am) Gm7 (Em7) Cm/G (Am) Gm (Em) Cm/G (Am)
face no more to smile on me, op-pressed by ev - ery e - ne - my,
I should die, give light to me; frus - trate my gloat-ing ad-ver-sary,
Gm7 (Em7) Gm7/F Eb (C) Eb/D Cm7 (Am7)
my soul en - dur - ing a - go - ny? Oh
up - lift my soul in ec - sta - sy, and

E♭/F
(C)
B♭/F
(G)
ans - wer me, my God; oh
I'll re - joice, my God; and
F7sus
(D7sus)
1.
B♭maj7
(Gmaj7)
E♭/B♭
(C)
2.
B♭maj7
(Gmaj7)
ans - wer me, my God!
I'll re - joice, my God!
Optional instrumental part
Verse 1
11
mp
Verse 2
mf expressivo
optional 8va
f
rit.

13C How long, O Lord

Words: from Psalm 13
Barbara Woollett
Music: Christopher Norton

Moderately with expression
Dm6 Dm(♯7) Dm7 Dm6 Gm7 B♭/C C/F F Em7 E♭9
1 How long, O Lord, will you for - get an ans - wer to my prayer?
2 How long, O Lord, will you for - sake and leave me in this way?
3 How long, O Lord – but you for - give, with mer - cy from a - bove.
mp
Dm9 Dm9(♯7) Dm9 G13/D Gm7 B♭/C C7
No to - kens of your love I see, your face is turned a -
When will you come to my re - lief? My heart is o - ver -
I find that all your ways are just, I learn to praise you
Fsus2 F Em7 A7 Dm Em7(♭5) A7
1.2. Dm G/A A7
3. Dm
- way from me; I wres - tle with des - pair.
- whelmed with grief, by e - vil night and day.
and to trust in your un - fail - ing love.

In your presence is fullness of joy 16B

From Psalm 16
Words and music: Mike Kerry
Music arranged Chris Rolinson

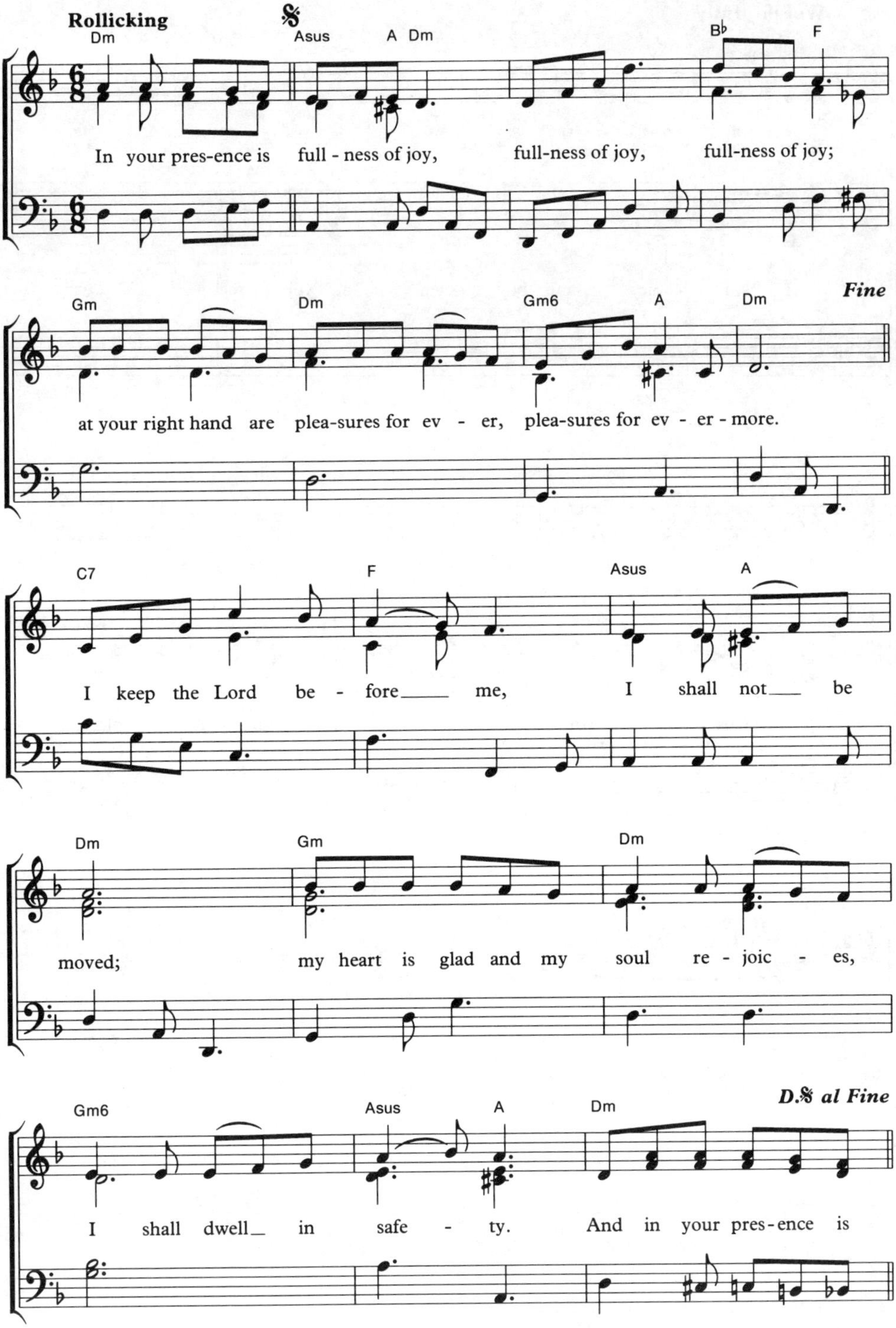

Rollicking

In your pres-ence is full - ness of joy, full-ness of joy, full-ness of joy;

at your right hand are plea-sures for ev - er, plea-sures for ev - er - more.

Fine

I keep the Lord be - fore ___ me, I shall not ___ be

moved; my heart is glad and my soul re - joic - es,

I shall dwell ___ in safe - ty. And in your pres-ence is

D.𝄋 al Fine

16C I will come and bow down

From Psalm 16
Words and music: Martin Nystrom
Music arranged David Peacock

Worshipfully
G/A
DESCANT
D
Bm
Em7
I will come and bow down at your feet, Lord
I will come and bow down at your feet, Lord
A7
F♯m
B7
Je - sus; in your pres - ence is full - ness of
Je - sus; in your pres - ence is full - ness of

Em
A7
Bm
joy. There is no - thing, there is
joy. There is no - thing, there is

C#/B
F#m
B7
no - one to com - pare with you; I take
no - one to com - pare with you; I take

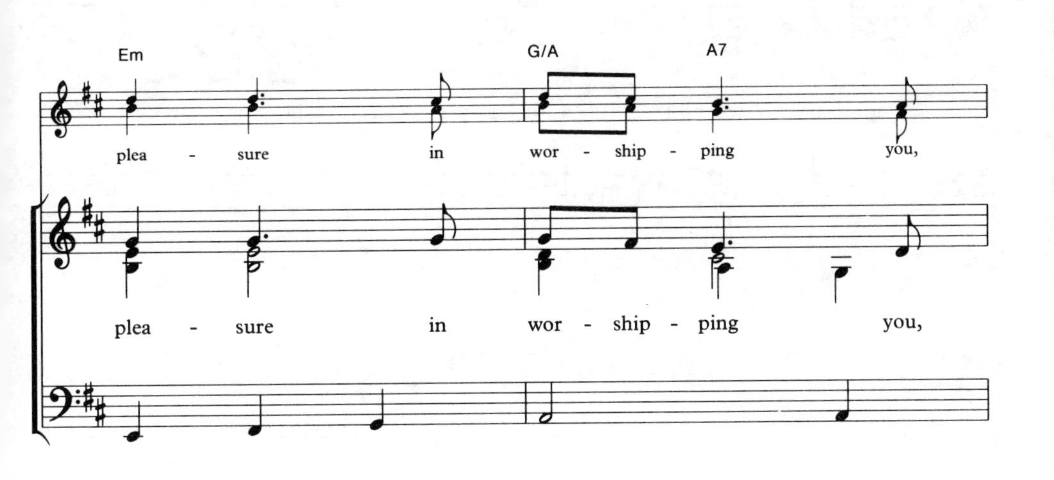
Em
G/A
A7
plea - sure in wor - ship - ping you,
plea - sure in wor - ship - ping you,

to repeat
last time
D
G/A
D
Lord. I will Lord.
Lord. I will Lord.

16D You will show me the path of life

From Psalm 16
Words and music: Norman Warren
Music arranged Christopher Norton

Gently
D G Dsus2 D F♯m
You will show me the path of life; you will show me the
Bm7(♭5) Bdim(no F) F♯m9 F♯m
Verse
D/C G/B B/A Gmaj7 Em/G
path of life. 1 In your pres-ence, in your pres-ence are
Em Asus A Em Asus A D
plea-sures ev-er-more, plea-sures ev-er-more. You will show me the
G Dsus2 D Em/D A7 D
path of life; you will show me the path of life.

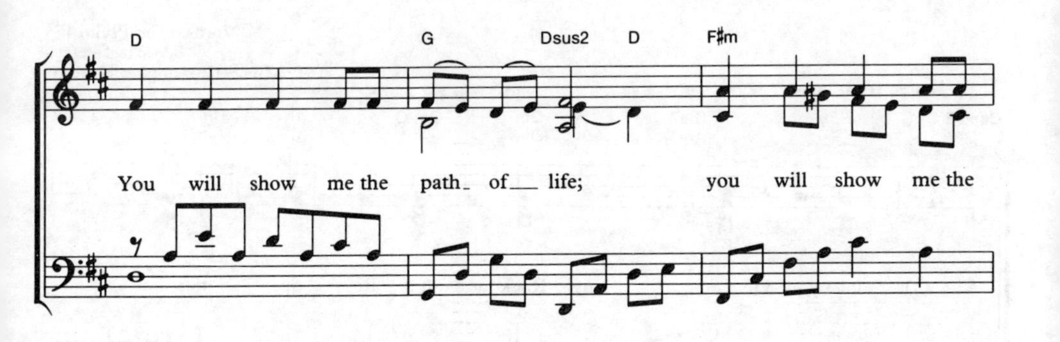
D G Dsus2 D F♯m
You will show me the path_ of__ life; you will show me the

Verse
Bm7(♭5) Bdim(no F) F♯m9 F♯m D/C G/B B/A Gmaj7 Em/G
path of__ life. 2 At your right hand, at your right hand are

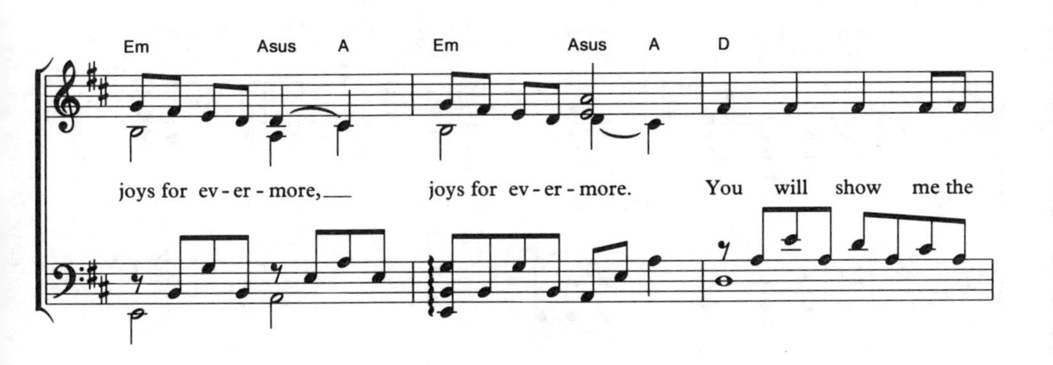
Em Asus A Em Asus A D
joys for ev - er - more,__ joys for ev - er - more. You will show me the

rall.
G Dsus2 D Em/D A7 D
path_ of__ life; you will show me the path_ of__ life.

18C I love you, O Lord

Words: from Psalm 18
Michael Perry
Music: Christopher Norton

Rock feel
Capo 5(C)
F (C)
Dm7 (Am7)
Gm7 (Dm7)
Gm/C
Bb/C (F)
C (G)
Bb/F (F)
F7 (C7)
I love you, O Lord, my Rock and my Re - dee - mer,
for you make me strong; I trust in you al-ways.
You are my shield, the hope of my sal - va - tion;
I cry out to you, and of - fer you my praise.
Fine

Verse
F♯dim
(C♯dim)
Gm
(Dm)
B♭m/G
(Fm)
B♭m/A F/A
(C)
1 The seas of death – their tor-rents ov-er - whelm me;
2 The moun-tains shake – they trem-ble at his an - ger,
3 My Sav-iour lives – his mer-cy has de - liv-ered me,
D7
(A7)
G7
(D7)
Gm/C
(Dm)
C7 F♯dim
(G7) (C♯dim)
in my per-plex-i-ty I call up-on the Lord; and from his
like burn-ing coals their fire con-sumes the skies; he tears the
he raised me up to this ex-alt-ed place; I wor-ship
Gm
(Dm)
B♭m/G
(Fm)
B♭m/A F/A
(C)
D7
(A7)
heaven he hears my voice and res-cues me, he rea-ches down
clouds, the light-ning strikes his en-e-mies, he guides me in
him who makes me share his vic-to-ries and ev-er-more
G7
(D7)
C7
(G7)
F
(C)
B♭/F F7 B♭/F F
(F) (C7) (F) (C)
C
(G)
D.𝄋 al Fine
and saves me by his word. I
the way and makes me wise.
will fol-low me with grace.

19D Everywhere the skies declare

Words: from Psalm 19
Barbara Woollett
Music: Christopher Norton
Moderato
Capo 3(A) C (A) Dm7/C (Bm7) C (A) Dm7/C (Bm7) C (A) Dm7/C (Bm7) C (A) Dm7/C (Bm7)
1 Ev - ery-where the skies de-clare the
2 Ev - ery-where the sun de-clares the
3 Ev - ery-where his word de-clares the
4 Ev - ery-where his saints de-clare the
f
Cm/E♭ (Am) F (D) C (A) E♭maj7 (Cmaj7) F (D)
glo - ry of the Lord! Day af - ter day they
glo - ry of the Lord! And like a bride - groom
glo - ry of the Lord! His per - fect law re -
glo - ry of the Lord! And they don't try to
C (A) E♭maj7 (Cmaj7) F (D) C (A)
shout his praise, night af - ter night they show his ways;
in his fame, a champ-ion run - ning in the game,
- vives the soul, his pro - mis - es our hearts con - sole;
hide their blame, but come to him in Je - sus' name;

A♭9 (F) B♭ (G) A♭9 (F) B♭ (G) A♭9 (F) B♭ (G)
ev - ery - where their voice is heard,
ev - ery - where it shines a - broad,
ev - ery - where his voice is heard,
ev - ery - where their lives re - cord,
in ev - ery cor - ner
A♭9 (F) B♭ (G) C (A) Dm7 (Bm7) Em7 (C♯m7) E♭7 (C7)
of the world – the glo - ry of the Lord, the
Dm7 (Bm7) C/E (A) F (D) G7 (E7) C (A) Dm7 (Bm7) C/E (A) F/G (D) C (A)
1–3.
4.
glo - ry of the Lord!

19E May the words of my mouth

From Psalm 19
Words and music: Bob Fraser

Worshipfully
Capo 3(C)
E♭ (C)
Gm7 (Em7)
Cm (Am)
E♭/B♭ (C)
p May the words of my mouth, the me-di - ta - tion of my
F/A (D)
E♭/B♭ (C)
A♭/B♭ (F)
last time to Coda
heart, be al - ways ac - cept - a - ble to
E♭ (C)
1.
A♭/B♭ (F)
2.
E♭ (C)
Edim (Adim)
you, O Lord; may the Lord. O
Fm7 (Dm7)
Gm/B♭ (Em)
Fm/B♭ (Dm)
Gm/B♭ (Em)
Fm/B♭ (Dm)
Fm/E♭
E♭ (C)
Edim (C♯dim)
Lord, my rock and my re - deem - er, O

Fm7 (Dm)
Gm/B♭ (Em) Fm/B♭ (Dm) Gm/B♭ (Em) Fm/B♭ (Dm)
Gsus (Esus)
G (E)
Lord, my strength_ and my shield!_ May the
E♭ (C)
Gm7 (Em7)
Cm (Am)
E♭/B♭ (C)
F/A (D)
words_ of my mouth,_ the me-di - ta - tion of my_ heart, be
E♭/B♭ (C)
A♭/B♭ (F)
E♭ (C)
Gm7/D (Em7)
Cm7 (Am7)
al-ways_ ac-cept-a-ble to_ you.
A♭/B♭ (F)
A♭maj7 (Fmaj7)
A♭/B♭ (F)
Gm7 (Em7)
A♭/B♭ (F)
D.𝄋 al Coda
Fm9 (Dm9)
Fm (Dm)
B♭sus (Gsus) B♭7 (G7)
May the
CODA
rit.
A♭ (F)
E♭/G (C)
Fm7 (Dm7)
E♭ (C)
you._

19F May our worship be acceptable

From Psalm 19
Words and music: Graham Kendrick
Music arranged Stuart Townend

Prayerfully
E Emaj7 E6 Emaj7 Amaj7 A/B E A/B B
May our wor-ship be ac-cept-a-ble _ in your sight, O Lord;
E Emaj7 E6 Emaj7 Amaj7 A/B B6 E D/E E7
may our wor-ship be ac-cept-a-ble _ in your sight, O Lord;
Amaj7 B/A G♯m7 C♯m7 F♯9 Amaj7 Dmaj7 A/B
may the words of my mouth be pure, and the me-di-ta-tion of my heart; _
B E Emaj7 E6 Emaj7 Amaj7 A/B B6 E
_ may our wor-ship be ac-cept-a-ble _ in your sight, O Lord.

May the Lord answer you

20B

From Psalm 20
Words and music: Philip Lawson-Johnston
Music arranged Christopher Norton

Lively
Em
Am
mp May the Lord_ ans - wer you when you are in dis - tress,
B7
Em
may the name of God pro - tect_____ you; may he send you help from the
Am
B7
Em B7 Em
sanc - tua-ry and grant you sup-port from Zi - on.
Am
May he give to you the de - sire of your heart and

B7
Em
make all your plans suc - ceed:
we will shout for joy when we see
Am
B7
you vic - to - ri - ous, - and we'll lift up our ban - ners in the
to Coda
Em
B7
Em
E7
Am
Am/G
f
name of our God!
Some will trust in earth-ly power,
D/F♯
D
G
Am
E7
Am
B7
some will trust in man, but we will trust in the name of our God.
E/G♯
E7
Am
Am/G
D/F♯
D
G
Am
E7
Am
They are brought down to their knees, they are doomed to fall, but we rise up and

1.
B
Em
B7
Em
B7
Em
stand firm.
2.
B
Slower
Em
D
Em
mf
O Lord, de - liv - er us,
C
D
G
B
Em
D
ans - wer when we call.
O Lord, de - liv - er
Em
C
D
accel.
B
D.𝄋 al Coda
us,
ans - wer when we call.
CODA
B
Slowly
Em
Am6
Em/B
B7
Em
God!
mf
May the Lord grant your re - quests.

20C May the Lord God hear your prayer

Words: from Psalm 20
Michael Perry
Music: Chris Rolinson
Prayerfully (slow 2)
Capo 3(D)
F (D)
F7sus (D7sus)
B♭/F (G)
B♭m/F (Gm)
MEN
1 May the Lord God hear your
2 May he grant your true de -
3 Now we know the Lord can
WOMEN
(1) may the Lord God hear your
(2) may he grant your true de -
(3) now we know the Lord can
(MEN)
prayer,
- sire,
save,
Am7 (F♯m7)
Dm7 (Bm7)
prayer;
- sire;
save;
may his name pro - tect you al - ways,
may he make your plans suc - cess - ful,
now we trust this world no lon - ger,

Fmaj7/C (Dmaj7) Bbmaj9 (Gmaj9) F/A (D) Dm (Bm) Gm7 (Em7)
may his name pro - tect you al - ways! May he
may he make your plans suc - cess - ful! May he
now we trust this world no lon - ger. Now we
May he
May he
Now we
Bb/C (G) C (A) Bb/C (G) C (A) Am7 (F#m7) C/D (A) D7 (B7) C/D (A) D7 (B7)
ALL
meet you in his house, lift - ing up your heart in
give you all you need, caus - ing ev - ery - one to
see he ans - wers prayer: praise him now for all his
Gm7 (Em7) F/A (D) Bb (G) F/C (D) A7/C# (F#7) Dm (Bm) Dm7
wor - ship, in wor - ship; lift - ing
thank him, to thank him; caus - ing
mer - cy, his mer - cy; praise him
Gm7 (Em7) F/A (D) Bb (G) Bb/C C (A) Fsus (Dsus) F (D)
up your heart in wor - ship.
ev - ery - one to thank him.
now for all his mer - cy!

20D Some trust in chariots

From Psalm 20
Words and music: John Pantry
Music arranged Christopher Norton

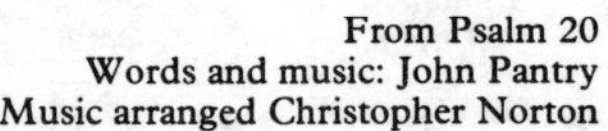

Brightly
A/C♯
D
E
A/C♯
D
f
A/E
E7
A
D/A
A
F♯m
E
1 Some trust in cha-ri-ots,
2 Long may he grant the de -
3 May the Lord hear you when -
D
A/C♯
Bm
A
some in their hor - ses; but we will trust in the
- sires of your heart, and with po - wer make all of your
- ev - er you're trou - bled, send to you help and
B
E
F♯m
E
D
name of the Lord. All those who lean on their own un - der -
plans to suc - ceed. We'll shout for joy when we hear of your
give you new heart; if you can trust in him, he will di -

A/C♯ Bm C♯ F♯m
- stand - ing will be brought to their knees and shall fall.
vic - to - ries, lift up our ban - ners and sing!
- rect you, and your feet will not fall from the path.
E A E A D Esus E A
But the sav - ing power of God's right hand will ne - ver
will ne - ver
E A E A D Esus
fail; the sav - ing power of God's right hand will ne -
fail; will
1.2. 3. 4.
E A/C♯ A E D.S. A/C♯ D
- ver fail. fail. But the fail.
ne - ver fail.
rit.
E A/C♯ D A/E E7 A D/A A

22B

In the presence of your people

From Psalm 22
Words and music: Brent Chambers
Music arranged Christopher Norton
Instrumental arrangements: David Peacock

Hebrew style
A A/C♯ Dm A A/C♯ Dm A7 Dm
mf 1 In the pre-sence of your peo - ple I will praise your name,
f 2 Lai, lai, lai, lai, lai, lai, lai, etc.
D D/F♯ Gm C F B♭ Gm/E A
for a - lone you are ho - ly, en-throned on the prais - es of Is - ra - el.
A A/C♯ Dm A A/C♯ Dm A7 Dm
Let us ce - le-brate your good - ness and your stead - fast love;
D D/F♯ Gm C F B♭ Gm/E A7 Dm
may your name be ex - alt - ed here on__ earth and in heaven a - bove!

Instrumental parts

FLUTES

a2
tr
tr
tr
tr

B♭ CLARINETS

a2

VIOLINS

O Lord my God

From Psalm 22
Words and music: John Bell

Expressively
Dm7 G Cmaj7 F
ALL O Lord my God, O Lord my God,
Dm7 G Cmaj7 F
why do you seem so far from me, O
far from me,
why do you seem so far from me, O
B♭maj7 C7/B♭ F/A Gsus G7
Fine
Lord my God?
O Lord my God, my God?
Lord, O Lord my God?

Verse
CHOIR/WORSHIP GROUP
Am Am(♯6) Gmaj7
1 Night and morn - ing I make my
2 Pain and suf - fering un - bound and
3 Why, oh why do the wick - ed
4 Turn a - gain as you hear my

G
B♭
C7/B♭
prayer: peace for this place, and
blind plague the pro - gress of
thrive, poor folk pe - rish, the
plea, tend the tor - ment in
Am7
F/A
D♭
help for there; wait - ing and
hu - man - kind, al - ways de -
rich sur - vive; begg - ing the
all I see; lov - ing and
A♭
B♭m
Fm/A♭
won - dering, wait - ing and won - dering –
- mand - ing, al - ways de - mand - ing –
ques - tion, begg - ing the ques - tion –
heal - ing, lov - ing and heal - ing –
Gm7
Csus
C
D.C. al Fine
does God care; does God care?
does God mind; does God mind?
is God a - live; is God a - live?
set me free, set me free!

23A The Lord my shepherd rules my life

Shoreham-by-Sea
Words: from Psalm 23
Christopher Idle
Music: Christopher Hayward
Instrumental arrangement: David Peacock
Flowing
Capo 3(G)
B♭ (G) B♭/A (G) Gm (Em) Dm/F (Bm)
1 The Lord my shepherd rules my life and gives me all I need; he leads me by refreshing streams, in pastures green I
(2) Lord revives my failing strength, he makes my joy complete; and in right paths, for his name's sake, he guides my faltering
(3) in a valley dark as death, no evil makes me fear; your shepherd's staff protects my way, for you are with me
E♭ (C) E♭/D (C) Cm7 (Am7) E♭/F (C)
B♭maj7 (Gmaj7) E♭maj7 (Cmaj7) Cm/A (Am) D7 (B7)
Gm (Em) Gm/F (Em) Cm7 (Am7) E♭/F (C) F7 (D7)

Alternative tunes: Bedfordshire May-Day Carol or Brother James' Air, *Psalms for Today* 23A.

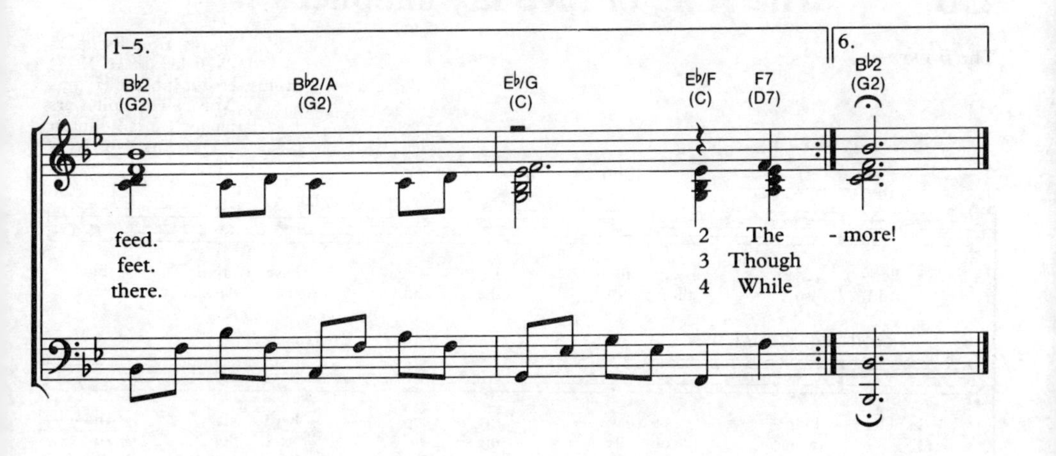
1–5.
6.
B♭2
(G2)
B♭2/A
(G2)
E♭/G
(C)
E♭/F
(C)
F7
(D7)
B♭2
(G2)
feed.
feet.
there.
2 The
3 Though
4 While
- more!

4 While all my enemies look on
you spread a royal feast;
you fill my cup, anoint my head,
and treat me as your guest.

5 Your goodness and your gracious love
pursue me all my days;
your house, O Lord, shall be my home –
your name, my endless praise.

6 To Father, Son and Spirit, praise!
to God, whom we adore,
be worship, glory, power and love,
both now and evermore!

Solo part for instrumental verse

23D The King of love my shepherd is

The Followers

Words: from Psalm 23
H W Baker (1821–1877)
in this version Jubilate Hymns
Music: The Followers
arranged Chris Rolinson
Descants: Ivor Keys

Sweetly flowing
D Bm7 Em7 A
GROUP DESCANT
(3 Per -) verse and fool - ish I have strayed, but
(6 And) so through all the length of days your
CONGREGATIONAL DESCANT
1 The king of love my shep - herd is, whose
(2) streams of liv - ing wa - ter flow, a
(3) - verse and fool - ish I have strayed, but
1 The king of love my shep - herd is, whose
(2) streams of liv - ing wa - ter flow, a
(3) - verse and fool - ish I have strayed, but
D Bm7 Em7 A
in his love he sought me; and
good - ness fails me ne - ver: Good
good - ness fails me ne - ver; I
ran - somed soul, he leads me; and
in his love he sought me; and
good - ness fails me ne - ver; I
ran - somed soul, he leads me; and
in his love he sought me; and

The congregation may be divided into two groups with each alternating between singing melody and congregational descant verses.

D
D7
G
Gm
Dmaj7
Bm7
on his shoul - der gent - ly laid, and home, re - joic - ing,
Shep - herd, may I sing your praise with - in your house for
no - thing lack if I am his and he is mine for
where the fer - tile pas - tures grow, with food from hea - ven
on his shoul - der gent - ly laid, and home, re - joic - ing,
1–5.
6.
Em7
A
Em7
A7
D
brought me. (3 Per -)
(6 And) ev - - - - er!
ev - er. 2 Where ev - - - - er!
feeds me. 3 Per -
brought me. 4 In

4 In death's dark vale I fear no ill
with you, dear Lord, beside me;
your rod and staff my comfort still,
your cross before to guide me.

5 You spread a banquet in my sight
of love beyond all knowing;
and O the gladness and delight
from your pure chalice flowing!

6 And so through all the length of days
your goodness fails me never:
Good Shepherd, may I sing your praise
within your house for ever!

23E

The Lord is my shepherd

From Psalm 23
Words and music: Bob Fraser
Music arranged Christopher Norton

With strength
Capo 1(D)
E♭ (D) B♭7 (A7) E♭ (D) A♭ (G) B♭ (A)
mp The Lord is my shep - herd – he knows the things I
E♭ (D) A♭ (G) B♭ (A) Gm7 (F♯m7) Cm7 (Bm7)
need; though I go through deep - est dark - ness he will
F9 (E9) B♭7sus (A7sus) B♭7 (A7) E♭ (D) B♭7 (A7)
guide and he will__ lead. The Lord is my
E♭ (D) A♭ (G) B♭ (A) E♭ (D) B♭ (A) Cm7 (Bm7) A♭ (G) B♭ (A)
shep - herd – I will not be a - fraid;_________ his good - ness and his

Gm7
(F♯m7)
Cm7
(Bm7)
Fm7
(Em7)
B♭7
(A7)
E♭
(D)
Fine
mer - cy will ne - ver, ne - ver fade.
B♭7
(A7)
E♭
(D)
p
1 You guide me on the right path –
2 And e - ven though sur - round - ed
B♭7
(A7)
E♭
(D)
D♭maj7
(Cmaj7)
I know you'll al - ways care; and when I need pro -
by ev - ery en - e - my, you've got the ban - quet
D.C. al Fine
Gm7
(F♯m7)
Fm7
(Em7)
B♭sus
(Asus)
B♭7
(A7)
- tec - tion, your rod and staff are there.
rea - dy, so ev - ery - one can see.

23F Because the Lord is my shepherd

From Psalm 23
Words and music: Christopher Walker
Meditatively ♩ = c.46
Verse
Capo 1(D)
E♭ (D)
A♭ (G)
B♭ (A)
E♭ (D)
mp
1 Be - cause the Lord is my shep - herd I have ev - ery - thing I need; he lets me rest in the mea - dow and
(2) when the road leads to dark - ness, I shall walk there un - a - fraid; ev - en when death is close I have
(3) love you make me a ban - quet for my e - ne - mies to see; you make me wel - come, pour - ing down
(4) good-ness al - ways is with me, and your mer - cy I know; your lov - ing - kind - ness strength - ens me
Fm/E♭ (Em)
E♭ (D)
Fm/E♭ (Em)
Gm (F♯m)

A♭ (G) E♭/G (D) Fm (Em) B♭sus (Asus) B♭ (A)
leads me___ to the qui - et streams; he re -
cour - age,___ for your help is there; you are
hon - our___ from your migh - ty hand; and this
al - ways___ as I go through life; I shall
E♭ (D) A♭ (G) E♭maj7 (Dmaj7) Fm (Em) B♭ (A)
- stores my soul and he leads me___ in the paths that are right.
close_ be - side me with com - fort,___ you are guid - ing my way.
joy___ fills me with glad - ness -___ it is too much to bear.
dwell in your pres - ence for ev - er,___ giv - ing praise to your name.
Chorus
E♭ (D) Fm/E♭ (Em) E♭ (D) B♭ (A) Cm (Bm) Gm/B♭ (F♯m)
Lord, you are my shep - herd, you are my friend: I want to fol - low you
1–3.
A♭ (G) E♭/G (D) Cm (Bm) A♭ (G) B♭sus (Asus) B♭ (A)
al - ways - just to fol - low my friend.
2 And
3 In
4 Your

4.
A♭ (G) rall.
E♭ (D) a tempo
Fm/E♭ (Em)
fol - low my friend.
E♭ (D)
Gm (F♯m)
C♯m (Bm) rall.
A♭ (G)
E♭ (D)
pp
Optional instrumental part
Verse
Chorus
2
1–3.
4.
rall.

This earth belongs to God

24D

Trumpet Voluntary
Words: from Psalm 24
Christopher Idle
Music: J Clarke (c.1674–1707)
arranged Christopher Norton
March style
1 This earth be - longs to God, the world, its wealth, and_ all its peo - ple;
2 Lift high your heads, you gates; rise up, you ev - er - last-ing doors, as
3 Lift high your heads, you gates, and fling wide o - pen the an-cient doors, for
4 All glo - ry_ be to God the Fa - ther, Son, and_ Ho - ly Spi - rit;
he formed the wa - ters wide and fash-ioned ev-ery sea and shore.
here now the King of glo - ry en - ters in - to full com-mand.
here comes the King of glo - ry tak - ing u - ni - ver - sal power.
from a - ges past it was, is now, and ev - er-more shall be.
Fine
Who may go up the hill of the Lord and stand in the place of ho - li - ness?
A Who is the King, this King of_ glo - ry, where is the throne he comes to claim?
Who is the King, this King of_ glo - ry, what is the power by which he reigns?
D.C. al Fine
On - ly the one whose heart is pure, whose hands and_ lips are clean.
B Christ is the King, the Lord of_ glo - ry, fresh from his vic - to - ry.
Christ is the King, his cross his glo - ry, and by_ love he rules.

24E Lift up your heads

From Psalm 24
Words and music: Michelle Stoodley
Music arranged: Christopher Norton

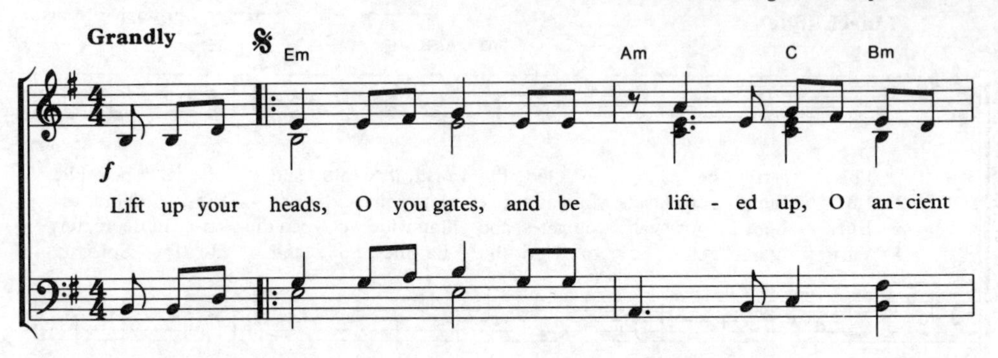
Grandly
Em
Am
C
Bm
f
Lift up your heads, O you gates, and be lift - ed up, O an-cient

Em
A
C
Bm
1.
Em
doors, that the King of glo - ry may come in. Lift up your

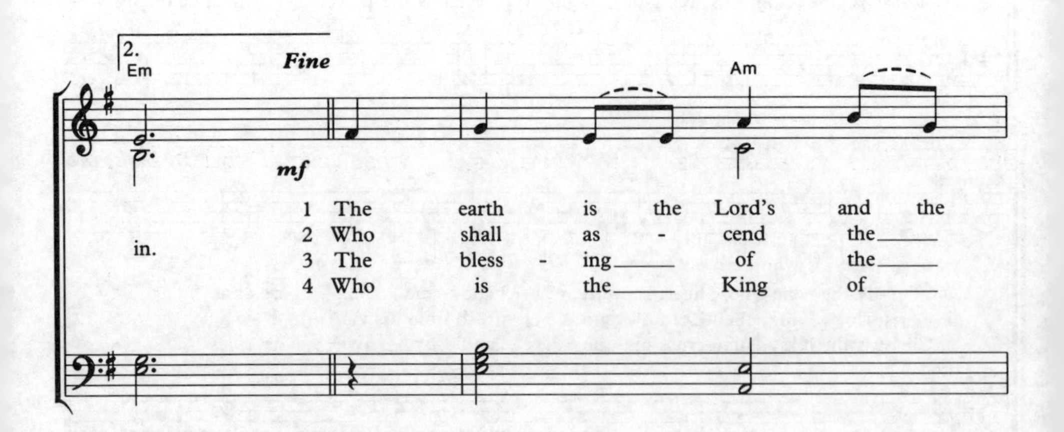
2.
Em
Fine
Am
mf
in.
1 The earth is the Lord's and the
2 Who shall as - cend the
3 The bless - ing of the
4 Who is the King of

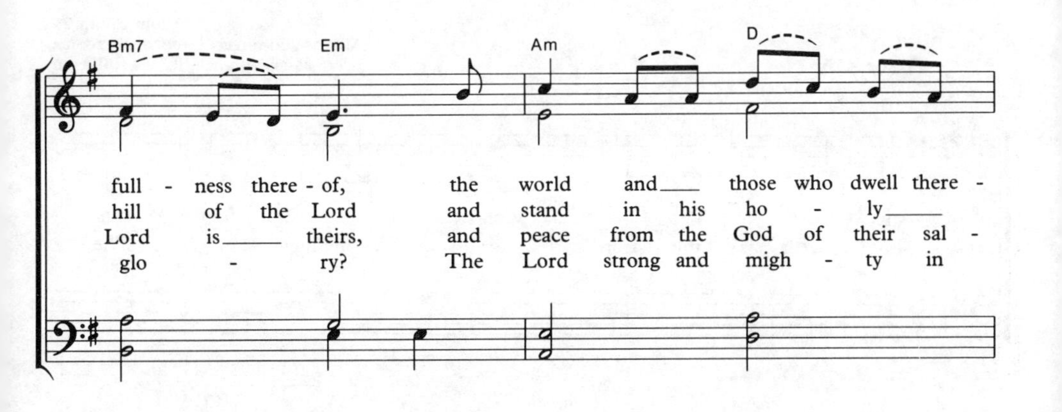
Bm7
Em
Am
D
full - ness there - of, the world and those who dwell there -
hill of the Lord and stand in his ho - ly
Lord is theirs, and peace from the God of their sal -
glo - ry? The Lord strong and migh - ty in

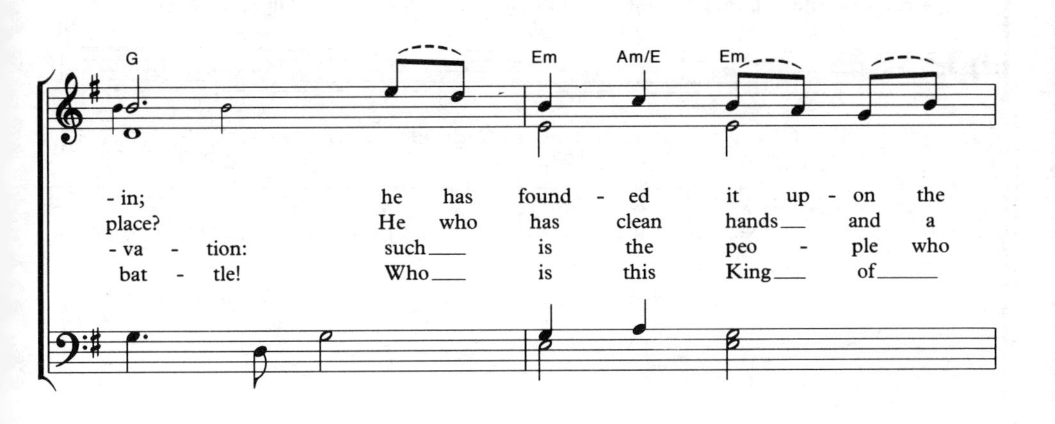
G
Em
Am/E
Em
- in; he has found - ed it up - on the
place? He who has clean hands and a
- va - tion: such is the peo - ple who
bat - tle! Who is this King of

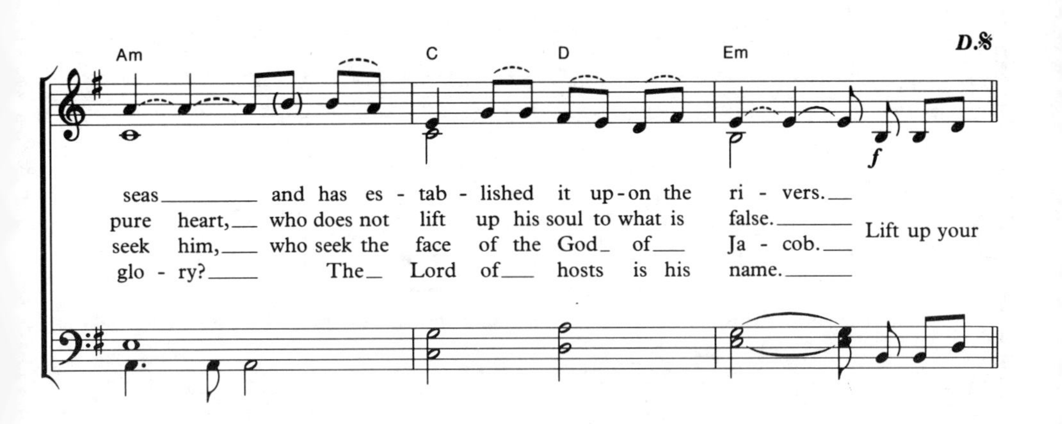
Am
C
D
Em
D.𝄋
f
seas and has es - tab - lished it up-on the ri - vers.
pure heart, who does not lift up his soul to what is false.
seek him, who seek the face of the God of Ja - cob.
glo - ry? The Lord of hosts is his name.
Lift up your

24F The earth is the Lord's

From Psalm 24
Words and music: Graham Kendrick
Music arranged Chris Rolinson

Forcefully
Chorus
D G D
MEN WOMEN MEN
The earth is the Lord's and ev - ery - thing in it. The
Em7 Asus A D
earth is the Lord's, the work of his hands. The earth is the
WOMEN MEN
3rd time to Coda
G D G D
WOMEN ALL
Lord's and ev - ery - thing in it: and all things were made for his
A D G/D D G/A
glo - ry! The
Verse
D Bm7 Em7 Asus A D
mountains are his, the seas and the is - lands, the cit - ies and

Bm7 Em7 Asus A D Bm7
towns, the hou - ses and streets: let re - bels bow down and
Em7 Asus A G D A
wor - ship be - fore him, for all things were made for his glo -
D.𝄋 al Coda
D G/D D G/A
- ry! The
CODA
G
all things were
allargando
D G D G D
made, yes, all things were made, and all things were made for his
a tempo
A D G/D D
glo - ry!

24G The earth and its fullness belong to God

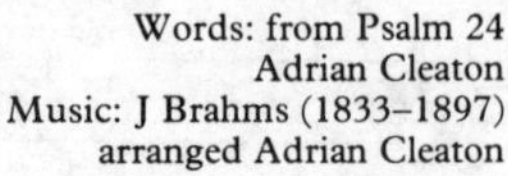
Words: from Psalm 24
Adrian Cleaton
Music: J Brahms (1833–1897)
arranged Adrian Cleaton

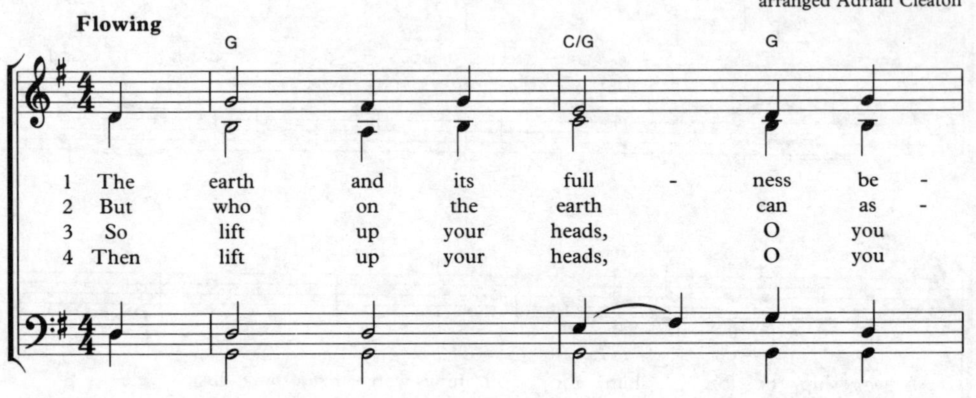

Flowing
G
C/G
G
1 The earth and its full - ness be -
2 But who on the earth can as -
3 So lift up your heads, O you
4 Then lift up your heads, O you

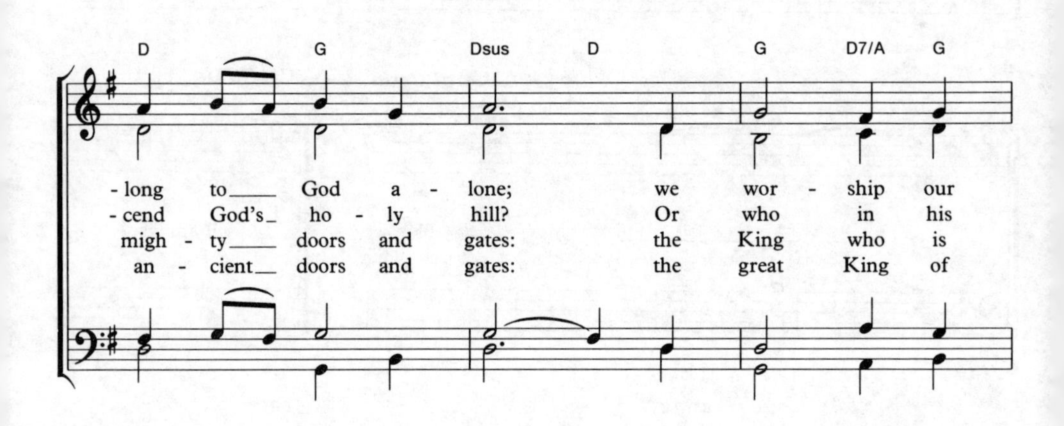

D
G
Dsus
D
G
D7/A
G
- long to God a - lone; we wor - ship our
- cend God's ho - ly hill? Or who in his
migh - ty doors and gates: the King who is
an - cient doors and gates: the great King of

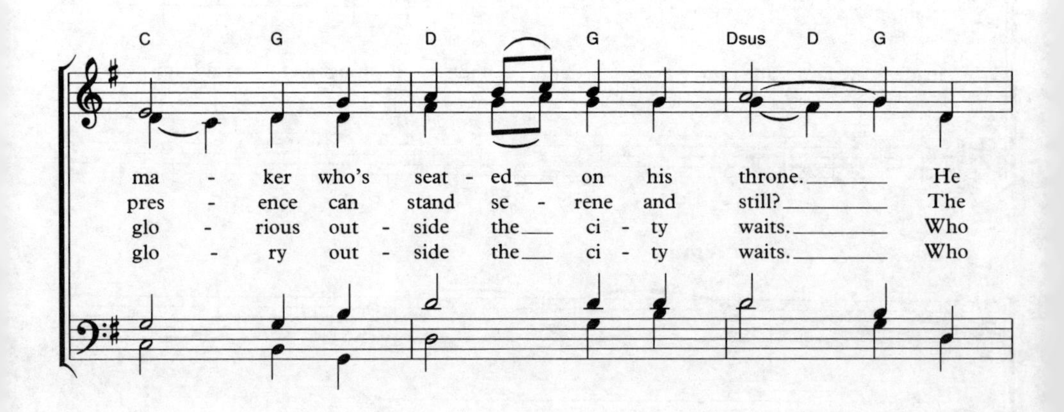

C
G
D
G
Dsus
D
G
ma - ker who's seat - ed on his throne. He
pres - ence can stand se - rene and still? The
glo - rious out - side the ci - ty waits. Who
glo - ry out - side the ci - ty waits. Who

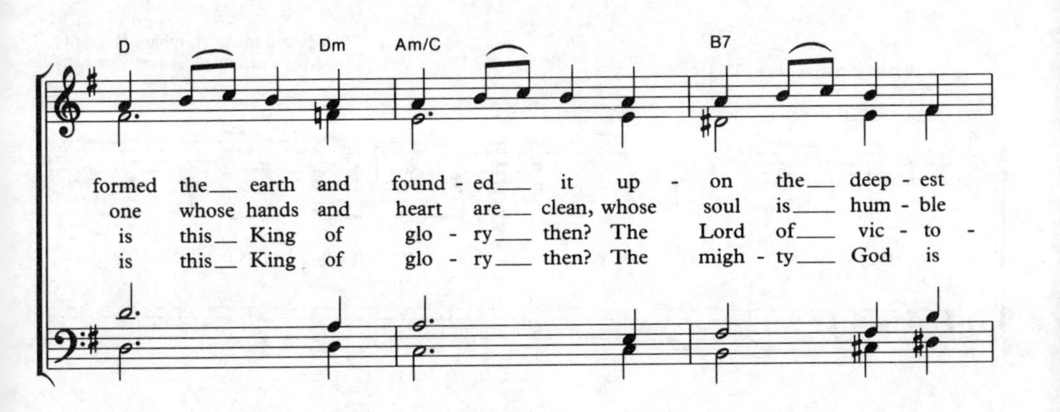
D Dm Am/C B7
formed the earth and found - ed it up - on the deep - est
one whose hands and heart are clean, whose soul is hum - ble
is this King of glo - ry then? The Lord of vic - to -
is this King of glo - ry then? The migh - ty God is

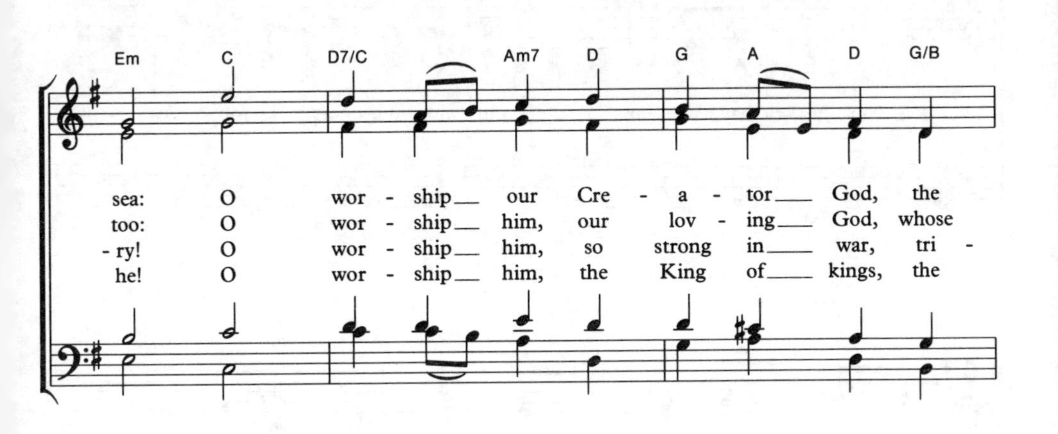
Em C D7/C Am7 D G A D G/B
sea: O wor - ship our Cre - a - tor God, the
too: O wor - ship him, our lov - ing God, whose
- ry! O wor - ship him, so strong in war, tri -
he! O wor - ship him, the King of kings, the

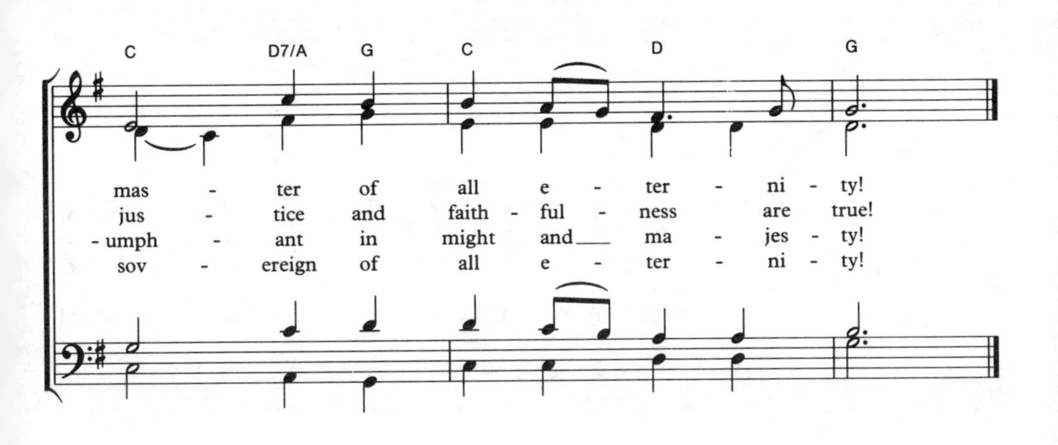
C D7/A G C D G
mas - ter of all e - ter - ni - ty!
jus - tice and faith - ful - ness are true!
- umph - ant in might and ma - jes - ty!
sov - ereign of all e - ter - ni - ty!

24H Fling wide your doors

From Psalm 24
Words and music: Graham Kendrick
Music arranged Stuart Townend
With vigour ♩ = 133
Capo 2(C)
D (C)
Fling wide your doors, O you streets; o-pen up, you hearts of men, that the
Bm7 (Am7) Em7 (Dm7) A7 (G7) D (C)
King of glo-ry may come in; fling wide your doors, O you streets; o-pen
3rd time to Coda
Bm7 (Am7) Em7 (Dm7) A7 (G)
up, you hearts of men, that the King of glo - ry may come
D (C) D7 (C7) G (F) D (C) Bm7 (Am7)
in!
WOMEN
Who is this King of glo - ry?
MEN
The Lord, strong and

D/A (C) G (A) G (F) Bm (Am)
WOMEN
MEN
migh - ty. Who is this King, this King of glo - ry? The
E7 (D7) G/A (F) A (G) G/A (F) A (G)
ALL
Lord – his name is Je - sus! Fling wide your
CODA
D (C)
LEADER ALL LEADER
in! Fling wide your doors, fling wide your doors, O you
Bm7 (Am7) Em7 (Dm7) A7 (G7)
ALL
streets, O you streets – o - pen up, you hearts of
1. D (C) 2. D (C) D7 (C7)
LEADER
men! Fling wide your doors, men!

241 Glory, glory, glory to the King

Glory to the King

From Psalm 24
Words and music: Tom McLain
Music arranged David Peacock

Joyfully
G/D D A7 D G Asus A
Glo - ry, glo - ry, glo - ry to the King;
G/D D A7 D G G/A D
Fine
glo - ry, glo - ry, glo - ry to the King!
Bm F♯m G G/A D
Who is the King of glo - ry? King Je - sus is his name; he is
Bm F♯m G Em7 Asus A
D.C. al Fine
high and lift-ed up a - bove the earth, and his name I will pro - claim.

Show me your ways, O Lord

25B

From Psalm 25
Words and music: Janice A Finn
Music arranged Chris Rolinson

Very expressively
D
Gmaj9
D
G
D
Em7
D
Dmaj7
Gmaj7
D
Dmaj7
Show me your ways, O Lord; teach me your
Gmaj7
Dmaj7/A
Em/G
paths and lead me in your
D
Gmaj9
D
Dmaj7
truth. Show me your

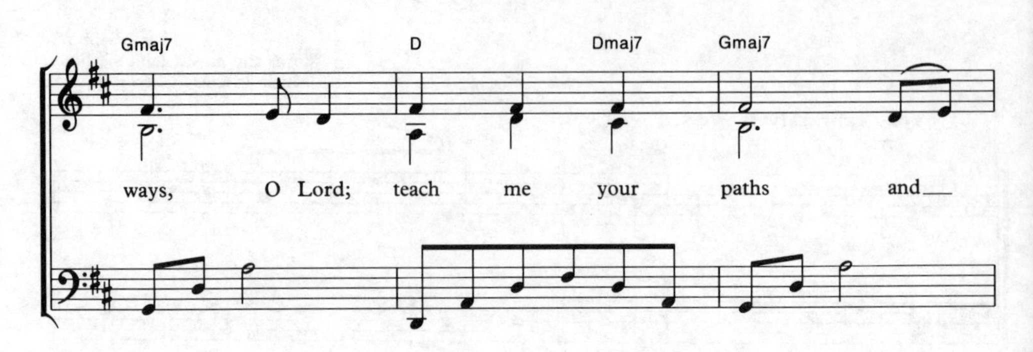
Gmaj7 D Dmaj7 Gmaj7
ways, O Lord; teach me your paths and

Dmaj7/A Dmaj7/F♯ Em/G Asus Dmaj7 D7
lead me in your truth. For

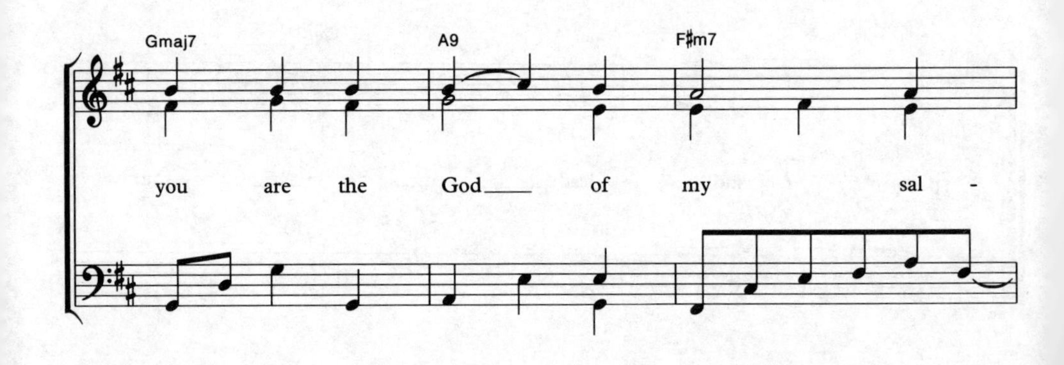
Gmaj7 A9 F♯m7
you are the God of my sal -

Bm7 Em7 A9 Dmaj7
- va - tion, on you do I wait all the day

D7
Gmaj7
A9
long; for you are the God of
F♯m7
Bm7
Em7
A7
my sal - va - tion, on you do I wait all the
to repeat
Gm
C9
last time
D
day.
day.
Gmaj9
rall. al fine
D
Gmaj9
D

25C To you, O Lord, I lift up my soul

Words: from Psalm 25
Malcolm Scott
Music: Charlotte Wright
arranged Christopher Norton

Joyfully
D G A
mp 1 To you, O Lord, I lift up my soul, in
2 Re - mem - ber, Lord, your mer - cy and love, for
3 O guard my life and res - cue me, let me
sim.
G A D D
you I trust, O my God; more than the watch-man
they have been from of old; re - mem - ber not the
not be put to shame; turn to me and be
G A G A D
waits for the morn my soul shall wait for the Lord.
sins of my youth or my re - bel - lious ways.
gra-cious un - to me, for my hope is in your name.
D G/D D G/D D G/D
WOMEN Show me your ways, O Lord; Teach me your truth, O
mf
MEN show me your ways, O Lord.

D G/D D G/D D G/D
Lord; and_ guide me in_ the way that leads_ to
teach me your truth, O Lord – and_ guide me in - to
A D/A A7 D G/D
life:
life.
You are the way,_ my
D G/D D G/D D G/D
Lord; You are the truth, my Lord; to_
you are the way,_ my Lord. you are the truth, my
D G/D D G/D D G/D D
know you is_ to have e - ter - nal life;
Lord – to_ know you is_ to have e - ter - nal life.

25D Remember, remember your mercy, Lord

From Psalm 25
Words of chorus and music: Paul Inwood
Words of verses from The Grail

Gentle syncopation ♩ = 72–76

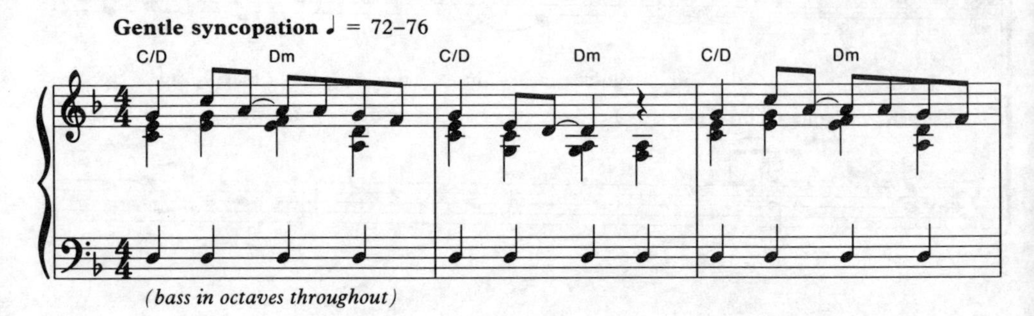
C/D
Dm
C/D
Dm
C/D
Dm
(bass in octaves throughout)

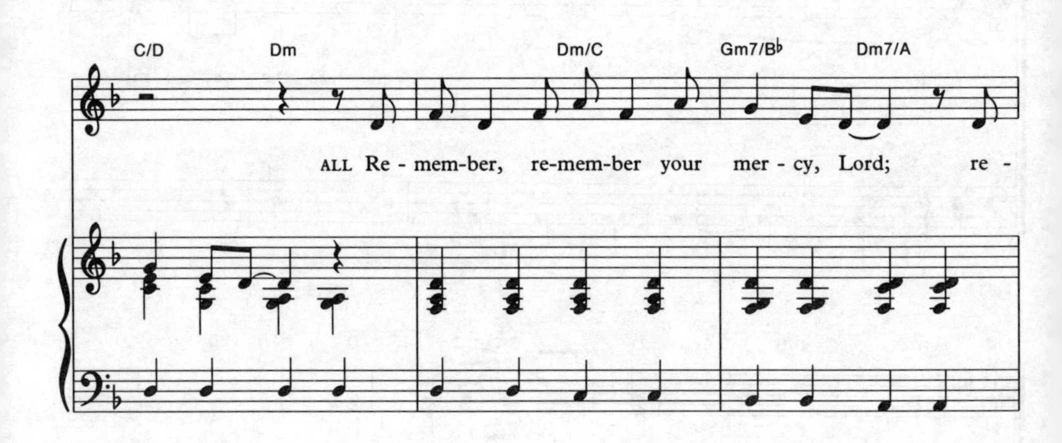
C/D
Dm
Dm/C
Gm7/B♭
Dm7/A
ALL Re - mem-ber, re-mem-ber your mer - cy, Lord; re -

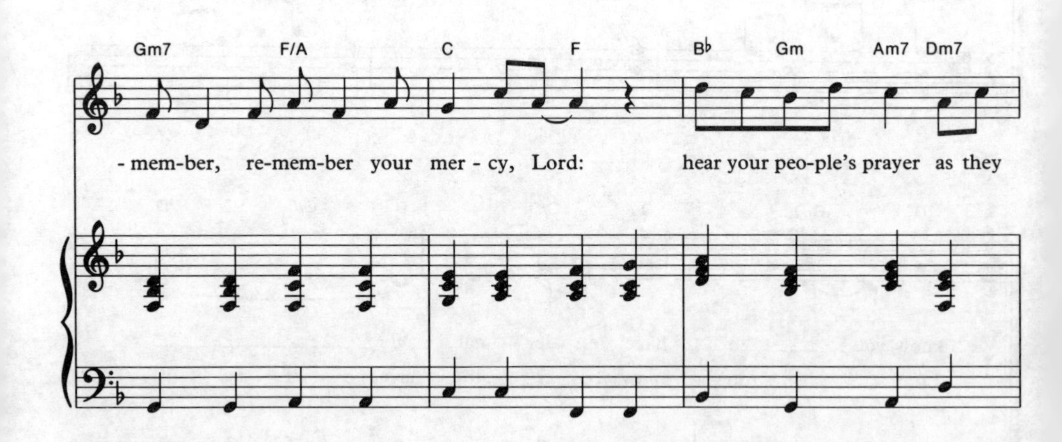
Gm7
F/A
C
F
B♭
Gm
Am7
Dm7
- mem-ber, re-mem-ber your mer - cy, Lord: hear your peo-ple's prayer as they

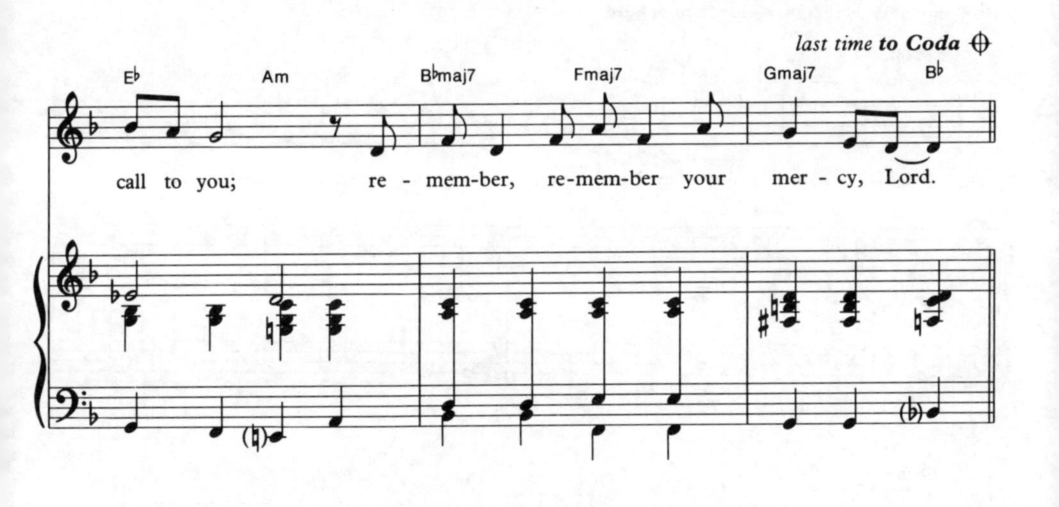
last time to Coda
E♭
Am
B♭maj7
Fmaj7
Gmaj7
B♭
call to you; re - mem-ber, re-mem-ber your mer - cy, Lord.

Verse 1
Dm
Dm/C
B♭maj7
Gm7
Fmaj7
Dm7/F
SOLO 1 Lord, make me know your ways, Lord, teach me your paths; make me

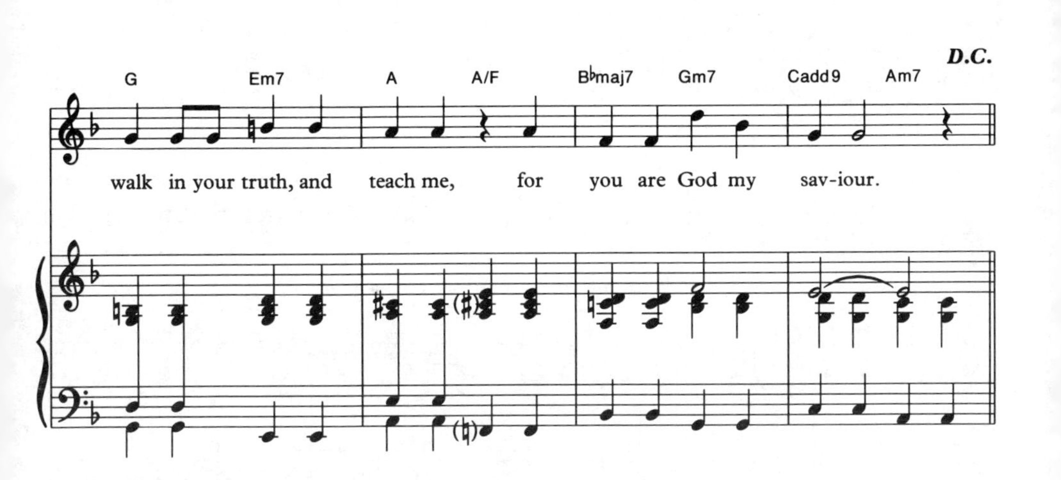
D.C.
G
Em7
A
A/F
B♭maj7
Gm7
Cadd9
Am7
walk in your truth, and teach me, for you are God my sav-iour.

25D Remember, remember your mercy, Lord

Verse 2
Dm
Dm/C
B♭
Gm7
Fmaj7 Dm7/F
SOLO 2 Re - mem-ber your mer-cy, Lord, and the love you have shown from of old;
E♭maj7
E♭6
Dm7
Dm6
E♭maj7
E♭6
do not re-mem-ber the sins of my youth.
E♭maj7
Cm7
F
Dm7
G
Em7
In your love re-mem-ber me, in your love re -
D.C.
A
A/F
B♭
Gm7
Cadd9
Am7
- mem-ber me be - cause of your good-ness, O Lord.

Verse 3
Dm
Dm/C
B♭maj7
Gm7
SOLO 3 The Lord is good and up - right, he shows the path to all who
Fmaj7
Dm7/F
G
Em7
A
A/F
stray; he guides the hum-ble in the right path, he
B♭maj7
Gm7
Cadd9
Am7
D.C.
teach-es his way to the poor.
CODA
C/D
Dm
C/D
Dm
C/D
Dm
C/D
Asus7/D

27B Safe in the hands of God who made me

Words: from Psalm 27
Michael Perry
Music: Christopher Norton

Strongly, rock style
C F/C C G/C C Em7/B
mf
1 Safe in the hands of God who made me,
2 This I have prayed and will seek af - ter,
3 God of my life, my Lord, my mas - ter,
4 Teach me your way and lead me on - wards,
Am7 C7/G F C/E Dm7 F G7sus G7 E E/D
what can there be that I should fear? God is my
that I may walk with God each day; then will he
fa - ther and mo - ther now to me: come, shield me
save me from those who do me wrong; give me the
Am/C Am B B7/D♯ Esus E/D A/C♯
light and my sal - va - tion, strong is his
give me his pro - tec - tion, no trou - ble
from the threat of e - vil, lift up my
grace to wait with pa - tience, help me to
1–3. 4.
Dm A7/E Dm/F F/G G7 C F/G G F/G G7 C
help when foes are near.
shall my heart dis - may.
soul and set me free!
trust, hold firm, be strong.

Alternative tune: Spiritus Vitae, *Hymns for Today's Church* 237

The God of heaven thunders 29B

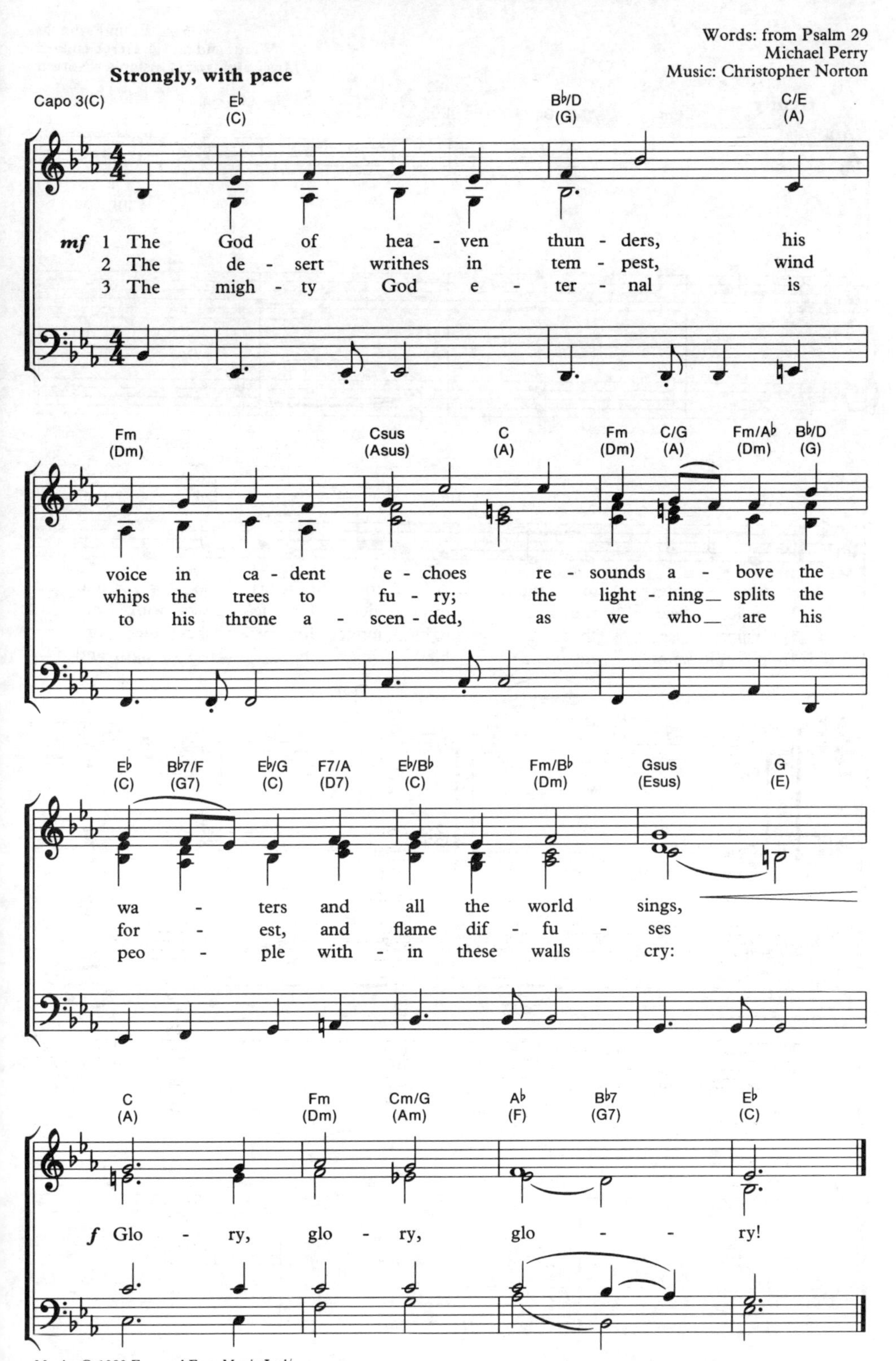
Words: from Psalm 29
Michael Perry
Music: Christopher Norton
Strongly, with pace
Capo 3(C)
Eb (C) Bb/D (G) C/E (A)
Fm (Dm) Csus (Asus) C (A) Fm (Dm) C/G (A) Fm/Ab (Dm) Bb/D (G)
Eb (C) Bb7/F (G7) Eb/G (C) F7/A (D7) Eb/Bb (C) Fm/Bb (Dm) Gsus (Esus) G (E)
C (A) Fm (Dm) Cm/G (Am) Ab (F) Bb7 (G7) Eb (C)
mf 1 The God of hea - ven thun - ders, his voice in ca - dent e - choes re - sounds a - bove the wa - ters and all the world sings,
2 The de - sert writhes in tem - pest, wind whips the trees to fu - ry; the light - ning splits the for - est, and flame dif - fu - ses
3 The migh - ty God e - ter - nal is to his throne a - scen - ded, as we who are his peo - ple with - in these walls cry:
f Glo - ry, glo - ry, glo - ry!

29C Bring your tributes to the Lord

From Psalm 29
Words and music: Derek Howell
Music arranged Christopher Norton

Gently
Em Bm E(no3rd)
1 Bring your
p
Em Bm7 Em Bm7
tri - butes to the Lord of hosts, praise his glo - ry and
(2) voice_ hear the____ thun - der, for he speaks with all
(3) voice_ see the____ light - ning, for it shakes the dry
(4) peo - ple know his____ bless - ing, he___ gives strength and
E(no3rd) Em Bm7
power; wor - ship him in his ho - li - ness, for___
power: the seas___ hear its_____ splen - dour and they
land: the trees___ break be - fore___ him, cre -
peace; for he reigns e - ter - nal - ly – lift___

Em
Bm7
E(no 3rd)
Am6
E(no 3rd) Em9
ev - er singing glo - ry.
e - cho with his glo - ry.
- a - tion shouts in glo - ry.
up your voice in glo - ry!
f Glo-ry, al - le - lu - ia,
f
Am6
E(no 3rd) Em9
Am6
E(no 3rd)
glo - ry to the Lord: you who stand in his glo - ry,
Bm7
E(no 3rd)
1–3.
4. Em9
praise the Lord of the storm.
p
2 In his
3 In his
4 His
p
ped.

30B You have changed my sadness

From Psalm 30
Words and music: Norman Warren

Hebrew style
Dm
OPTIONAL DESCANT
Gm
A
La la la etc.
WOMEN
1 You have changed my sad - ness in - to a joy - ful dance;
2 So I will not be si - lent, I will sing praise to you;
Dm
Gm
A
MEN
you have changed my sad - ness in - to a joy - ful dance.
so I will not be si - lent, I will sing praise to you.
B♭
F
A7/E
Dm
A7/C♯
A
ALL
You have ta-ken a - way my sor - row and sur - round-ed me with joy;
Lord, you are my God, I will give you thanks for ev - er; so

To be sung with increasing speed, adding descant on the last verse.

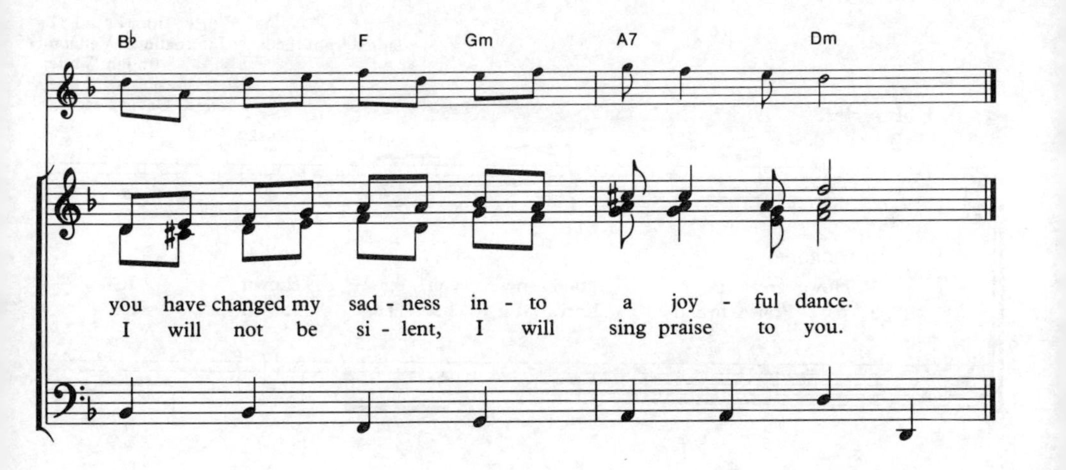
B♭
F
Gm
A7
Dm
you have changed my sad - ness in - to a joy - ful dance.
I will not be si - lent, I will sing praise to you.

B♭ melody

B♭ version of optional descant

31B How great is the goodness

Words: from Psalm 31
adapted from the New International Version
by Ian White
Music: Ian White
arranged David Peacock

Unhurried
G
Em7
Csus2
SOLO/GROUP
1 How great is the good - ness you have shown to
2 Praise to the Lord, for he has shown his
D
G
Em7
those___ who seek your name; the good-ness you give in the sight of
won-der - ful___ love to me!____ When I was sure I was far a -
Csus2
D
Em
A7
all who seek you as__ a re - fuge! In the rock of your pre -
- way you heard my cry_ for mer - cy.__ Show your love to the Lord,
D
D7/F#
G
C
- sence you__ hide them________ safe from all in - trigues of men,
__ all of you his saints._ The Lord will pre - serve___ the faith - ful one,_

G Em Am7 D7 G F/G
— and you keep them safe from cru - el tongues.
— but he will re - pay the proud in full.
ALL
Be
C Cm G F/G G
strong, take cour - age in — your heart,
C Cm G G/B C
all of you whose hope is in the Lord; — be strong, take
Cm G F/G G C
cour - age in — your heart, all of you — whose
Fine
1.
D.C.
2.
D.𝄋 al Fine
Cm G C/D F/G
hope is in the Lord! — Be

32B Happy is the one

From Psalm 32
Words and music: Bill Batstone

Joyfully
Capo 4(C)
E (C) B/E (G) E (C) A/E (F) E (C) B/E (G) E (C)
Hap - py is the one whose sin free - ly is for -
A (F) B/D♯ (G) E (C) B/E (G) E (C) A/E (F) E (C)
- giv - en, whose in - no - cence has been de - clared
C♯m7 (Am7) G♯m7 (Em7) F♯m7 (Dm7) Amaj7/B (Fmaj7) E (C) Esus2 (Csus2) E (C)
by the Lord of hea - - ven!
1. A/E (F) Esus (Csus)
2. Esus (Csus) A/B (F) G♯m7 (Em7)
- ven!
1 I cried till I could cry
2 When I let my heart

Amaj7 (Fmaj7) G♯m7 (Em7) Amaj9 (Fmaj9)
__ no more when my guilt in me re - mained; __ I
__ be known and my con - fes - sion made, __
D2 (B♭) A/C♯ (F) D (B♭) Bsus (G) D.C.
fell be-neath the burn - ing sun till for - give-ness brought the rain. __
then I saw _ your mer - cy flow to __ wash my guilt a - way. __
E (C) B/E (G) E (C) A/E (F) E (C) B/E (G) E (C)
Hap - py is __ the one __ whose sin ____ free - ly is __ for -
A (F) B/D♯ (G) E (C) B/E (G) E (C) A/E (F) E (C)
- giv - en, whose in - no - cence has been __ de - clared _

C♯m7
(Am7)
G♯m7
(Em7)
F♯m7
(Dm7)
Amaj7/B
(Fmaj7)
E
(C)
Esus2
(Csus2)
E
(C)
by the Lord of__ hea - - ven!__
1.
A/E
(F)
Esus
(Csus)
2.
Esus
(Csus)
A/B
(F)
F
(C♯)
C/F
(G♯)
F
(C♯)
B♭2
(F♯)
F/G
(C♯)
- ven!
B♭/C
(F♯)
C7
(G♯7)
Fmaj7
(C♯)
3 Peo-ple, let__ your voice__ be heard in prayer be - fore_ your God:
C/D
(G♯)
F/G
(C♯)
B♭/C
(F♯)
Fmaj7
(C♯)
he a - lone_ can res - cue you_ from

B♭maj9
(F♯)
Asus2/C♯
(F)
F♯m7
(Dm7)
A/B
(F)
trou-ble like a flood.
B
(G)
E
(C)
B/E
(G)
E
(C)
A/E
(F)
E
(C)
Hap - py is the one whose sin
E
(C)
B/E
(G)
E
(C)
A/E
(F)
B/D♯
(G)
E
(C)
B/E
(G)
E
(C)
A/E
(F)
free - ly is for - giv - en, whose in - no - cence has been
E
(C)
C♯m
(Am)
G♯m7
(Em7)
F♯m7
(Dm7)
Amaj7/B
(Fmaj7)
E
(C)
de - clared by the Lord of hea - - ven!

33B All you that are righteous

From Psalm 33
Words and music: Sarah Lacy
Music arranged Christopher Norton

Strongly
ff
D G/D A/D D G/D A/D
D G A D/F♯ F
All you that are right - eous, shout for joy what the
G A Bm F♯m Em7 G
Lord has done! Praise him, all you that o - bey him; give thanks to him
D/F♯ Em A7 D G/D A/D
Fine
and sing to him a new song.
(give thanks),

D Asus A Em Bsus Bm
mp
1 The Lord's words are true; for he is just and_ right-eous. When he
2 The Lord looks down from heaven, he watch-es o - ver his peo - ple, o - ver
G D/F♯ C G/A A
spoke, the world was cre - a - ted._
those who trust in his love._ We
D Asus A Em Bsus Bm Bm/A
mf
Wor-ship him, you_ peo - ples;_ hon-our him, you na-tions, for the
put our hope in the Lord,_ for he is our_ pro - tec-tor; in his
G Esus E Asus A
cresc.
Lord is in con - trol!_
name we shall be glad._

34C O taste and see

From Psalm 34
Words and music: Phil Rogers
Music arranged Chris Rolinson

Tempo di beguine – with a light feel

Capo 5(C) Fmaj9 (Cmaj9)
Gm7 (Dm7) C7 (G7) Fmaj7 (Cmaj7)
O taste and see that the Lord is good:
F6 (C6) Gm6/E (Dm6) A7 (E7) Dm (Am)
how bless-ed is the man who hides him-self in him!
D7 (A7) Gm7 (Dm7) E♭9 (B♭9) Fmaj7 (Cmaj7)
I sought the Lord and he ans - wered me,
D7 (A7) Gm7 (Dm7) C7 (G7) Fmaj9 (Cmaj9)
and set me free from all my fears.

F♯dim (C♯dim)
Gm7 (Dm7)
C7 (G7)
I will give thanks to him, for he is good;
Fmaj7 (Cmaj7)
F6 (C6)
F♯dim (C♯dim)
Gm7 (Dm7)
C7 (G7)
his stead-fast love to me will ne-ver end.
to repeat
Fmaj9 (Cmaj9)
optional D.𝄋
2nd time
last time
Fmaj9 (Cmaj9)
Gm9 (Dm9)
Fmaj9 (Cmaj9)
Gm9 (Dm9)
Fmaj9 (Cmaj9)

34D

Praise to the Lord

From Psalm 34
Words and music: Graham Kendrick

Brightly
Capo 3(D)
B♭ (G) C (A) F (D) B♭ (G) F (D)
1 Praise to the Lord! Sing al - le - lu - ias
2 Praise to the Lord! The wind and the waves, the
3 Praise to the Lord! O taste and see his
Gm (Em) F (D) B♭ (G) Csus (Asus) C (A)
to the king of all the earth.
thun - der and rain, dis - play his power:
good - ness and mer - cy ne - ver fail.
B♭ (G) C (A) F (D) B♭ (G) F (D)
Praise to his name! Let ev - ery crea - ture
raise now the shout; come, lift up your voice and
Praise to his name, who gives to his child - ren
Gm (Em) F (D) Csus (Asus) C (A)
join in the joy - ful song.
join with all na - ture's song.
gifts from his gen - erous hand.

Chorus
F
(D)
C
(A)
F
(D)
C
(A)
MEN
WOMEN
I will praise him, I will praise him;
Dm
(Bm)
G
(E)
Dm
(Bm)
G
(E)
MEN
WOMEN
I will ex - alt him, I will ex - alt him –
Dm
(Bm)
G
(E)
Dm
(Bm)
G
(E)
Dm
(Bm)
Dm7/C
(Bm7)
MEN
WOMEN
ALL
for his love, for his love, for his
last time
G7/B
(E7)
G7
(E7)
Csus
(Asus)
C
(A)
F
(D)
love en - dures for ev - er!

34E Holy, holy, holy Lord

Sanctus Dominus II

From Psalm 34
Words and music: Taizé – Jacques Berthier

Continuous response

♩. = 56
ALL
D
Em7/D
mp
Ho - ly, ho - ly, ho - ly Lord,
Sanc - tus, sanc - tus, Do - mi - nus,

Alternative response

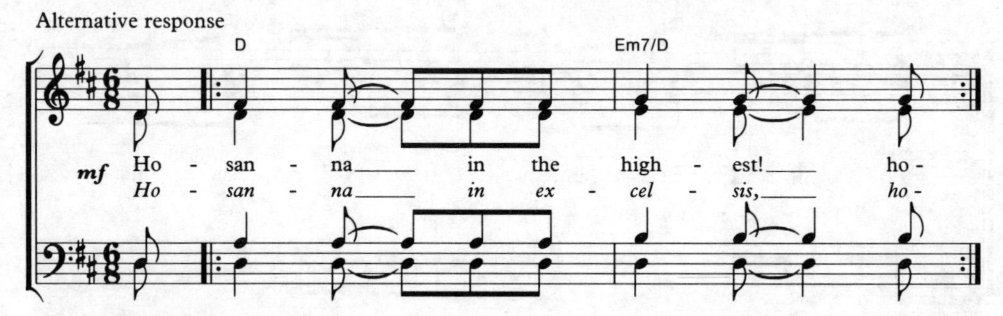

D
Em7/D
mf
Ho - san - na in the high - est! ho -
Ho - san - na in ex - cel - sis, ho -

Accompaniment

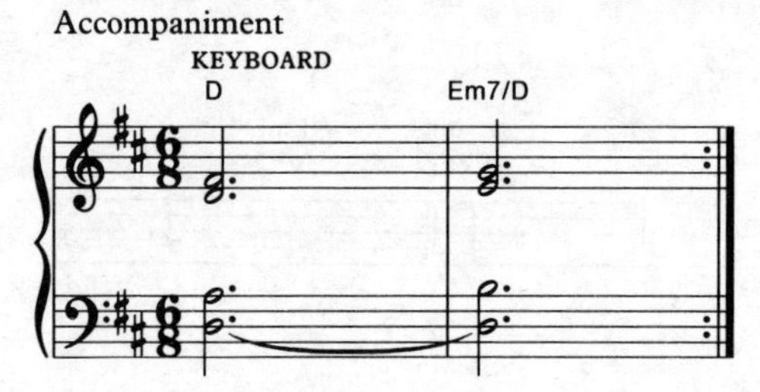

KEYBOARD
D
Em7/D

Verses (sung above continuous response)

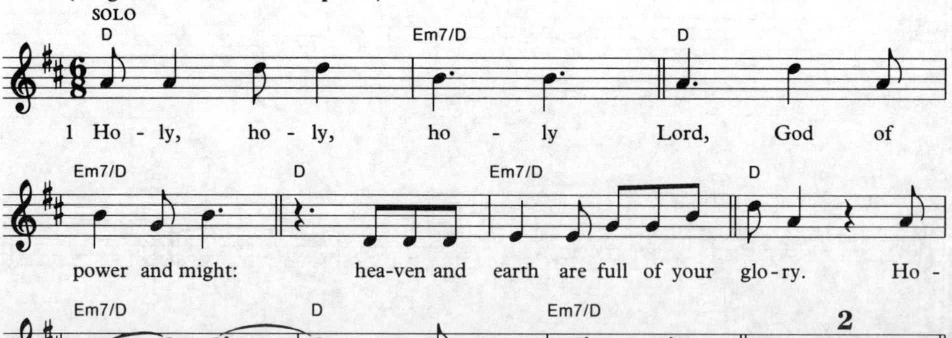

SOLO
D
Em7/D
D
1 Ho - ly, ho - ly, ho - ly Lord, God of
Em7/D
D
Em7/D
D
power and might: hea-ven and earth are full of your glo-ry. Ho -
Em7/D
D
Em7/D
2
- san - na in the high - est!

D
Em7/D
2 I will bless the Lord at all times, his
D
Em7/D
D
Em7/D
praise shall al - ways be on my lips: glo - ri - fy the Lord with me,
D
Em7/D
D
Em7/D
to - geth - er let us praise his name!
GUITAR
RECORDER DUO
DESCANT
TREBLE

37B The steadfast love of the Lord

From Psalm 37
Words and music: Edith McNeill
Music arranged Chris Rolinson

Worshipfully
E A/E E
The stead - fast love of the Lord ne - ver cea - -
B/E E Bm9 E9sus E7
- ses, his mer - cies ne - ver come to an end; they are
A B/A G#m C#m F#m A/B B7
new ev - ery morn - ing, new ev - ery morn - ing: great is your faith - ful -
E/G# B E F#m A/B B7 E
Fine
- ness, O Lord, great is your faith - ful - ness!
1.
A B7/F# G#m7
1 The Lord is my por - tion, says my soul,

D.C.
C♯m7
F♯m7
E/G♯
A
C♯m6/A♯
A/B
Emaj7/B
A/B
— therefore I will hope in him.
2–4.
A
B7/F♯
G♯m
C♯m
2 The Lord is good to those who wait for him,
3 The Lord will not cast off for ev - er,
4 So let us ex - a - mine all our ways,
F♯m7
B7
E
A
E/G♯
A
B7/F♯
to the soul that seeks him; it is good that we should wait
but will have com - pas - sion; for he does not will - ing -
and re - turn to the Lord; let us lift up our hearts and
G♯m7
C♯m
F♯/A♯
E/G♯
F♯7
A/B
B7
D.C.
qui - et - ly for the sal - va-tion of the Lord.
- ly af - flict or grieve the sons of men.
hands to God in heaven.

37C Delight yourself in the Lord

From Psalm 37
Words and music: Phil Potter
Music arranged Christopher Norton

Calypso
D
mf
Chorus
D
G
De - light your - self in the Lord, and he'll give
A
G/D
D
you the de - sires of your heart; de-light your - self
G
A
D
Repeat first and last times only
in the Lord and he'll give you all you need.

Verses
D
G
A
1 Praise him,
2 Seek him,
3 Trust him,
thank_ him,
serve_ him,
fol - low him,
give him
give him
give him
D
Em/D
D
love;
love;
love;
praise him,
seek him,
trust him,
G
A
D
thank_ him,
serve_ him,
fol - low him,
give him
give him
give him
love.
love.
love.
1.2.
last time

The chorus and verses may be sung by different groups simultaneously.

40B I waited patiently for the Lord

Words: from Psalm 40
Michael Baughen
Music: Christopher Norton

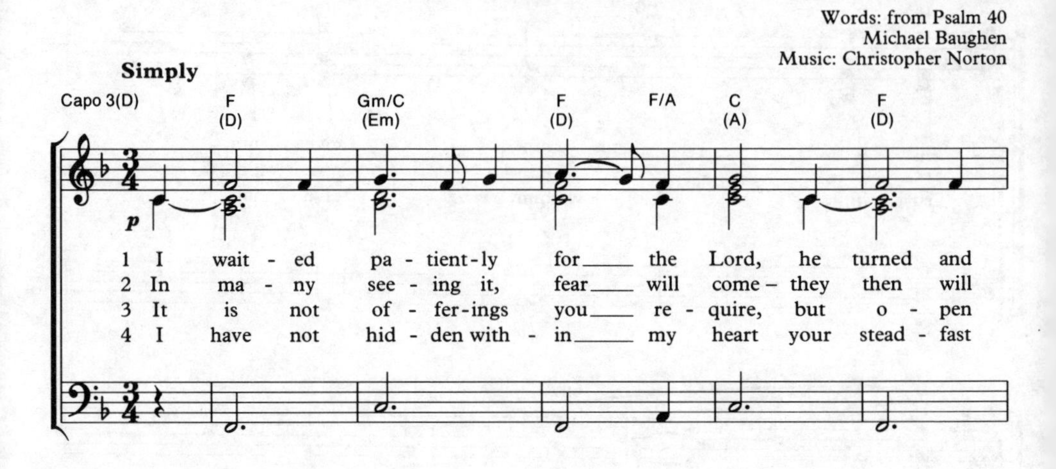
Simply
Capo 3(D)
F (D) Gm/C (Em) F (D) F/A C (A) F (D)
p
1 I wait - ed pa - tient - ly for the Lord, he turned and
2 In ma - ny see - ing it, fear will come – they then will
3 It is not of - fer - ings you re - quire, but o - pen
4 I have not hid - den with - in my heart your stead - fast

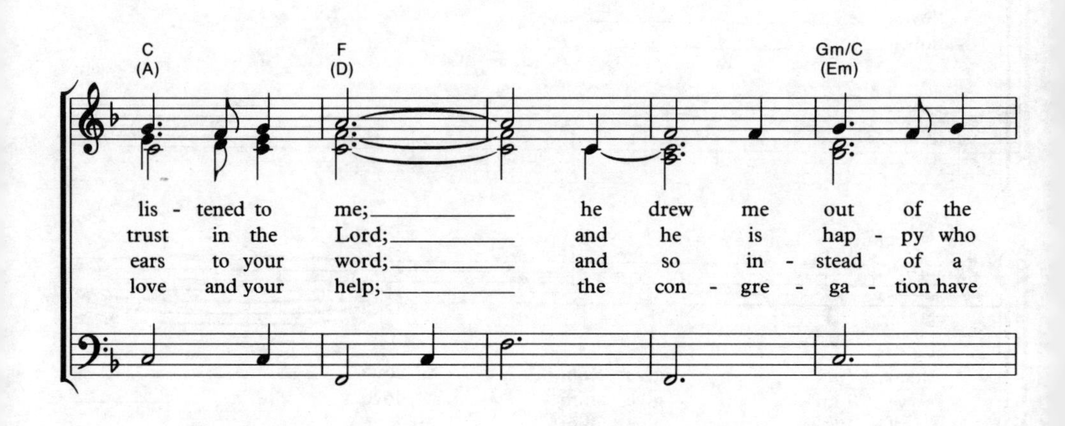
C (A) F (D) Gm/C (Em)
lis - tened to me; he drew me out of the
trust in the Lord; and he is hap - py who
ears to your word; and so in - stead of a
love and your help; the con - gre - ga - tion have

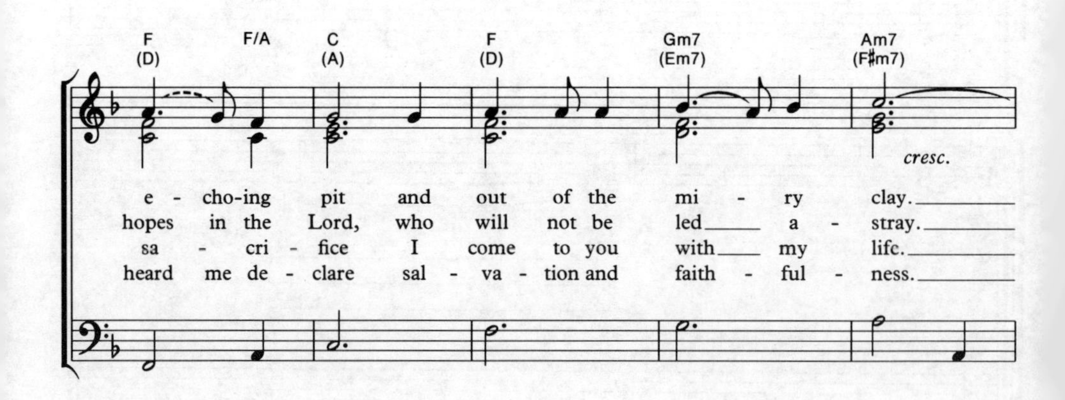
F (D) F/A C (A) F (D) Gm7 (Em7) Am7 (F♯m7)
cresc.
e - cho - ing pit and out of the mi - ry clay.
hopes in the Lord, who will not be led a - stray.
sa - cri - fice I come to you with my life.
heard me de - clare sal - va - tion and faith - ful - ness.

D7 (B7) Gm7 (Em7) B♭maj7 (Gmaj7) C (A) C/E F (D) Am7 (F♯m7) B♭ (G)
mf
— He set my feet up - on a rock, my
— Your won - drous deeds and thoughts to us are
— I love to do your will, O God, with -
— And so when e - vils cir - cle me have
Am7 (F♯m7) Dm7 (Bm7) Gm7 (Em7) C7 (A7) B♭ (G)
mp
foot - steps he made se - cure; with - in my
mul - ti - plied, O my God; they num - ber
- in my heart is your law; de - li - verance
mer - cy on me, O Lord; may all who
A7 (F♯7) Dm (Bm) B♭m6/D♭ (Gm) F/C (D) Gm7 (Em7)
cresc.
mouth he put a new song – a song of praise to
more than we can pro - claim – Lord, none com - pares with
is the news I have told – my lips have not been
love you thank - ful - ly say, The Lord is great in -
Am7 (F♯m7) D7 (B7) Gm7 (Em7) C7 (A7) F (D)
f
dim.
God, a song of praise to God.
you; Lord, none com - pares with you.
sealed, my lips have not been sealed.
- deed, the Lord is great in - deed!

40C I waited, I waited on the Lord

From Psalm 40
Words and music: John Bell

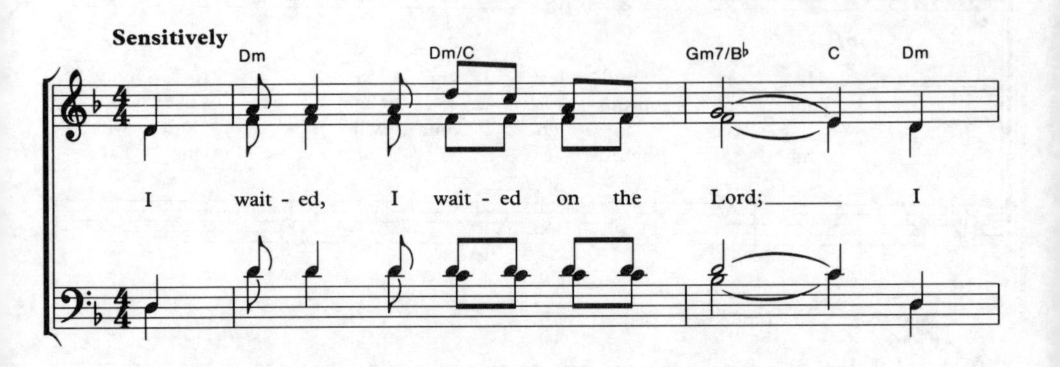
Sensitively
Dm
Dm/C
Gm7/B♭
C
Dm
I wait - ed, I wait - ed on the Lord; I

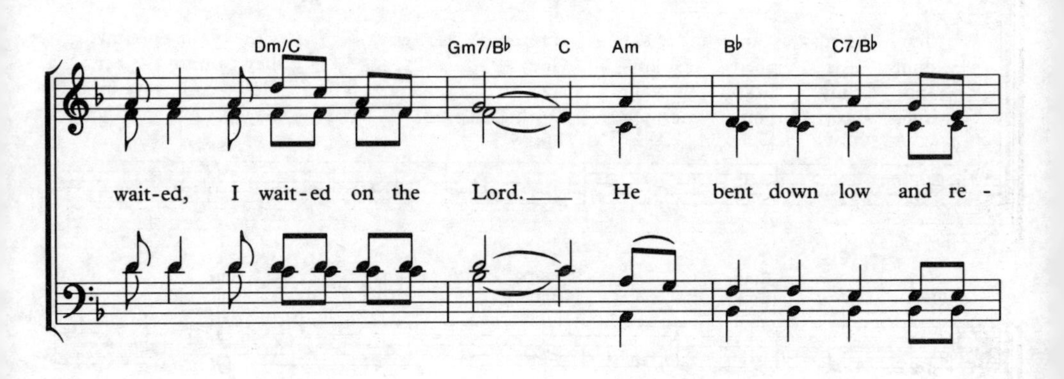
Dm/C
Gm7/B♭
C
Am
B♭
C7/B♭
wait-ed, I wait-ed on the Lord. He bent down low and re -

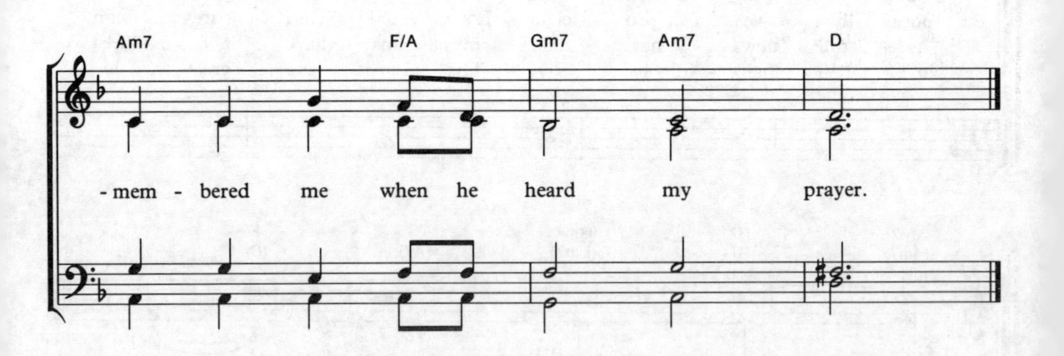
Am7
F/A
Gm7
Am7
D
-mem - bered me when he heard my prayer.

Just as a lost and thirsty deer 42C

From Psalm 42
Words and music: John Bell

With expression
Am Bm7 Dm7 Esus Em7 A
1 Just as a lost and thirs - ty deer
2 Both day and night I cry a - loud;
3 Bro - ken and hurt I call to mind
4 Why am I now so lost and low;
Am Bm7 Dm7 Esus Em7 A
longs for the cool and run - ning stream,
tears have be - come my on - ly food
how in the past I served the Lord,
why am I trou - bled and con - fused?
Am Fmaj7 G Em7 F Dm7 Esus E7
I thirst for you, the liv - ing God,
while all a - round cruel voi - ces ask,
wor - shipped and walked with hap - py crowds,
Gi - ven no ans - wer, still I hope
Am Bm7 Dm7 Esus Em7 A
anx - ious to know that you are near.
'Where is your God, where is your God?'
sing - ing and shout - ing praise to God.
and trust my Sav - iour and my God.

42D As the deer pants for the water

From Psalm 42
Words and music: Martin Nystrom

Flowing
D
A/C♯
Bm
Bm/A
p
1 As the deer pants_ for the wa - ter, so my
2 I want you more than gold or sil - ver, on - ly
3 You're my friend and you are my bro - ther, e - ven

G
Asus
A
D
A/C♯
soul longs af - ter you; you a - lone are my
you can sa - tis - fy; you a - lone are the
though you are a king; I love you more than

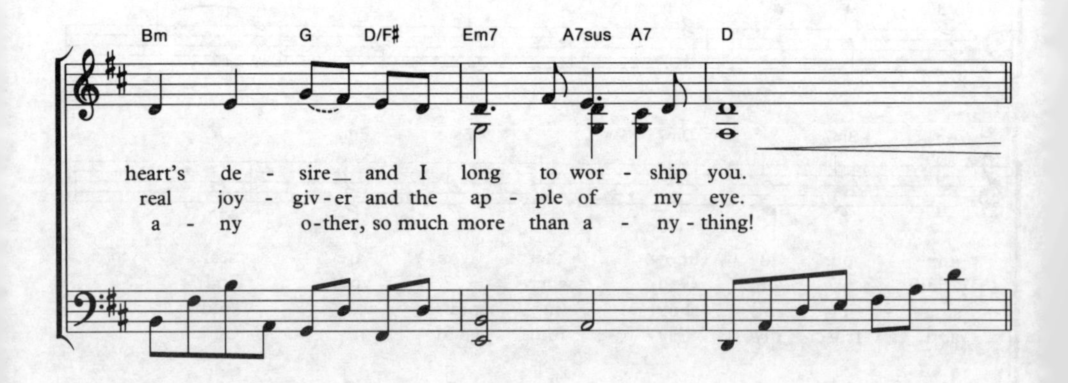
Bm
G
D/F♯
Em7
A7sus
A7
D
heart's de - sire_ and I long to wor - ship you.
real joy - giv - er and the ap - ple of my eye.
a - ny o - ther, so much more than a - ny - thing!

Bm
Bm/A
G
D/F♯
f
You a - lone are my strength, my shield, to

rit.
a tempo
G
Bm/F♯
Em
F♯sus
F♯
D
A/C♯
mp
you a - lone may my spi - rit yield; you a - lone are my

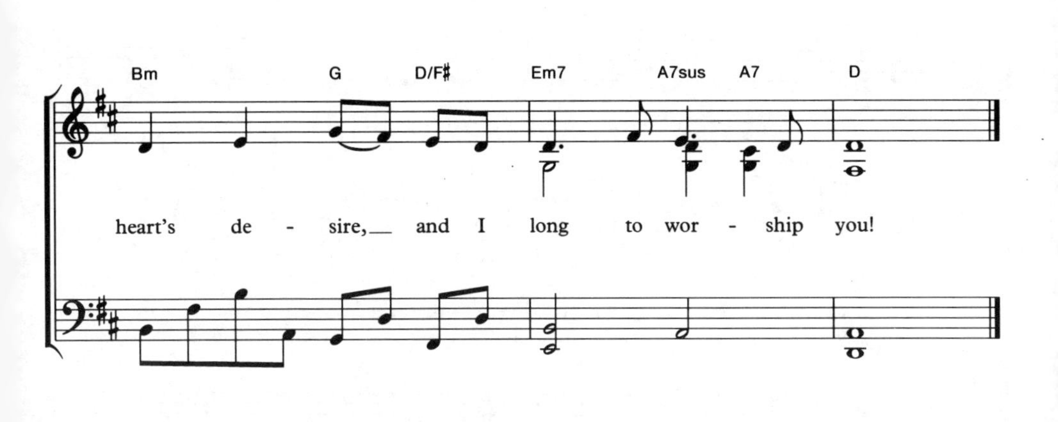
Bm
G
D/F♯
Em7
A7sus
A7
D
heart's de - sire,__ and I long to wor - ship you!

43c O Father, send your light

From Psalms 43 and 44
Words and music: Rae Ranford
Music arranged David Peacock

Light Hebrew feel
Em B Em B Em
1 O Fa-ther, send your light;_ O Fa-ther, send your truth, and let them
(2) God and King_ who gives me ev - ery - thing, and in whose
B Em B Em
lead me back to you in Zi - on._ O Fa-ther, send your light; O Fa-ther,
name I can de-feat my e-ne-mies. I will not trust the bow, I will not
B Em B Em
send your truth, and let them lead me back to you in Zi - on._ I will
trust the sword, for you have saved me from all those who ha-ted me._ My heart
G D C D
come to your Tem-ple_ where you live,_ then I'll come to your al - tar, O
yearns for your pres-ence,_ migh - ty God; my soul thirsts for your right - eous -

Em
G
God; there I'll play my harp and sing
- ness. I will sing your praise, I will
D
Em
B7
Em
praise to you – you're the source of my hap - pi - ness.
bless your name –
Em
Am
Em
Lai, lai, lai, lai; lai, lai, lai, lai; lai, lai, lai, lai, lai;
B
Em
Am
lai, lai, lai; lai, lai, lai, lai; lai, lai, lai, lai;
1.
2. Optional repeat from
to end
Em/B
B7
Em
Em
Em
lai, lai, lai, lai, lai; lai, lai. 2 You are my lai. lai.

44 We have heard, O Lord our God

Words: from Psalm 44
Michael Perry
Music: Chris Rolinson
Moderato maestoso
Capo 3(C)
1 We have heard, O Lord our God, the story of your grace; and how you gave to us this land, defending us with your right hand and showing us your face.
2 You are great, O Lord our God, we trusted in your name; we did not triumph by the sword, but through the victory of your word you put our foes to shame.
3 Yet, today, O Lord our God, the weak – who once were strong – cry out to you, 'O come, arise, reveal your light to darkened eyes, and turn our sighs to song!'
Alternative tune: Great Glen, Psalms for Today 44

Be still and know that I am God

46C

From Psalm 46
Words and music: Unknown
Music arranged Christopher Norton

Simply

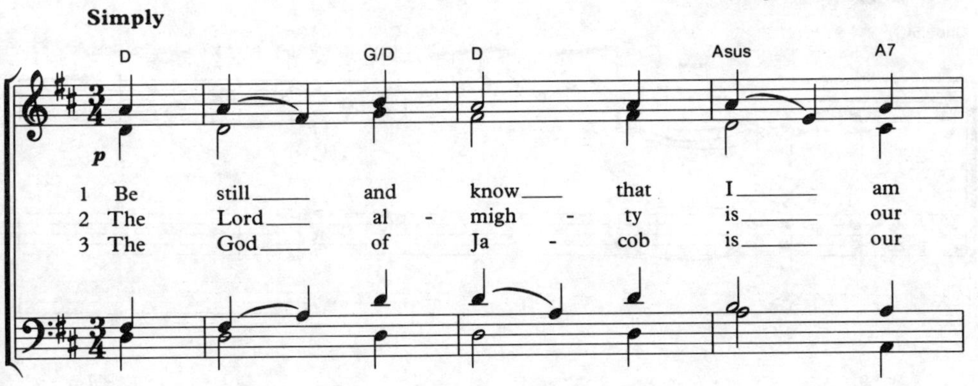

D
G/D
D
Asus
A7
p
1 Be still and know that I am
2 The Lord al - migh - ty is our
3 The God of Ja - cob is our

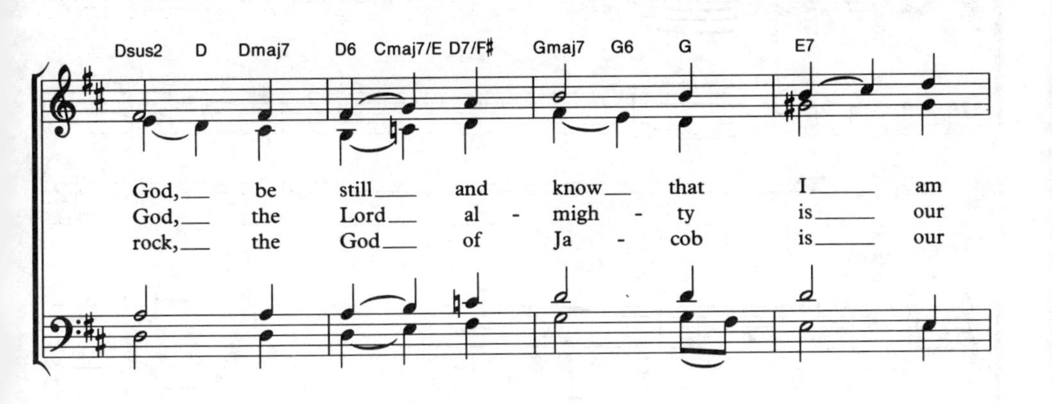

Dsus2
D
Dmaj7
D6
Cmaj7/E
D7/F♯
Gmaj7
G6
G
E7
God, be still and know that I am
God, the Lord al - migh - ty is our
rock, the God of Ja - cob is our

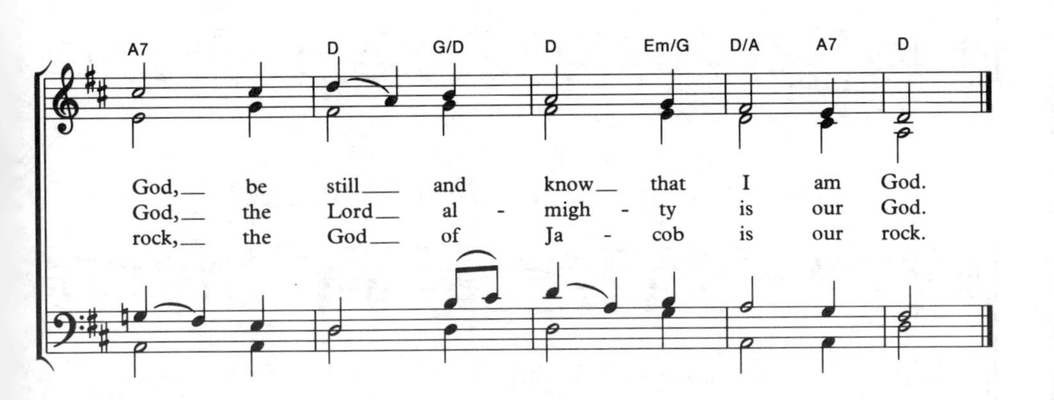

A7
D
G/D
D
Em/G
D/A
A7
D
God, be still and know that I am God.
God, the Lord al - migh - ty is our God.
rock, the God of Ja - cob is our rock.

46D Emmanuel, God is with us

From Psalm 46
Words and music: Dave Fellingham
Music arranged Chris Rolinson
Rock-style
Capo 5(C) B♭+9 (F+9)
C/D (G) Dm (Am)
B♭+9 (F+9)
C/D (G) Dm (Am)
B♭/C (F) C/F (G) F (C) C/F (G) F (C)
Em - ma - nu - el, God is with us,
C/F (G) F (C) F/E F/A C/D (G) Dm7 (Am7)
Em - ma - nu - el, God is with us.

B♭maj7
(Fmaj7)
Am7
(Em7)
The Lord of hosts, he is with us, the
Gm7
(Dm7)
Dm/A
(Am)
A
(E)
Dm
(Am)
B♭
(F)
C/B♭
(G)
God of Ja - cob is our strong-hold; the Lord most
F/A
(C)
Dm7
(Am7)
Gm7
(Dm7)
B♭/C
(F)
high is our re-fuge and strength. God is
B♭/F
(F)
F
(C)
B♭/F
(F)
F
(C)
B♭/F
(F)
F
(C)
B♭/F
(F)
F
(C)
with us, God is with us,

46D Emmanuel, God is with us

F♯dim (C♯dim) F/G (C) Gm (Dm) F/C (C) C (G) B♭/F (F) F (C) B♭/F (F)
dwell-ing in the midst of his peo - ple; God is with_ us,
F (C) B♭/F (F) F (C) B♭/F (F) F (C) Gm (Dm) C (G)
God is with_ us, mak-ing glad the
Am (Em) Dm (Am) B♭ (F) C (G) Am (Em) D (A)
ci - ty of God_ as the ri - ver of life flows from the throne
B♭ (F) C/B♭ (G) F/A (C) C (G) F (C) Gm7 (Dm7)
bring - ing life and strength to all._ We shall not_ be moved;

Csus
(Gsus)
B♭/F
(F)
F
(C)
B♭/F
(F)
F
(C)
B♭m/G
(Fm)
God is with us, Em - ma - nu - el,
F♯dim
(C♯dim)
B♭maj7/F
(Fmaj7)
Gm7
(Dm7)
C+9
(G+9)
B♭+9
(F+9)
God with us, God is now with us.
C/D
(G)
Dm
(Am)
B♭+9
(F+9)
C/D
(G)
Dm
(Am)
F/C
(C)
B♭/C
(F)
F
(C)

46E Be still and know that I am God

The Father's Song

From Psalms 46 and 1
Words and music: Garth Hewitt

Gently ♩ = 104
D
E7
1 'Be still and know that I am
A
D
God; I stand a - mong you
E7
A
and I am God. Though the moun - tains
D
E7
crum - ble ___ and dis - ap -

A
D
- pear
I will be with you –
E7
A
to Verse 2
to end
you need not
fear.' ___
D
E7
2 There's a ri-ver of
joy
flows on and
A
F♯m/C♯
D
on, ___
flows through the ci - ty –

E
A
it's the Fa - ther's song;
there's a tree of
D
E7
A
life
by the ri - ver - side,
F♯m/C♯
D
the leaves are for healing
E7
A
D.𝄋
where the tears have been cried.
3 'Be still and

Clap your hands, all you people

From Psalm 47
Words and music: Jimmy Owens
Music arranged David Peacock

1
2
3
4
C
G7
Clap your hands, all you peo-ple; shout to our God with a voice of tri-umph!
Clap your hands, all you peo-ple; shout to our God with a voice of praise! Ho -
- san - na, ho - san - na: shout to our God with a voice of tri-umph!
Praise him, praise him: shout to our God with a voice of praise!

This may be sung as a round.

47D Sing praises to our God

From Psalm 47
Words and music: Melva Lea
Music arranged Chris Rolinson
Forcefully
A D A
Sing prais - es to our God, sing prais - es; sing
A D A A D
prais-es to our God, sing prais - es; sing prais-es to our God, sing prais -
1.3. 2.4. Fine
A E E7 A A
- es: Al - le - lu - ia! Sing - ia!
A E D
For God is the king o - ver all the

A A E
earth: sing prais - es now to him with un - der -
D A A
- stand - - - ing; O clap your hands and
E D A
shout, all you peo - - - ple, for
A E D C9
D.𝄋 al Fine
he is to be great - ly praised. Sing
Ped.

Clap your hands

From Psalm 47
Words and music: Herbert Chappell

With excitement ♩ = 120
Dm7/G
(marcato)
F/G
Dm7/G
F/G
Dm/G
ff
(stacc.)
(sim. stacc.)
C6
C
p
SOLO Clap your hands, clap your hands; shout to God with the voice of tri-umph.
G7/C
ALL Clap your hands, clap your hands; shout to God with the voice of tri-umph.

On repeated sections
1st time: SOLO
2nd time: ALL
A♭/E♭
D♭/E♭
A♭/E♭
D♭/E♭
1.
A♭/E♭
For the Lord most high is pow-er-ful – he's the king of all the earth. For the
ff
sfz
sfz
2.
Dm7/G
F/G
Dm7/G
F/G
Dm/G
earth.
(stacc.)
C6
C
C6
C
C6
C
G7/C
C
He'll sub-due the peo-ple un-der us, and the na-tions un-der our feet.
p subito

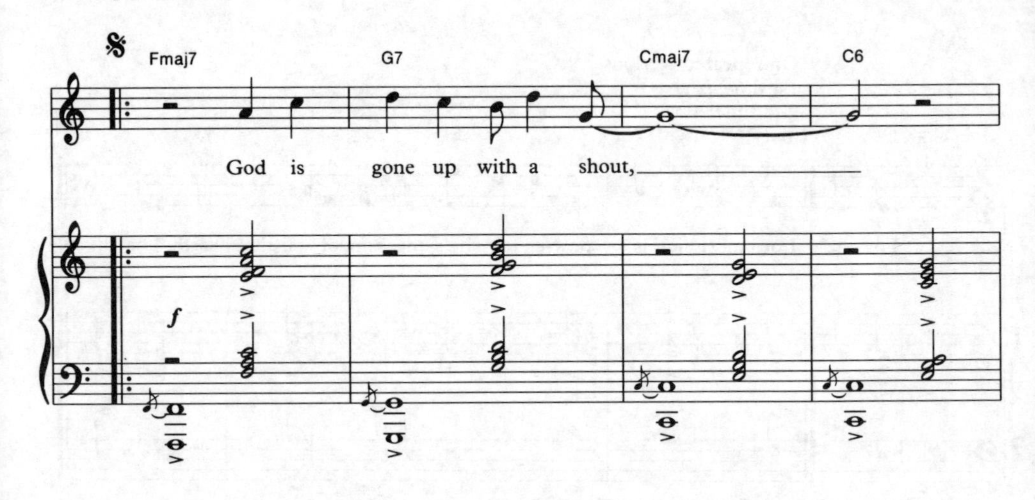
Fmaj7
G7
Cmaj7
C6
God is gone up with a shout,
f

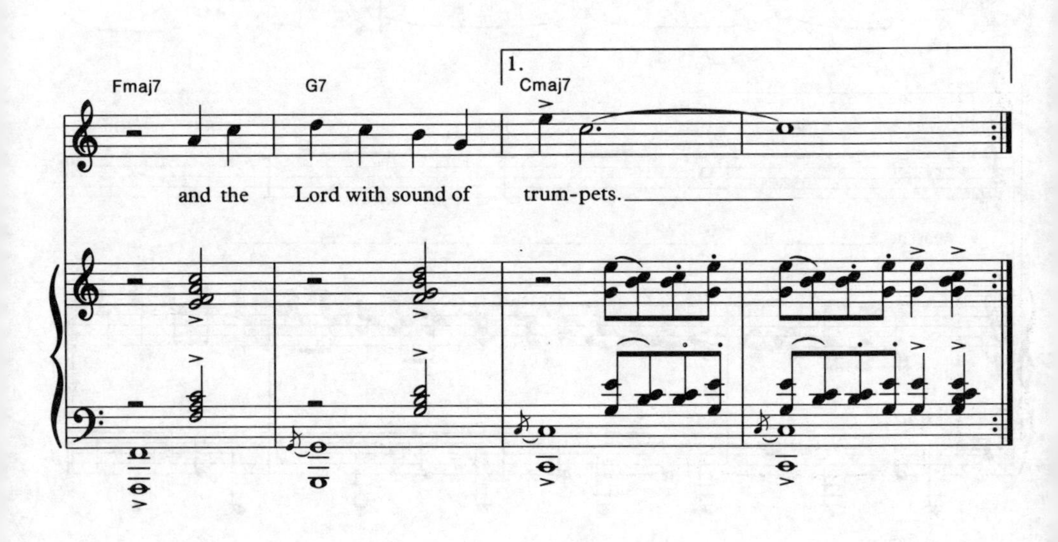
1.
Fmaj7
G7
Cmaj7
and the Lord with sound of trum-pets.

2.
Dm7/G
F/G
Dm7/G
F/G
Dm/G
trum-pets.

D.𝄋 (optional)
C6
C
C6
C
C6
C
G7/C
C
Clap your hands, clap your hands, shout to God with the voice of tri-umph.

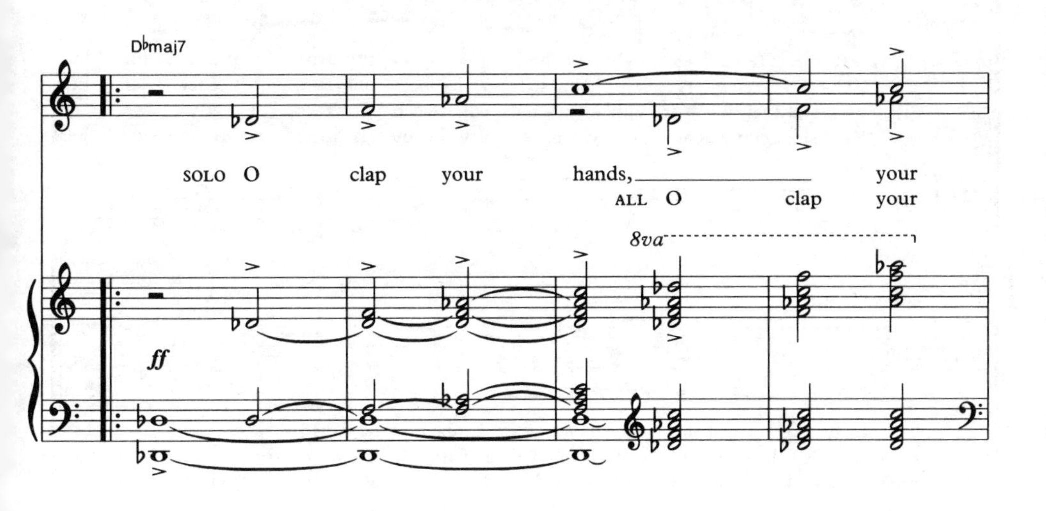
D♭maj7
SOLO O clap your hands, your
ALL O clap your
8va
ff

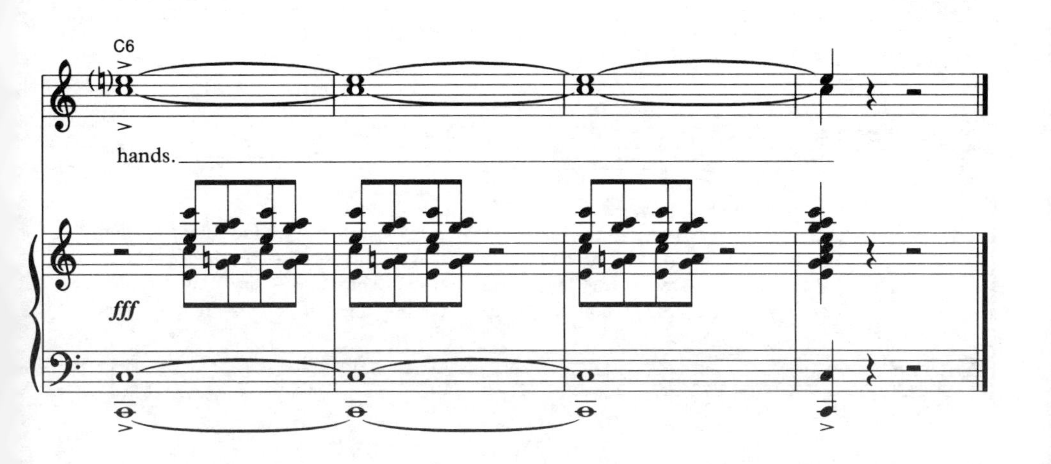
C6
hands.
fff

48B How great is God almighty

Battle Hymn
Words: from Psalm 48
Richard Bewes
Music: American traditional melody
arranged Christopher Norton
In a march style
Capo 3(G) Gm (Em) Cm/E♭ (Am) Cm B♭/F (G) F7 (D7) B♭ (G) E♭/B♭ (C) B♭ (G)
f
mf
1 How
B♭ (G) B♭/D
great is God al - migh - ty and how wor - thy to be praised, for the
(2) Zi - on ci - ty God him-self will be our sure de - fence – all the
(3) east - ward wind your migh - ty arm will sweep your foes a - way; we have
(4) day shall come at last when ev - ery wrong is turned to right; we shall
E♭ (C) B♭ (G)
ci - ty of our ho - ly God shall make the world a - mazed; his
kings of earth who ev - er reigned are stripped of vain pre - tence; they
seen ful-filled in Zi - on all the truth of what you say: we
see in Zi - on's ci - ta - del the end - ing of the night: in
D/A (B) Gm (Em) B♭7/F (G7)
moun - tain ev - er beau - ti - ful be - fore our vis - ion raised – the
see his throne in glo - ry and in fear they scat - ter thence – the
think of your e - ter - nal love and wor - ship ev - ery day the
ev - ery ge - ne - ra - tion we are pass - ing on his light – the

Cm/E♭ (Am) Cm (Am) B♭/F (G) F7 (D7) B♭ (G) E♭/B♭ (C) B♭ (G)
Joy of all the earth!
Power of all the earth!
Praise of all the earth!
God of all the earth!
B♭ (G) E♭ (C)
f
Glo - ry be to God the Fa - ther, glo - ry be to God the
B♭ (G) D/F♯ (B) D Gm (Em) B♭7/F (G7)
Sav - iour, glo - ry to the Ho - ly Spi - rit, for
1–3. 4.
Cm/E♭ (Am) Cm B♭/F (G) F7 (D7) B♭ (G) E♭/B♭ (C) B♭ (G) B♭ (G) E♭/B♭ (C) B♭ (G)
ev - er, Three - in - One!
2 In
3 Like One!
4 The

48C Great is the Lord

SATB version

From Psalm 48
Words and music: Steve McEwan

♩ = 73
Verse
A
D2/A
3
A
Great is the Lord_ and most wor-thy of praise: the
D2/A
F#m7
A/E
ci-ty of our God, the ho - ly place, the joy of the_ whole earth.
Bm7
C#m7 D2/E
A
D2/A
— Great is the Lord in whom we have the vic - to-ry;
A
D2/A
— he aids_ us a - gainst the e - ne - my,_

F♯m7
A/E
Bm7
D/E
we bow down on our knees. And,
Chorus
A
C♯m7
Lord, we want to lift your name on high, and,
D2
A/C♯
Bm7
D/E
Lord, we want to thank you for the works you've done in our lives. And,
A
C♯m7
D2
A/C♯
Lord, we trust in your un-fail-ing love – for you a-lone are God e-ter-nal
Bm7
D/E
A
through-out earth and hea-ven a-bove.

51C(i) Have mercy, Lord, as you promise

Words: from Psalm 51
Jonathan Barnes
Music: Christopher Norton

Calmly
C/E Am9 Dm7 G9
1 Have mer - cy, Lord, as you pro - mise,
2 Your sen - tence on me is right - eous,
3 Lord, wash me from my un - clean - ness,
p
Em7 Am7 Dm7 G7sus G/F Esus E
wash me and cleanse me from my guilt: for I can see the
for I have sinned since my be - gin - ning; and, Lord, you look for
fill me with joy where once was sad - ness; give me a heart re -
Am7 D9 G7sus G7
wrong in my life; a - gainst you, Lord, have I
truth in my heart – so teach me wis - dom, I
- newed, O my Lord, your ho - ly spi - rit with -

C/E
Am9
Dm7
G7
Csus2
C
F
C(no 3rd)
sinned.
pray.
- in.

4 Turn from my sins and destroy them
but let me never be forsaken;
O give me joy in knowing you save,
and make me love your command.

5 Lord, take my lips: I will praise you!
No sacrifice I bring redeems me;
all you require is my broken heart –
a gift you will not refuse.

6 Lord, give your peace to your servant,
protect and stay by me for ever;
through your great love accept what I give,
and fill my life with your praise!

Instrumental part

p
3
3
mf
dim.
p

51C(ii) Have mercy, Lord, as you promise

Lavender

Words: from Psalm 51
Jonathan Barnes
Music: David Wilson

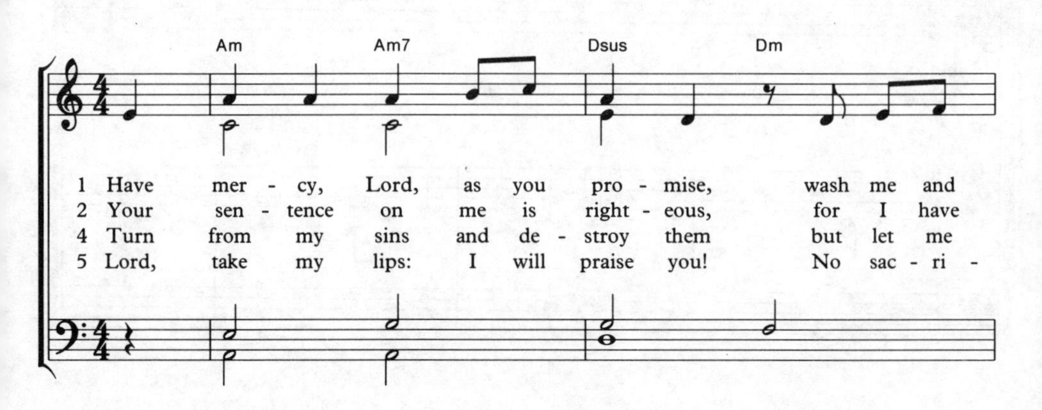
Am
Am7
Dsus
Dm
1 Have mer - cy, Lord, as you pro - mise, wash me and
2 Your sen - tence on me is right - eous, for I have
4 Turn from my sins and de - stroy them but let me
5 Lord, take my lips: I will praise you! No sac - ri -

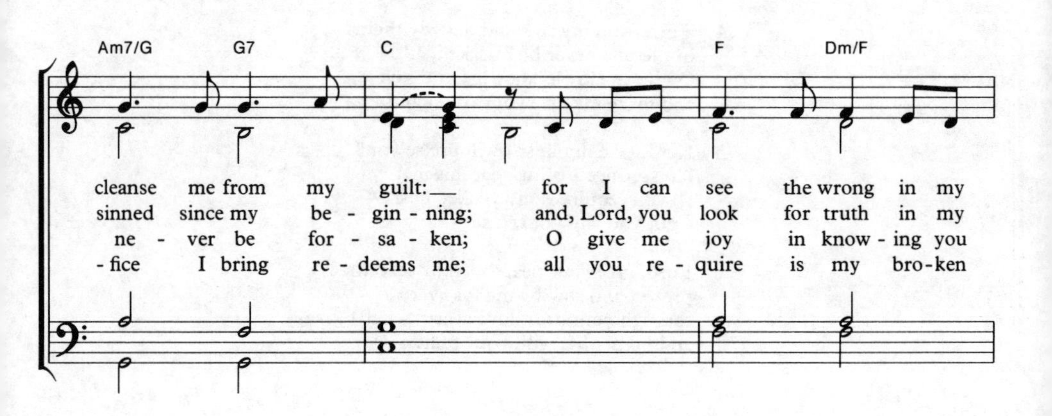
Am7/G
G7
C
F
Dm/F
cleanse me from my guilt:— for I can see the wrong in my
sinned since my be - gin - ning; and, Lord, you look for truth in my
ne - ver be for - sa - ken; O give me joy in know - ing you
- fice I bring re - deems me; all you re - quire is my bro-ken

Esus
E
Dm7
E7
Am
life; a - gainst you, Lord, have I sinned.
heart – so teach me wis - dom, I pray.
save, and make me love your com - mand.
heart – a gift you will not re - fuse.

HARMONY VERSION
Verses 3 and 6
Am Am7 Dsus Dm
3 Lord, wash me__ from my un - clean - ness, fill me with
6 Lord, give your__ peace to your ser - vant, pro - tect and

Am7/G G7 C F Dm
joy where once was sad - ness; give me a heart re-newed, O my
stay by me for ev - er; through your great love ac - cept what I

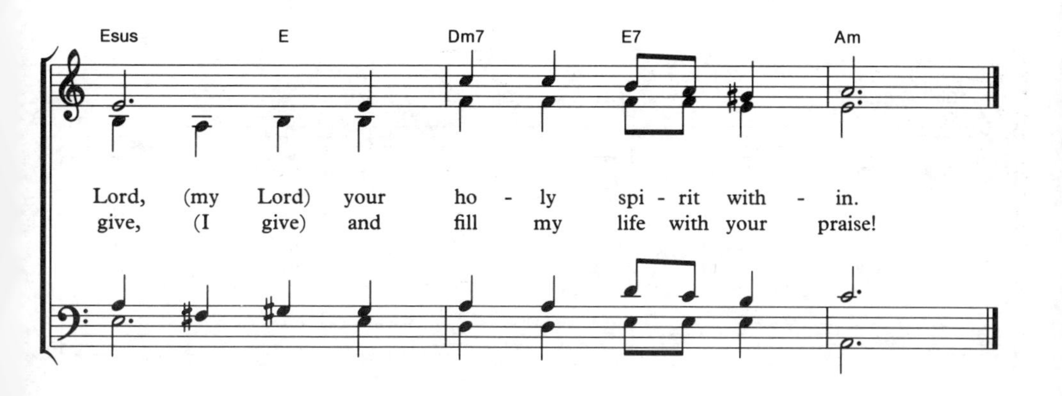
Esus E Dm7 E7 Am
Lord, (my Lord) your ho - ly spi - rit with - in.
give, (I give) and fill my life with your praise!

53 Only the fool will say

Words: from Psalm 53
Michael Perry
Music: Christopher Norton

Moderato
Csus2
C
Em7/B
Am7
mp
1 On - ly the fool will say 'There is no
2 On - ly from Zi - on shall sal - va - tion

Em7
Am7
Dm7
F/G
God'; on - ly the one whose way
come; on - ly in God we all

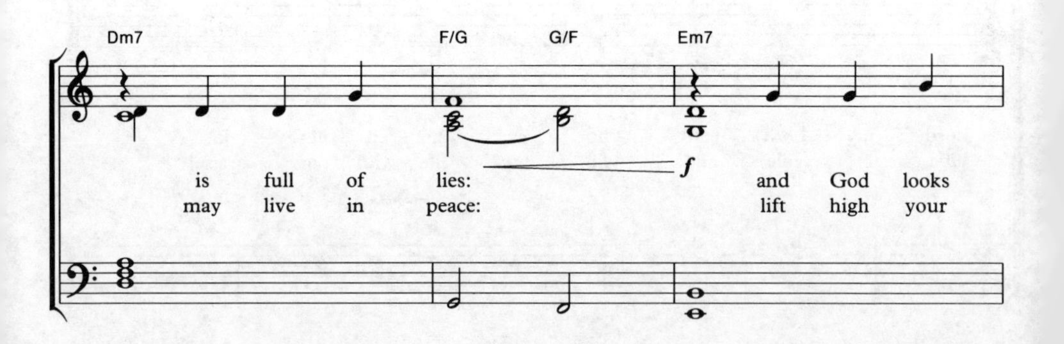
Dm7
F/G
G/F
Em7
is full of lies: and God looks
may live in peace: lift high your
f

Alternative tune: Astwood, *Psalms for Today* 53

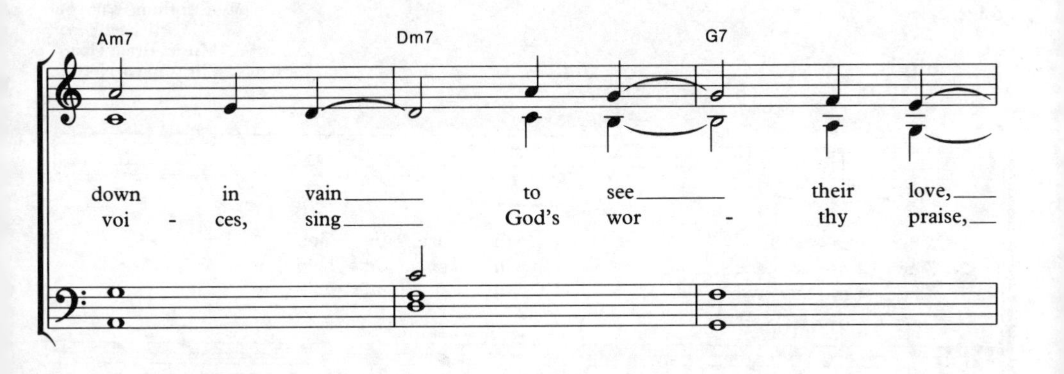
Am7
Dm7
G7
down in vain___ to see___ their love,___
voi - ces, sing___ God's wor - thy praise,___

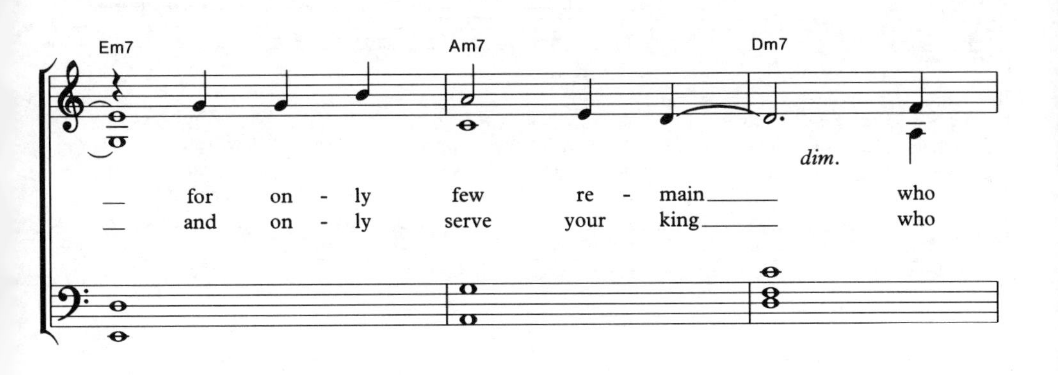
Em7
Am7
Dm7
___ for on - ly few re - main___ who
___ and on - ly serve your king___ who
dim.

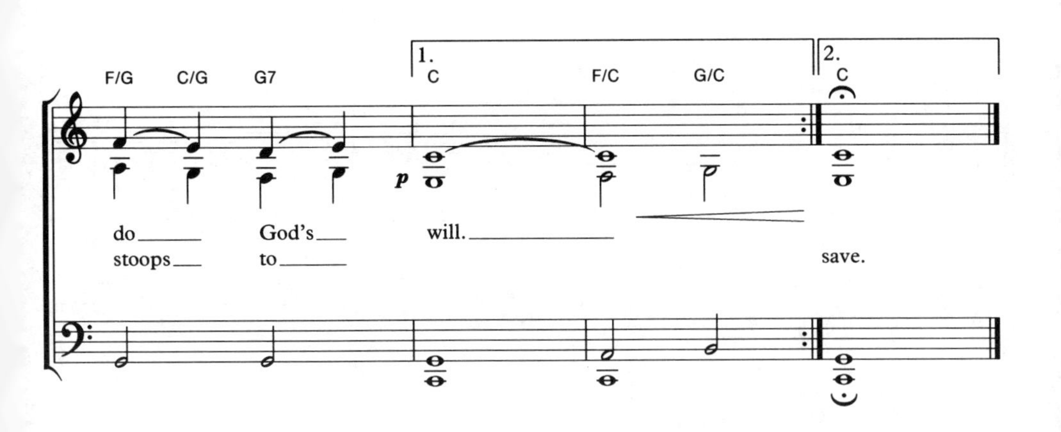
F/G
C/G
G7
1.
C
F/C
G/C
2.
C
p
do___ God's___ will.___
stoops___ to___ save.

56B When I'm afraid

Silverdale
Words: from Psalm 56
Michael Perry
Music: Brian Hoare
arranged Christopher Norton
Simply
UNISON
C Dm7 G7 Em Am
1 When I'm a - fraid I will trust in God,
2 When I'm a - lone I will ask God's help,
3 While I'm a - live I will tell God's praise,
F Dm G/D C/E F Gsus G
when I'm a - fraid I will say, 'What can a - ny -
when I'm a - lone I will pray – how can a - ny -
while I'm a - live I will sing: who can a - ny -
C Dm7 G/F Em7 Am
- one do to me –
- one spoil my peace,
- more come be - tween
1.2.
C/G Am Dm7 G C
God is mine to - day?'
I am God's to - day?
3.
C/G Am Dm7 Dm A
me and God my king?

Simply
HARMONY VERSION
C Dm7 G7 Em Am
1 When I'm a - fraid I will trust in God,
2 When I'm a - lone I will ask God's help,
3 While I'm a - live I will tell God's praise,
F Dm G/D C/E F Gsus G
3
when I'm a - fraid I will say, 'What can a - ny -
when I'm a - lone I will pray – how can a - ny -
while I'm a - live I will sing: who can a - ny -
C Dm7 Em7 Am
- one do to me –
- one spoil my peace,
- more come be - tween
1.2.
F C/E Dm7 G7 C
God is mine to - day?'
I am God's to - day?
3.
F C/E Dm7 G7 A
me and God my king?

57B I will give thanks to you

From Psalm 57
Words and music: Brent Chambers
Music arranged Christopher Norton
Majestically
Capo 3(G)
mf
B♭ (G) E♭/B♭ (C) B♭ (G) E♭/B♭ (C)
I will give thanks to you, O Lord, a-mong the
B♭/A (G) Gm (Em) F (D) E♭ (C)
peo - ple; I will sing prais-es to you a-mong the
E♭/B♭ B♭ (G) Cm7 (Am7) F (D) B♭ (G) E♭/B♭ (C)
na - tions: for your stead - fast love is
3
B♭ (G) E♭/B♭ (C) B♭ (G) B♭/A Gm7 (Em7)
great, is great to the hea - vens, and your faith-ful-ness, your
C11 (A11) C7 (A7) F (D) F7 (D7) E♭/F (C) F7 (D7)
cresc.
faith - ful-ness to the clouds. Be ex -

B♭ (G)
F (D)
C7/G (A7)
F/A (D)
f
-alt-ed, O God, a-bove the hea - vens; let your
1.3.
Cm (Am)
F7 (D7)
B♭ (G)
E♭/F (C)
F7 (D7)
glo-ry be o-ver all the earth: be ex-
2.
Cm (Am)
F7 (D7)
B♭ (G)
E♭/B♭ (C)
B♭ (G)
D.𝄋
glo-ry be o-ver all the earth! I will
4.
Cm (Am)
G7/D (E7)
Cm/E♭ (Am)
F (D)
F/E♭
Dm7 (Bm7)
D/F♯ (B)
Gm (Em)
glo - ry, let your glo - ry, let your
Cm (Am)
F7 (D7)
B♭ (G)
E♭/B♭ (C)
B♭ (G)
glo-ry be o-ver all the earth!

61A Listen to my prayer, Lord

Words: from Psalm 61
J E Seddon (1915–1983)
Music: Christopher Norton

Calmly
Capo 3(Am) Cm (Am) B♭/C (G) A♭sus2 (F) Gm7sus (Em7) Fm9 (Dm9) Gm7sus (Em7)
1 Lis - ten to my prayer, Lord, hear my hum - ble
2 In earth's farth - est cor - ner you will hear my
MEN 3 You have been my shel - ter when the foe was
A♭maj7 (Fmaj7) B♭(no 3rd) (G no 3rd) Cm (Am) B♭/C (G) A♭sus2 (F) E♭6 (C6)
cry: when my heart is faint - ing,
voice: set me on your rock, Lord,
near, as a tower of re - fuge
1.3.5. Dm7 (Bm7) E♭6 (C6) F (D) F/G G (E) 2.4.6. Dm7 (Bm7) F/G (D) G7 (E7)
(1) to your throne I fly. (2) then I shall re -
(3) shield-ing me from fear.

The melody can be sung in canon. Second part begins at *
Verses 3 and 4 may be omitted.

Alternative tunes: Caswall, *Hymns for Today's Church* 126,
Listening, *Psalms for Today* 61A.

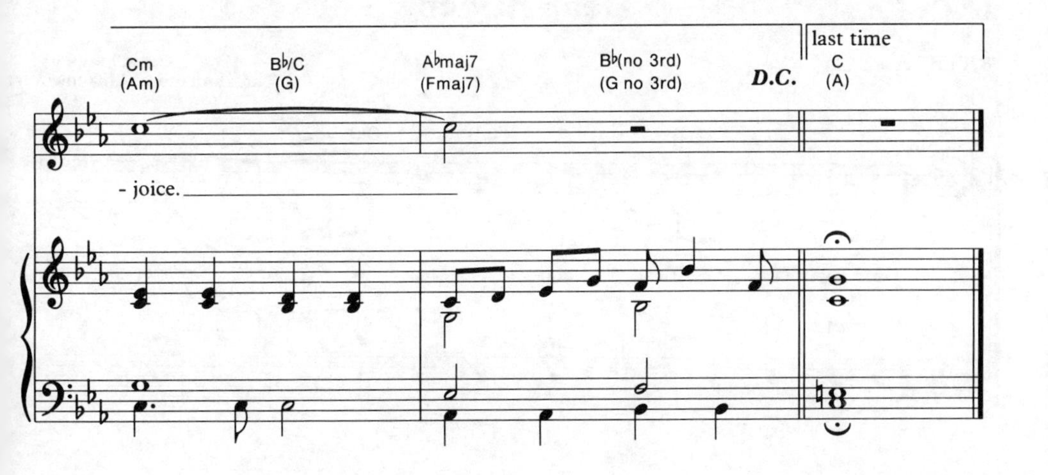
last time
Cm
(Am)
B♭/C
(G)
A♭maj7
(Fmaj7)
B♭(no 3rd)
(G no 3rd)
D.C.
C
(A)
- joice.

WOMEN
4 I will rest for ever
in your care and love,
guarded and protected
as by wings above.

ALL
5 All that I have promised,
help me to fulfil;
and in all who love you
work your perfect will.

6 May your truth and mercy
keep me all my days;
let my words and actions
be my songs of praise!

Instrumental part

1.3.5.
2.4.6.
D.C.
last time

61C Hear my cry

SATB version

From Psalm 61
Words and music: Unknown

♩ = 71
D
C/D
G/D
D
Hear my cry, O Lord, and lis - ten to my prayer:

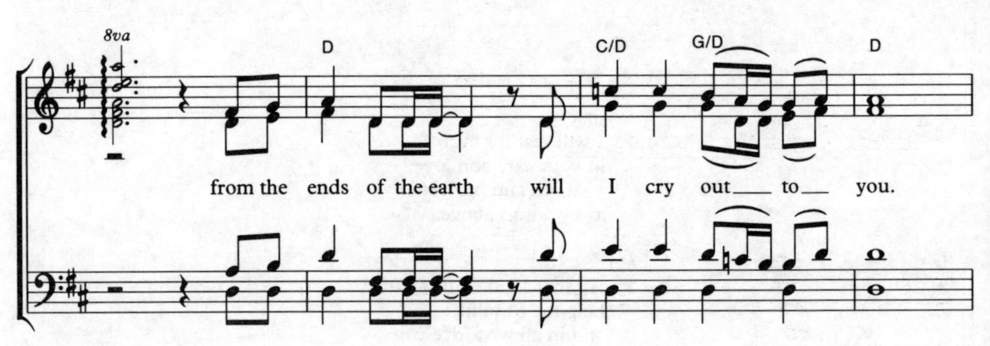

8va
D
C/D
G/D
D
from the ends of the earth will I cry out to you.

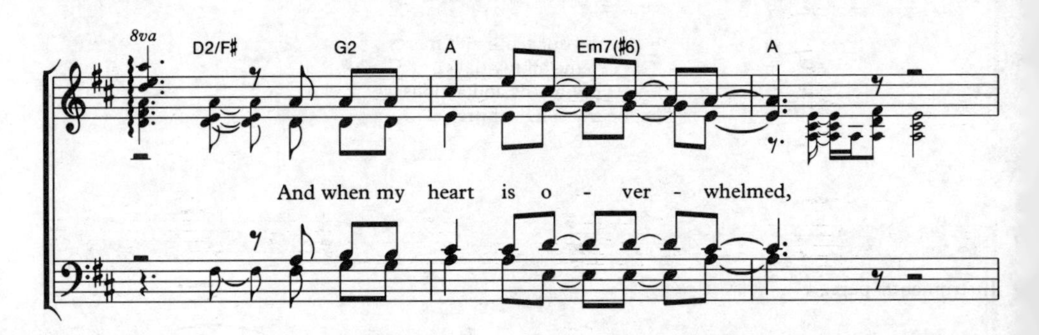

8va
D2/F♯
G2
A
Em7(♯6)
A
And when my heart is o - ver - whelmed,

G
D/F♯ Em7 D
A/C♯ Bm7
A
Em7sus
lead me to the Rock that is high - er than I,

A
D
that is high - er than I.
For
D
C/D
G/D
D
8va
you have been a hid - ing - place for me,
a high
D
C/D
G/D
D
8va
D2/F♯
G2
tow - er, Lord, a - gainst the e - ne - my.
And when my
A
Em7(♯6)
A
G
D/F♯ Em7
D
heart is o - ver - whelmed,
lead me to the Rock
A/C♯Bm7
A
Em7sus
A
D
that is high-er than I,
that is high-er than I.

62C I rest in God alone

From Psalm 62
Words and music: John Daniels
Music arranged Christopher Norton

With confidence
Capo 3(D)
F (D)
Am7 (F♯m7)
Dm7 (Bm7)
Am7 (F♯m7)
mf
I rest in God a - lone, from
B♭ (G)
Gm7 (Em7)
F/C (D)
C (A)
him comes my sal - va - tion;

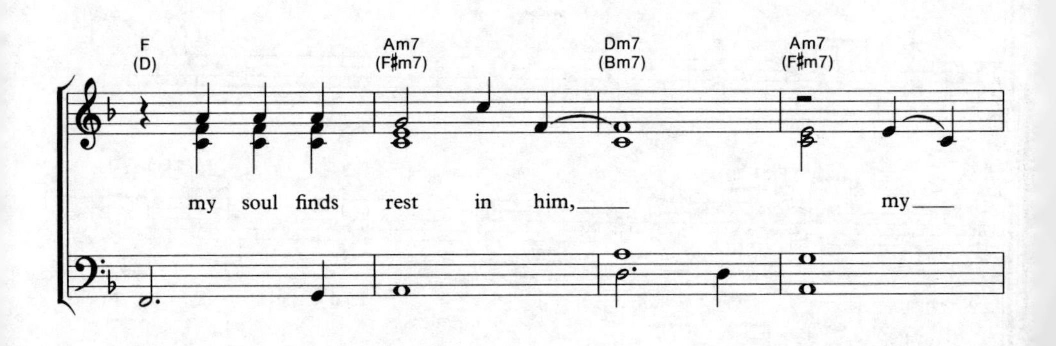
F (D)
Am7 (F♯m7)
Dm7 (Bm7)
Am7 (F♯m7)
my soul finds rest in him, my

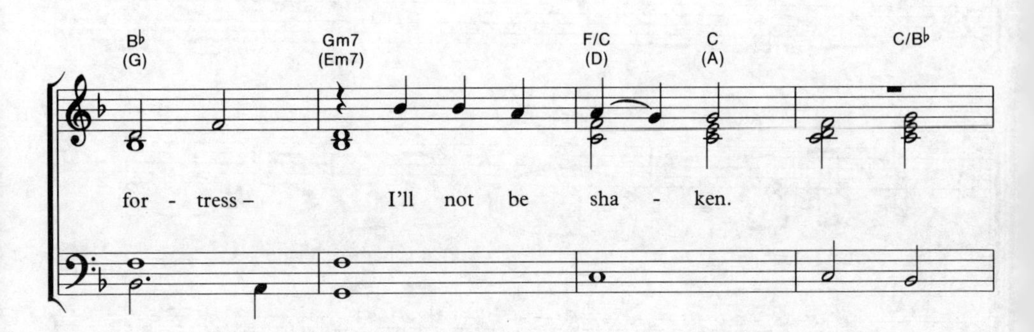
B♭ (G)
Gm7 (Em7)
F/C (D)
C (A)
C/B♭
for - tress – I'll not be sha - ken.

F/A (D)
B♭ (G)
C (A)
A/C♯ (F♯)
f
1 My hope is in the Lord my hon-our and strength; my
2 O trust in him, you peo - ple, pour out your hearts; for
Dm (Bm)
G7 (E7)
B♭/C (G)
C7 (A7)
C/B♭
re - fuge is in him for ev - er,
God is our re - fuge for ev - er,
F/A (D)
C/B♭ (A)
Cm/E♭ (Am)
D7 (B7)
my trust and all of my heart
Gm7 (Em7)
C7sus (A7)
C7
1.
F (D)
B♭/F (G)
2.
F (D)
in him a - lone my soul finds rest. rest.

63C I seek you, Lord God

Words: from Psalm 63
Basil E Bridge
Music: Christopher Norton
Calmly
Csus2 Am G/C C
p
1 I seek you, Lord God, I yearn for you;
2 In wor - ship I come to seek your face:
3 The bless - ing of your un - chang - ing love
Am G/C C G/C C
with long - ing my soul cries out for you
O show me your glo - ry and your grace –
I trea - sure all earth - ly good a - bove:
Dm7 Em7 Fmaj7 Fmaj7/G C
as the parched earth thirsts for rain.
let that vis - ion quick - en me.
let my voice de - clare your praise.
Am G/C C F/G Csus2

4 I'll praise you as long as life shall last;
your mercy provides a rich repast,
and my soul is satisfied.

5 In quiet my spirit shall recall
your mercies so great to each and all –
I am safe within your care.

Because your love is better than life

63D

From Psalm 63
Words and music: Phil Potter
Music arranged Christopher Norton

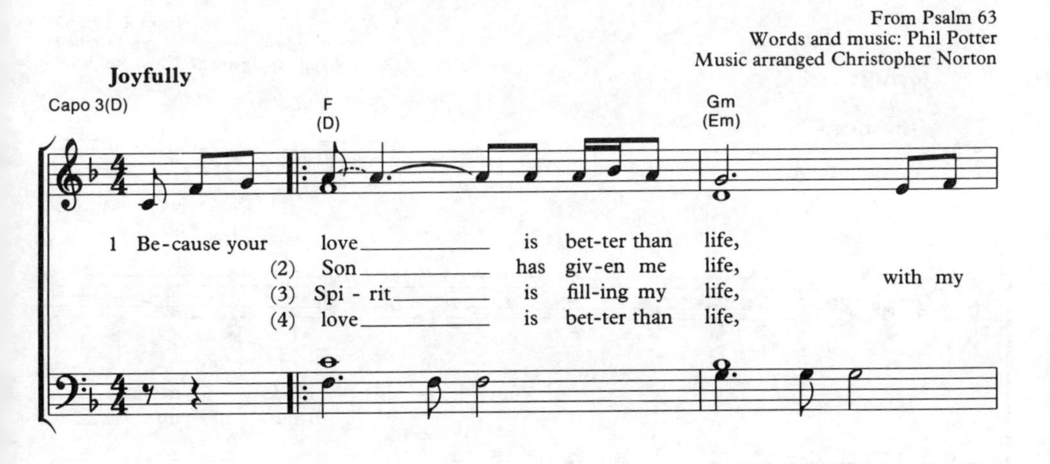
Joyfully
Capo 3(D)
F
(D)
Gm
(Em)
1 Be-cause your love is bet-ter than life,
(2) Son has giv-en me life,
(3) Spi - rit is fill-ing my life,
(4) love is bet-ter than life,
with my

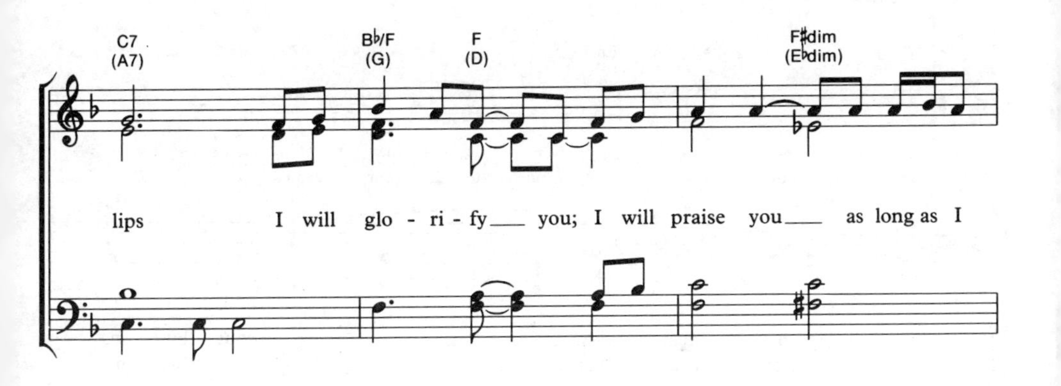
C7
(A7)
B♭/F
(G)
F
(D)
F♯dim
(E♭dim)
lips I will glo - ri - fy you; I will praise you as long as I

1–3.
4.
Gm
(Em)
C7
(A7)
F
(D)
F
(D)
live – in your name I lift my hands.
2 Be-cause your
3 Be-cause your
4 Be-cause your
hands.

63E Your loving-kindness is better than life

From Psalm 63
Words and music: Hugh Mitchell
Descant and arrangement: Chris Rolinson

Joyfully
G/A
DESCANT
A
D
1 Your lov - ing -
2 I lift my
1 Your lov - ing - kind - ness
(2) hands up
D6
Em7
A7
- kind - ness is bet - ter than life,
hands up un - to your name,
is bet - ter than life, your lov - ing -
un - to your name, I lift my
Em7
A7
D
your lov - ing - kind - ness is bet - ter than
I lift my hands up un - to your
- kind - ness is bet - ter than life;
hands up un - to your name:

D6
D
D7
life;
name:
my lips shall praise you –
– my lips shall praise you – so will I
G
Gm
D/A
G/A
so will I bless you; for your kind - ness is bet - ter than
bless you; your lov - ing - kind - ness is bet - ter than
1.
D
G/A
2.
E♭6
D6
life.
life.
life. 2 I lift my
life.

65C(i) The earth is yours, O God

Rossleigh 6 6 8 6 (SM)

Words: from Psalm 65
Michael Saward
Music: Brian and Sheila Dunning
arranged John Barnard

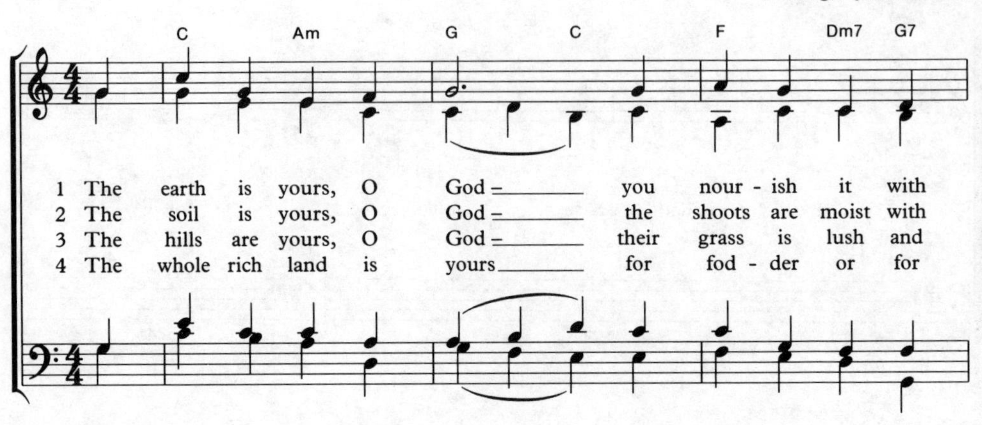

C Am G C F Dm7 G7
1 The earth is yours, O God — you nour-ish it with
2 The soil is yours, O God — the shoots are moist with
3 The hills are yours, O God — their grass is lush and
4 The whole rich land is yours for fod-der or for

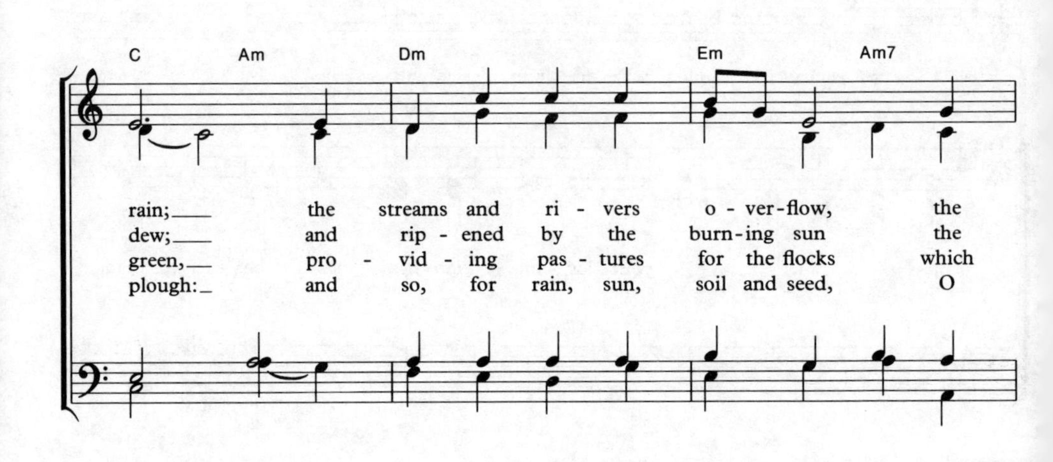

C Am Dm Em Am7
rain; the streams and ri-vers o-ver-flow, the
dew; and rip-ened by the burn-ing sun the
green, pro-vid-ing pas-tures for the flocks which
plough: and so, for rain, sun, soil and seed, O

1–3.
Dm Gsus G
land bears seed a-gain.
corn grows straight and true.
ev-ery-where are seen.
4.
Dm Dm7/G C
God, we thank you now!

The earth is yours, O God 65C(ii)

Franconia 6 6 8 6 (SM)
Words: from Psalm 65
Michael Saward
Music: *Harmonischer Liederschatz* 1738
Capo 3(C)
E♭ (C) B♭7 (G7) E♭ (C)
1 The earth is yours, O God – you
2 The soil is yours, O God – the
3 The hills are yours, O God – their
4 The whole rich land is yours for
A♭ (F) B♭ (G) E♭ (C)
nour - ish it with rain; the streams and ri - vers
shoots are moist with dew; and rip - ened by the
grass is lush and green, pro - vid - ing pas - tures
fod - der or for plough: and so, for rain, sun,
F (D) B♭ (G) Cm (Am) B♭7 (G7) E♭ (C)
o - ver - flow, the land bears seed a - gain.
burn - ing sun the corn grows straight and true.
for the flocks which ev - ery - where are seen.
soil and seed, O God, we thank you now!

66B Come, let us rejoice in him

Words: from Psalm 66
adapted from the New International Version
by Ian White
Music: Ian White

With confidence
C F Dm Dsus2
1 Shout with joy to God, all the earth! Sing to the
(2 All the) earth bows down to you, they sing their
(3 Praise our) God, O peo-ples – let the sound of all his
(4 Come and) lis - ten, all who fear the Lord, and let me
(5 If I) cher-ished sin with-in my heart, the Lord would
G F Dm G
glo - ry of his name and of - fer him praise and
praise to you – praise to your name, to your
praise be heard: he has pre-served our lives, our feet from
tell what he has done: my praise was on my tongue as I cried to
not have heard my cry, but sure - ly he has turned and he has

The verses may be sung by a soloist, with the congregation singing each chorus.

Csus2 F/G C F Dm
glo - ry. Say to God, 'How awe - some are your
name. Come and see what God has
slip - ping. As with sil - ver, you re - fined us,
him; if I cher - ished sin with - in my
lis - tened. He has heard my voice – praise be to
Dsus2 Gsus2 G
deeds, how great your pow - er o - ver all – your
done, how awe - some are his works for us: he turned the
Lord, put us through wa - ter and through fire, and
heart, the Lord would not have heard my cry, but
God! – my prayer he has not turned a - way, and

66B Come, let us rejoice in him

F
Dm
G
C
e - ne - mies will fall down be - fore you!'
sea in - to dry land and they crossed o - ver!
brought us to a place of a - bun - dance.
sure - ly he has turned and he has lis - tened.
he has not with - held his love from me!
Chorus
Am
G
F
F G Am
G
Come, let us re - joice in him, Come, let us re -
1.
F
- joice in him,
2.
F
- joice in him!
Fine
G7
2 All the
3 Praise our
4 Come and
5 If I

May God be gracious 67D

From Psalm 67
Words and music: Phil Potter
Music arranged Christopher Norton

Worshipfully
Capo 3(D)
F (D)
B♭ (G)
C (A)
mf
May God be gra - cious to us and
bless us, and make his face shine up - on us;
may God be gra - cious to us and
bless us, and make his face shine up - on us.

67E Let the people praise you, O God

From Psalm 67
Words and music: Chris Rolinson

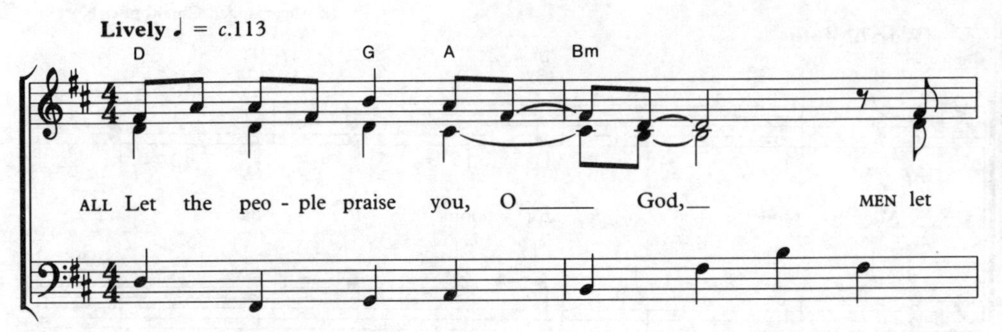
Lively ♩ = c.113
D G A Bm
ALL Let the peo - ple praise you, O___ God,__ MEN let

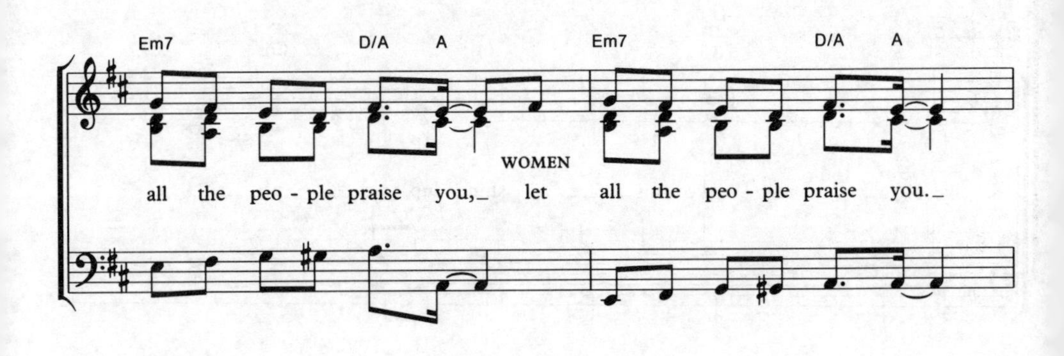
Em7 D/A A Em7 D/A A
all the peo - ple praise you,_ WOMEN let all the peo - ple praise you._

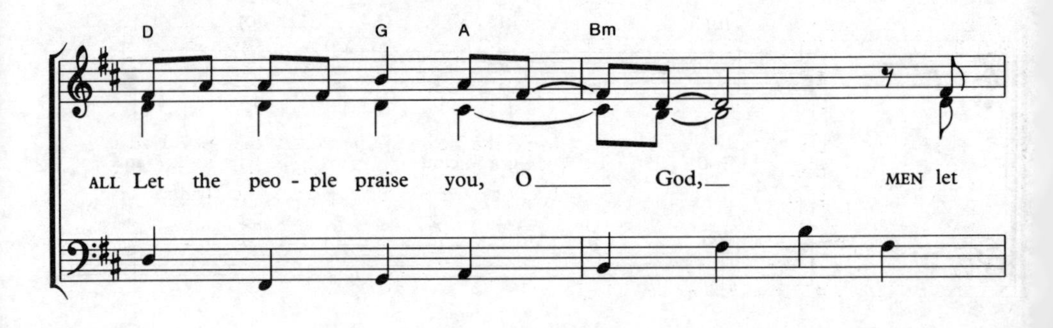
D G A Bm
ALL Let the peo - ple praise you, O___ God,__ MEN let

Em7 D/A A Em7 D/A A
all the peo - ple praise you,_ WOMEN let all the peo - ple praise you,_ ALL let

Fine
Em7 Asus A D G D
all the peo - ple praise you.
Esus E A E A Esus E
1 May your ways be known on earth, and your power to
2 We'll be glad and sing for joy, for you rule with
3 For you are a gra - cious God, we de - light to
Asus A F♯sus F♯ Bm F♯ Bm Bm/A
save us: then the peo - ples of the world shall
jus - tice; then the ends of all the earth shall
praise you: then our land shall see the fruits of
E7 Asus A G/A A
fear you, shall fear you.
fear you, shall fear you.
bless - ing, your bless - ing.

68B Let God arise

From Psalm 68
Words and music: Graham Kendrick
Music arranged Chris Rolinson
Forcefully – slightly march-like
Chorus
D A6 D G D Em7 A D
Let God a - rise, and let his e - ne - mies be scat - tered, and
Em7 G/A A Em7 A7
let those who hate him flee be - fore him;
D G D G D Em7 A D
let God a - rise, and let his e - ne - mies be scat - tered, and
Em7 G/A A D G
to verse
D
let those who hate him flee a - way.

to end
Fine
Verse
D
A
Em
A7
D
MEN But let the right - eous be glad;
WOMEN the
G/D
D
E7
A
let them ex - ult be - fore God,
right - eous be glad,
let them ex -
A7
F#
Bm
let them re - joice with glad -
- ult be - fore God;
O let
E7/G#
E7
A
Bm7
- ness, build - ing up a high - way for the king. We go in the
them re - joice for the king;
rall.
D.C. al Fine
A/C#
D
A7/E
D/F#
G6
Asus
A
name of the Lord: let us shout, 'Go up in the name of the Lord!'
let us shout, 'Go up in the name of the Lord!'

69B When my sorrows cover me

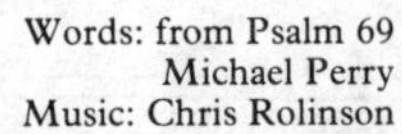
Words: from Psalm 69
Michael Perry
Music: Chris Rolinson

Worshipfully (moderate 4)
G
Bm7/E
Cmaj9
C/D

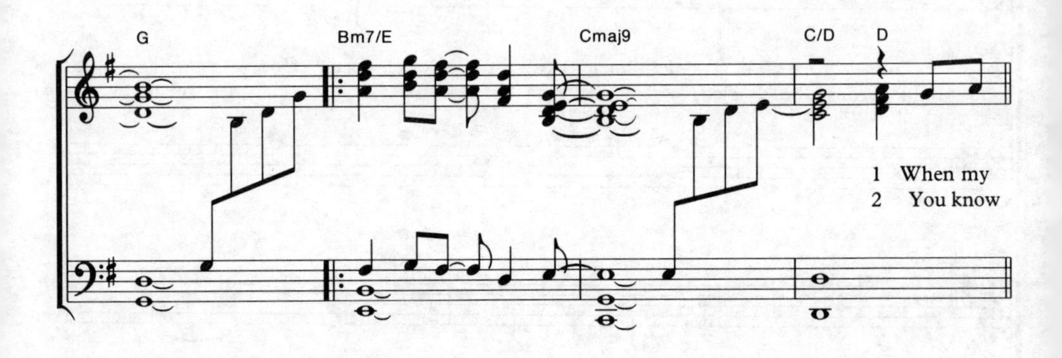
G
Bm7/E
Cmaj9
C/D
D
1 When my
2 You know

G
D/F#
Em
Gmaj7/D
Cmaj9
sor - rows co - ver me, save me, O
all my guil - ty fears, thank you, O

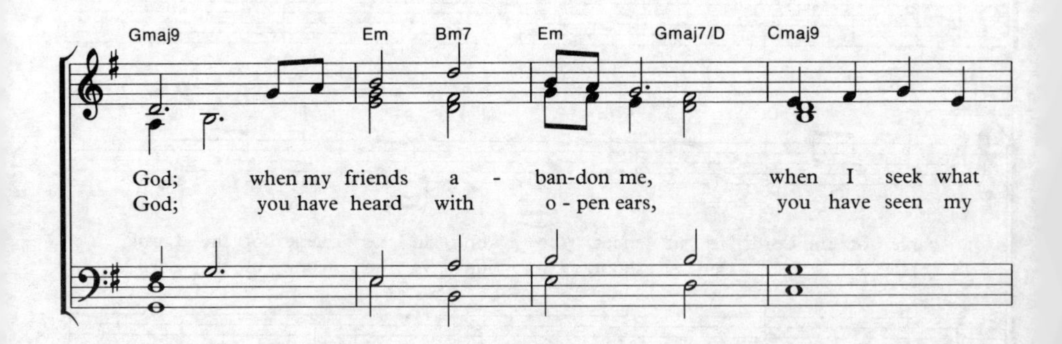
Gmaj9
Em
Bm7
Em
Gmaj7/D
Cmaj9
God; when my friends a - ban-don me, when I seek what
God; you have heard with o - pen ears, you have seen my

G/B
Am7(+4)
Gmaj9
Cmaj9
can - not be, when I look and can - not see,
con - trite tears, you will bless my fu - ture years,
Cmaj7/D
Gmaj7
Bm7/E
Cmaj9
save me, O God,
thank you, O God,
Cmaj7/D
Gmaj7
Bm7/E

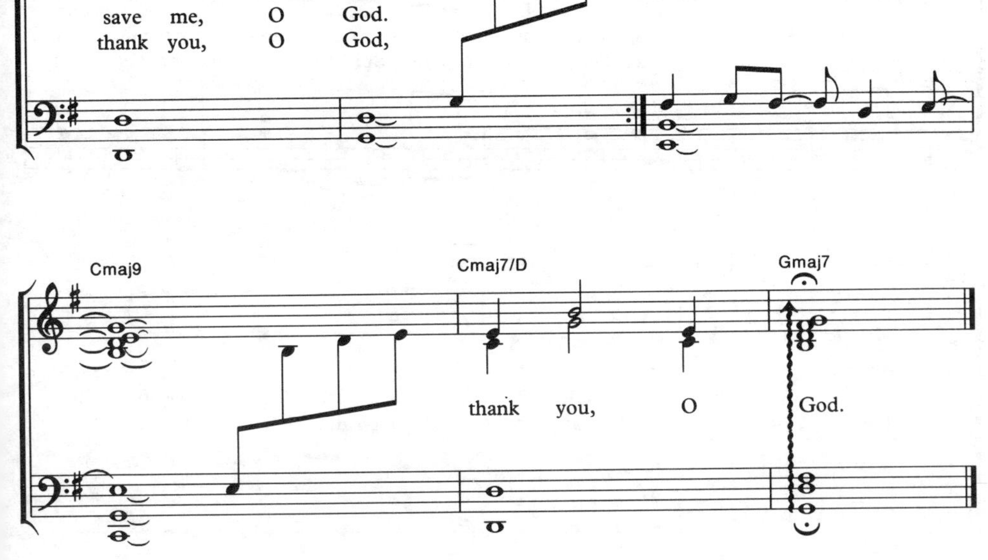

save me, O God.
thank you, O God,
Cmaj9
Cmaj7/D
Gmaj7
thank you, O God.

71A From time beyond my memory

O Tannenbaum
Words: from Psalm 71
Michael Perry
Music: Traditional melody
arranged Noël Tredinnick
Capo 5(C)
1 From time be-yond my me-mo-ry your love has been my rock, O Lord; since
3 We praise you, God, the ho-ly One, pro-claim your love from day to day, ex-
child-hood days I trust-ed you, and in my youth de-clared your word: 2 But
-alt your tri-umphs to the skies and trust your mer-cy come what may: 4 Sing
when the years are pass-ing by, as friends de-part and spi-rits fail, O
glo-ry to the Fa-ther, Son – and to the Spi-rit glo-ry be; let
God come quick-ly to my side that in your strength I may pre-vail.
psalms to God on earth be-gun re-sound through all e-ter-ni-ty!

I will praise you with the harp

71B

Words: from Psalm 71
adapted from the New International Version
by Ian White
Music: Ian White

Joyful rock-feel
Gm7
Am7
B♭
C
D♭
C
I will
A
B♭
C
G
praise you with the harp for your faith - ful - ness,
Those who want to harm me are put to shame
F
B♭
C
O my God; I will sing my praise to you
and con-fused; I will sing my praise to you

2nd time D.𝄋 (B)
3rd time to Coda 𝄌
G
F
Gm
with the lyre, with the lyre. O Ho-ly One of
with the lyre, with the lyre. when I sing my
I'll speak of all your
F
Gm
F
Is - ra-el, O Ho-ly One of Is - ra-el,
praise to you, when I sing my praise to you,
right - eous acts, I'll speak of all your right - eous acts,
Gm
F
B♭
O Ho-ly One of Is - ra-el: my lips will shout for
when I sing my praise to you – for I have been re -
I'll speak of all your right - eous acts, and tell it all day

Return to B for vv. 2, 3 then
return to A, repeat, then Coda
C
Gm7
C7/G
F
joy, my lips will shout for joy,
- deemed, for I have been re - deemed!
long, and tell it all day long. I will
Coda
F
D♭
I've been re - deemed I've been re -
to repeat
C
to end
- deemed I've been re - deemed.

84D How lovely is your dwelling-place

From Psalm 84
Words and music: Tom Howard

Moderately
Verse 1 and Chorus
C G/C F/C C Dm7 G7
1 How love - ly is your dwell - ing - place, al - migh - ty Lord!
C G/B Am D7
There's a hun - ger deep in - side my
Gsus G C G/C F/C
soul: on - ly in your pres -
C B7sus E Am Am/G
- ence are my heart and flesh re - stored – how

1.
2.3.4.
Fmaj7
Gsus
G7
F
love - ly.
How love - ly is your
Gsus
G
C
F/C
G/C
C
Fine
dwell - ing - place.
(3 A)
Verse 2
F/C
G/C
C
F/C
G/C
2 In your courts there's shel - ter for the great-est and the small;
C
Dm
C2/E
F
F/G
the spar - row has a place to build her nest,

C G/C F/C C
Eb
the pil - grim finds re -
Bbmaj7/D
Cm
A/C#
- fresh - ment in the rains that fall; and
Dm D7 Gsus F/G G
D.S.
each one has the strength to meet the test. How
Verse 3
F/C G/C C F/C G/C
(3) sin-gle day is bet-ter when spent in hum - ble praise,

C
Dm
C2/E
F
F/G
than a thou - sand days of liv - ing with-out
C
G/C
F/C G/C
C
E♭
you: the Lord be - stows his
B♭maj7/D
Dm7
Cm7
A7/C♯
fa - vour on each one who o - beys and
D.𝄋 al Fine
Dm
D7
Gsus
G C/G G7
bless-ings on the one whose heart is true. How

84E How lovely is your dwelling-place

Words: from Psalm 84
Jonathan Asprey
Music: Scottish traditional melody
arranged Christopher Norton
Flowing
F
B♭/F
p 1 & 4 How_ love - ly is___ your___ dwell-ing - place,
2 Ev - en the spar - row___ finds a home
3 And I'd ra - ther be___ a___ door-keep - er___
F
B♭/F
F
— O Lord of hosts,_ to__ me.___
— where he can set - - tle__ down;___
— and on - ly stay__ a__ day,___
B♭/F
— My_ soul is long - ing and faint -
— and the swal - low, she___ can build___ a__
— than_ live the life of a sin -
F
B♭/F
- ing the_ courts of the Lord___ to see;___
nest where she may_ lay___ her young___
- ner and_ have to__ stay___ a - way;___

F
B♭
my heart and flesh, they are sing -
with - in the courts of the Lord of
for the Lord is shin - ing as the
F
B♭/F
- ing for joy to the liv - ing God:
hosts, my king, my Lord, and my God:
sun, and the Lord, he's like a shield
F
B♭/F
how love - ly is your dwell-ing - place,
and hap-py are those who are dwell-ing where
and no good thing does he with - hold
F
B♭/F
F
O Lord of hosts, to me!
the song of praise is sung!
from those who walk his way.

85B Grant to us your peace, Lord

Dona nobis pacem II

From Psalm 85
Words and music: Taizé – Jacques Berthier

Continuous response

ALL ♩ = 80
D
Em7/D
Grant to us your peace, Lord
Do - na no - bis pa - cem

Accompaniment

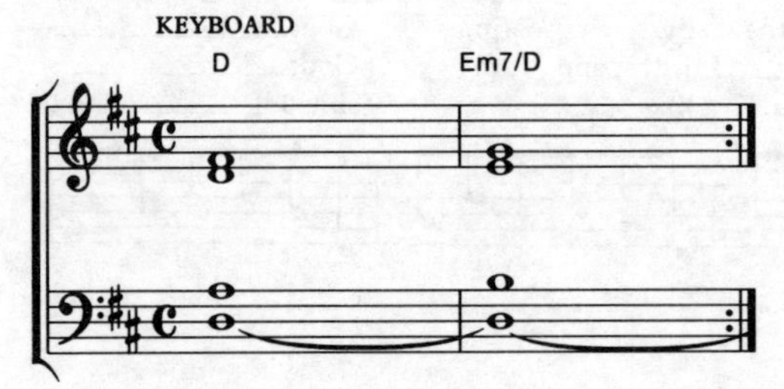
KEYBOARD
D
Em7/D

Solo verses (sung above continuous response)

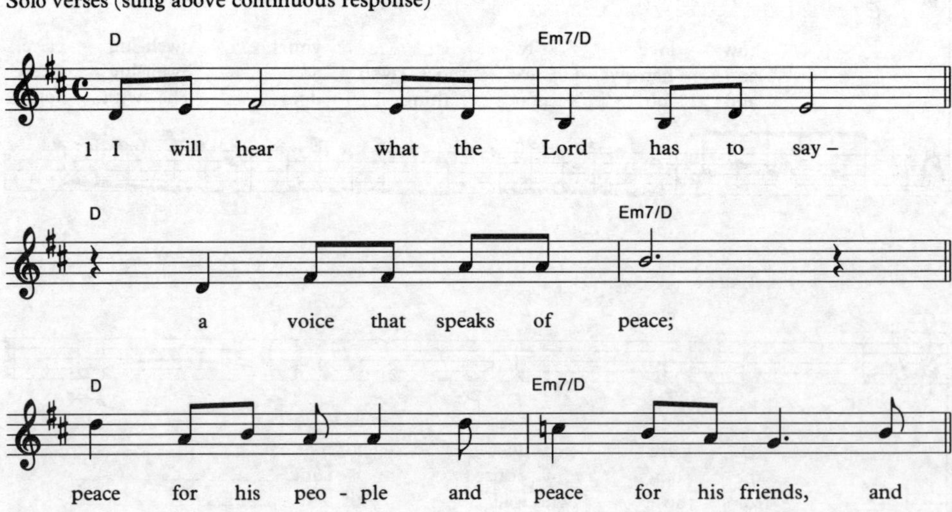
D
Em7/D
1 I will hear what the Lord has to say –
a voice that speaks of peace;
peace for his peo - ple and peace for his friends, and

D
Em7/D
peace for those who turn to him in their hearts.
2 His help is near for those who a - dore him,
his glo - ry will dwell in our land.
3 Mer - cy and faith - ful - ness have met,
jus - tice and peace have em - braced;
faith-ful-ness shall spring from the
earth, and jus - tice look down from hea - ven.
4 The Lord will grant us his joy, and our
earth shall yield its fruit;
jus - tice shall walk be -
- fore him, and peace shall fol - low his steps.

Instrumental parts overleaf

Accompaniments and solos

GUITAR

FLUTE

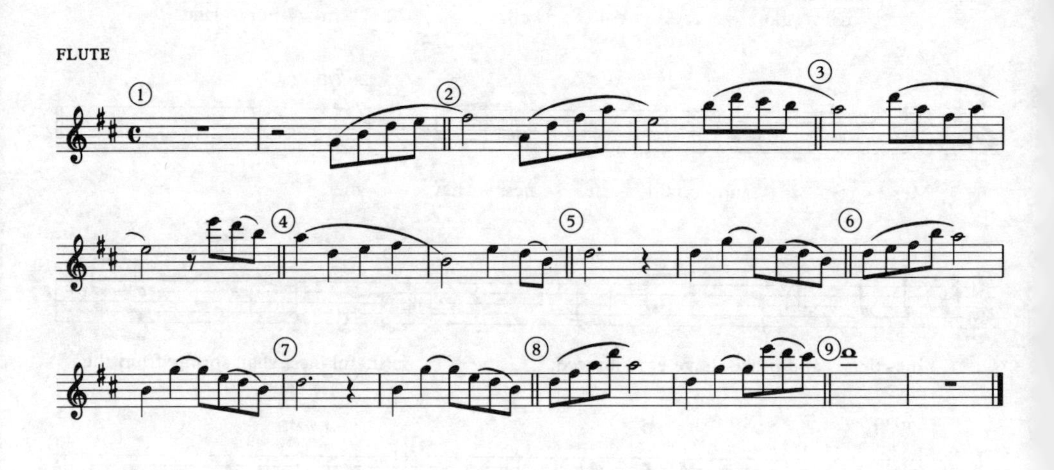

OBOE

BASSOON OR CELLO

1
2
3
4
5
6
7
8

COR ANGLAIS

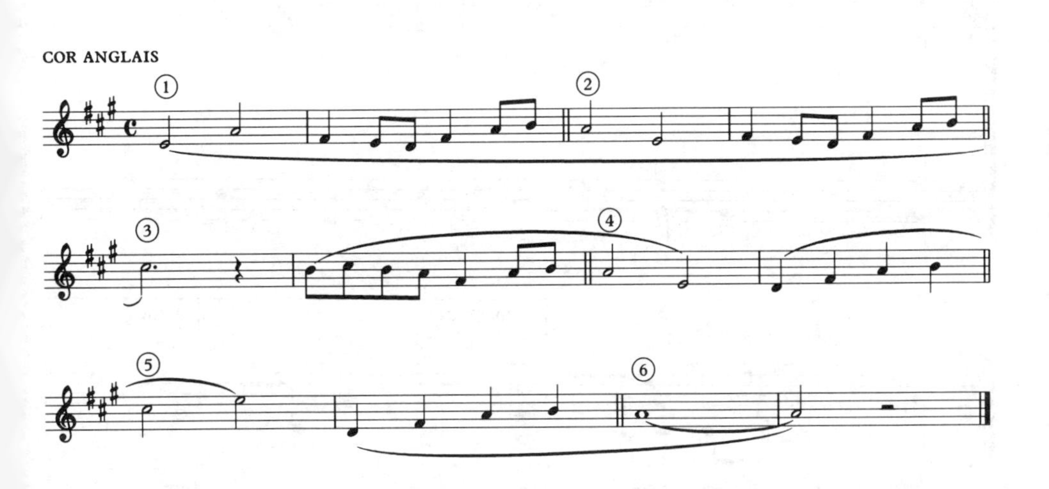
1
2
3
4
5
6

86B Teach me your way

From Psalm 86
Words and music: John Daniels
Music arranged Christopher Norton

Prayerfully
C Baug B D/E Em A7
Teach me your way, O Lord,
Dm7 F/G G F/C C G/B
and I will walk_ in your truth;
Am7 Baug B D/E Em A7
give me an un - di - vi - ded heart
Dm7 F/G C/G G7
to continue
C
to end
C
that I may fear_ your name.
name.

Gm7
B♭/C
C7
Fmaj7
B♭maj7
And I will praise you, O Lord my God,
Gm7
B♭/C
C7
F7sus
F♯dim
with all of my heart;
Gm7
B♭/C
C7
Fmaj7
B♭maj7
and I will praise you, O Lord my God,
Gm7
B♭/C
C7
F7sus
F/G
G
D.C.
and I will glo - ri - fy your name for ev - er.

89B I will sing of the Lord for ever

From Psalm 89
Words and music: Richard Henderson
Music arranged Christopher Norton

Joyfully
mp
Em D Em Bsus Bm Em G A Bsus B
I will sing of the Lord for ev-er, for his pro-mis-es are good;
Fine
Em D Em Bsus Bm C G B7sus B7 Em
I will sing of the Lord for ev-er, for his pro-mis-es are good!
E E/G♯ Am D D/F♯ G C C/E Am/F♯ F♯ Bsus B
His love ne-ver chan-ges, he is al-ways faith-ful – he will re-store Je-ru-sa-lem;
D.C. al Fine
E E/G♯ Am D D/F♯ G C C/E Am/F♯ B7sus Bm7 Em
his love ne-ver chan-ges, he is al-ways faith-ful – he will re-store Je-ru-sa-lem.

O Lord, the refuge of each generation

90C

Words: from Psalm 90
Basil E Bridge
Music: Christopher Norton
Not too fast
Capo 3(D)
1 O Lord, the re-fuge of each ge-ne-ra - tion, you
(2) thou - sand years like yes-ter - day in pass - ing, our
(3) Ho - ly Lord, for-give our self-de-ceiv - ing – our
(4) rush - es on: give us a heart of wis - dom that
reigned be-fore the u-ni-verse be-gan; we bear your stamp, the marks of your cre-
fleet-ing lives like half-re-mem-bered dreams, or weeds that flower at noon but die by
se-cret sins are clear be-fore your face: grant us re-lease, the joy of those be-
seeks your will and fol-lows your com-mands; show us your deeds, your glo-ry to our
-a - tion, and yet how frail we are, how brief life's span! 2 One
eve - ning – so, Lord, to you our tran-sient glo - ry seems. 3 O
-liev - ing they are re-stored by your e - ter - nal grace. 4 Time
child-ren, work out your time-less pur-pose through our hands.
mp

90D Lord, you have been our dwelling-place

Words: from Psalm 90
collected J G Wagner
and in this version Word & Music
Music: Christopher Norton
Rhythmically
A
C/D
1 Lord, you have been_ our dwell-ing - place
2 O teach us all___ to count our days,
3 O send the day__ of joy and light,
4 So let there be___ on us be - stowed
Em7add A
D
A
Asus
through all the a - ges of our race;
and set our hearts on wis-dom's ways;
for long has been our sor-row's night!
the beau - ty of the Lord our God;
A
C/D
be - fore the moun - tains had their birth
turn, Lord, to us___ in our dis - tress,
Af - flict - ed through the wea - ry years,
the work ac - comp - lished by our hand

Em7add A
D
Esus
E
or ev - er you had formed the earth, from
in pi - ty now your ser - vants bless; let
we wait un - til your help ap - pears: O
be pleased to bless, and make it stand; let
B♭/F
A
C
G/D
ev - er - last - ing you are God, to
mer - cy's dawn dis - pel our night, and
God be pres - ent at our side, your
all we do in deed or word, en -
B♭/F
A
C
G/D
D
1–3.
A
4.
A
ev - er - last - ing our a - bode.
all our day with joy be bright.
name in us be glo - ri - fied.
- dure to glo - ri - fy our Lord!

91B I will dwell in his secret place

From Psalm 91
Words and music: Gail Cole and Glen Cummings
Music arranged Christopher Norton

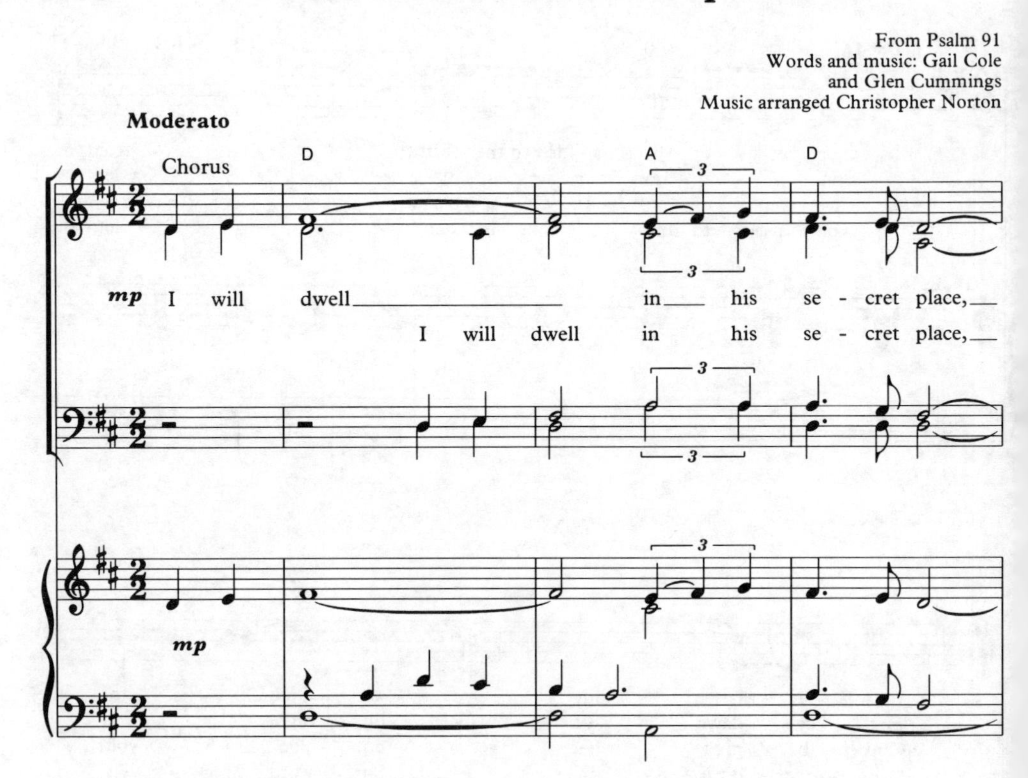
Moderato
Chorus
D
A
D
mp I will dwell in his se - cret place,
I will dwell in his se - cret place,
mp

A7
D
D/C♯
in his sha - dow I will a - bide;

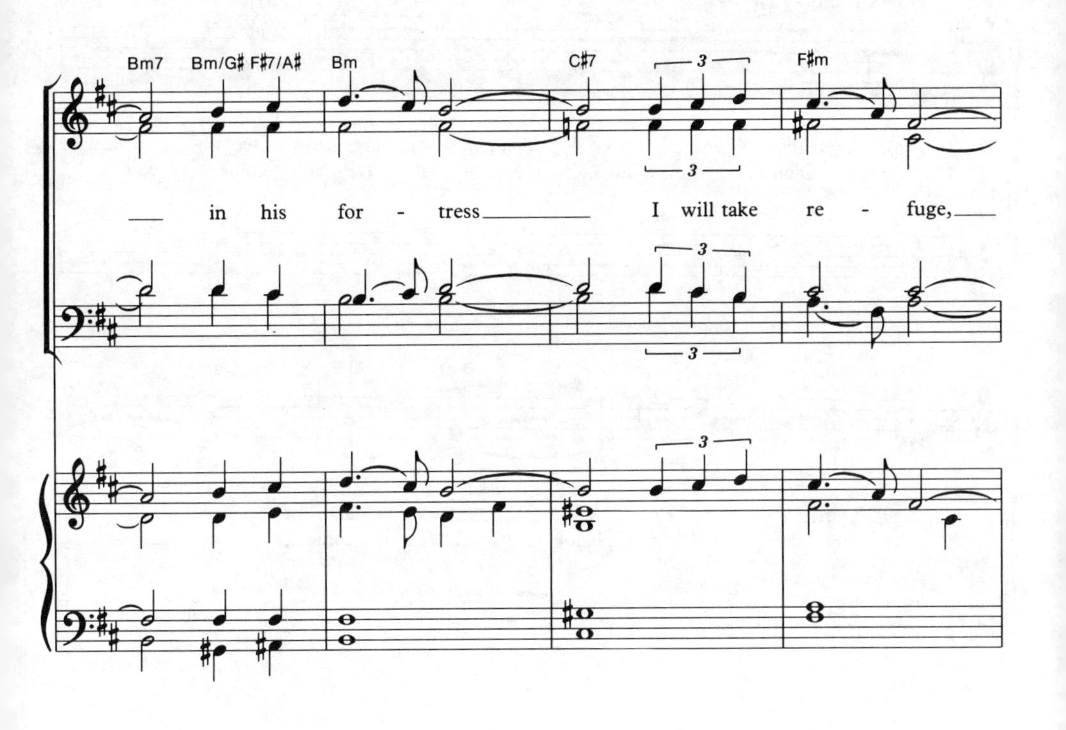
Bm7
Bm/G♯ F♯7/A♯
Bm
C♯7
F♯m
in his for - tress I will take re - fuge,

D/F♯
Em
A7
D
Fine
in my God, the most high.

91B I will dwell in his secret place

Verses 1 and 2
Bm A7 D D/C♯
3
1 From plague and from snare you are pro - tect - ed;
2 There shall no ev - il ov - er - come you,
Bm7 D/A G D Bm7 Em7 Em7/A A
you need not fear the dark of night,
nei - ther shall the plague come near;
G/A A G D D/C♯
and with his wing you will be co - vered,
for he shall place his an - gels o - ver you
Bm7 D/A Em7 Em7/A A
D.C.
de - liv - ered from the wick - ed's might.
to keep you safe from all your fear.

Verse 3
Bm
A7
3
D
D/C♯
3 When I call to the Lord he will ans - wer,
Bm7
D/A
G
D
Bm7
Em7
Em7/A
A
he will set my soul on high;
G/A
A
G
D
D/C♯
he will be near in time of trou - ble,
Bm7
D/A
Em7
Em7/A
A
D.C.
give long life, and sa - tis - fy.

91C I will live within the shadow

From Psalm 91
Words and music: Elaine Davis
Music arranged Christopher Norton

Moderato
Em
C
Bm
Em
p
1 I will live with - in the sha - dow
2 I shall not fear the dark - ness of night,
C
3
D
Em
of the al - migh - ty God of all;
or the dan - gers of day;
C
Bm
Em
by his wings I shall be pro - tect - ed,
dis - as - ter or fear shall ne - ver ov - er - whelm me
C
3
D
Em
for ev - er trust - ing in him.
while I am trust - ing in him.

C
D
Em
mf
He a - lone is my re - fuge,
C
D
G
he a - lone is my God;
Em
C
Bm7
Em
C
and he'll ne - ver, ne - ver fail me –
he is
3
D
Em
to repeat
C
D
faith-ful un - to me,
he is faith-ful un - to
3
Em
last time
C
Slower
D
Em
me.
he is faith-ful un - to me.
3

92B It is good to give thanks

SATB version
From Psalm 92
Words and music: Tom Howard and Bill Batstone
Moderately ♩ = 78
Capo 3(D) F (D) B♭maj9 (G) B♭/C F (D) F/A
It is good to give thanks to___ the Lord, sing-ing
B♭ (G) F/A (D) Gsus (Dsus) G (E) B♭/C (G) C (A) F/E♭ (D) B♭/D (G)
prais - es to___ our God___ on high:______ sing of mer-cies through -
A/C♯ (F♯) A Dm (Bm) Gm7 (Em7) B♭/C (G)
- out______ the day__ and of faith - ful - ness___ by______
Fine
Dm (Bm) Am (F♯m7) Gm7 (Em7) B♭/C (G) F (D) B♭/F (G) F (D) Am7 (F♯m7)
night,______ and of faith - ful - ness_ by____ night.________

Verse
Dm (Bm) C/D (A) B♭ (G) B♭/C F (D) F/A
1 I will re - joice in the work of your hands, for
2 From the strings of an in - stru - ment my
B♭ (G) B♭/C F (D) B♭/F (G) F (D)
you have made me glad; your
of - fer - ing will pour: the
E♭maj7 (Cmaj7) Cm7 (Am7) Am/D (F♯m) D7sus (B7) Gmaj7 (Emaj7)
e - ne - mies scat - ter, they fall a - way, but the
God of right - eous - ness is my Rock, ex -
E♭maj7 (Cmaj7) Gm/C (Em)
D.C. al Fine
right - eous one shall stand!
- alt - ed ev - er - more!

92C How good it is to give thanks

Words: from Psalm 92
in the Good News Bible version
Music: John Barnard

♩ = 130
G C G/B Am C
mf
D C/D D G C C/D D G
mf GROUP/CHOIR/SOLO
How good it is to give thanks to you, O Lord;
C/D Am/C Bm Em Am7 C/D D7 G C Am7
to sing in your hon - our, O most high God!
D C/D D G C C/D D G
f ALL
How good it is to give thanks to you, O Lord;
f

1–3. to Verses
4. Fine
C/D Am/C Bm Em Am7 C/D D7 G C Am7 G
to sing _ in your hon - our, O most high God: God!
Verse 1
Am7/D G(add A) G F♯m7 B7 Esus Em
mp
GROUP/CHOIR/SOLO
To pro - claim your con-stant love ev - ery morn - ing
mp
Bm7/D Em7/D C Am7 C/D Dsus D Gsus G
and your faith-ful-ness ev - ery night, with the
F♯m7 B B7/E Em Em/C♯ G/A A7 Am7/D Am7
D.𝄋
mu-sic of stringed in-stru-ments and with me-lo-dy on the harp.

Verse 2
Am7/D
G(add A)
G
F♯m7
B7
mp
GROUP/CHOIR/SOLO
Your_ migh - ty deeds, O Lord, make me
mp
Esus
Em
Bm7/D
Em/D
C
Am7
C/D
Dsus
D
glad;___ be-cause of what you have done,___ I sing___ for
Gsus
G
F♯m7
B
joy.___ How_ great are your
B7/E
Em
Em/C♯
G/A
A7
Am7/D
Am7
D.𝄋
ac-tions, Lord; how_ deep___ are your thoughts!___

Verse 3
Am7/D G(add A) G F♯m7 B7 Esus Em
mp
GROUP/CHOIR/SOLO
The righ-teous will flour-ish like palm trees,
mp
Bm7/D Em7/D C Am7 C/D Dsus D Gsus G
they will grow like the ce-dars of Le-ban-on;
F♯m7 B B7/E Em
they are like trees plant-ed in the house of the Lord,
D.𝄋 al Fine
Em/C♯ G/A A7 Am7/D Am7
that flour-ish in the Tem-ple of our God.

95D Come, let us sing out with joy

From Psalm 95, *Venite*
Words and music: Stephen Dean

With vigour
Chorus
Capo 3(G)
Bb (G) Gm (Em) Cm (Am) F7 (D7) Bb (G) F/A (D)
ALL
Come, let us sing out with joy to the Lord;
Gm♮6 (Em) Dm (Bm) Cm7 (Am7) Fsus (Dsus) F (D) Db (Bb) Bbm7 (Gm7)
hail the rock of sal - va - tion! Come in - to his
Ebm7 (Cm7) Fm/Ab (Dm) F7/A (D7) Bb (G) Ebmaj7 (Cmaj7) C7/E (A7) F7 (D7) Bb (G)
Fine
pres-ence to give him thanks, sing - ing psalms of tri - umph.

Verses
E♭7/D♭ (C)
Fm7/E♭ (Dm7)
E♭7 (C7)
D♭/B (B♭)
WORSHIP LEADER/GROUP
1 In his hands are the depths of the earth, the moun - tain peaks be -
2 Bow down be - fore him in prayer, kneel be - fore the
3 Lis - ten to the voice of the Lord, do not grow stub-born nor
4 Praise the Fa - ther who made all things, praise the Son who
E♭ (C)
C (A)
F (D)
C (A)
- long to him; his is the sea, he cre - a - ted it,
Lord and a - dore: he is the Lord our shep - herd,
hard - en your hearts; put not your God to the test,
died for us, praise the Spi - rit who glad-dens our hearts;
Gm/E♭ (Em)
D♭/F (B♭)
B♭m (Gm)
Cm (Am)
Fsus (Dsus)
F7/E♭ (D7)
D.C.
his is the dry land, formed by his hands.
we his peo - ple, the flock that he feeds.
well you know how he cares for us.
praise un - ceas - ing fill hea - ven and earth!

95E Let us sing to the God of salvation

Give me joy

Words: from Psalm 95, *Venite*
Richard Bewes
Music: traditional
arranged Christian Strover

Joyfully

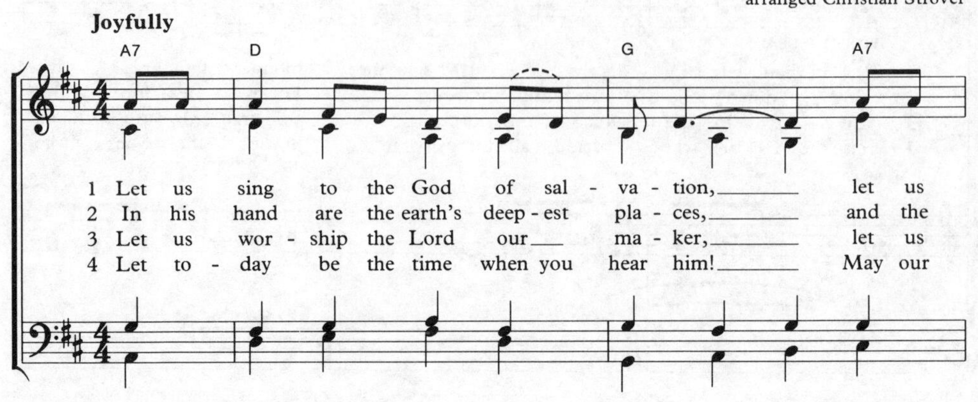

A7 D G A7
1 Let us sing to the God of sal - va - tion, let us
2 In his hand are the earth's deep - est pla - ces, and the
3 Let us wor - ship the Lord our ma - ker, let us
4 Let to - day be the time when you hear him! May our

D E7 A D D7
sing to the Lord our rock; let us come to his house with thanks -
strength of the hills is his; all the sea is the Lord's, for he
kneel to the Lord our God; for we all are the sheep of his
hearts not be hard or cold, lest we stray from the Lord in re -

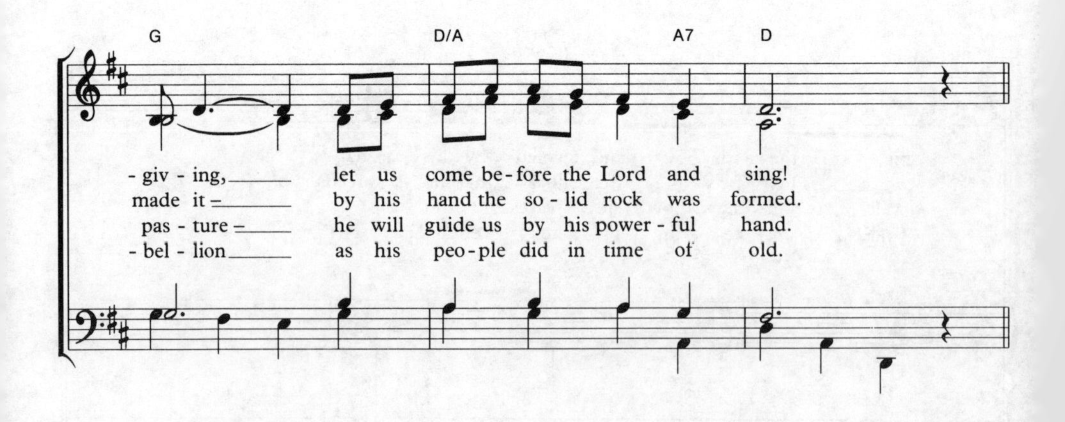

G D/A A7 D
- giv - ing, let us come be - fore the Lord and sing!
made it – by his hand the so - lid rock was formed.
pas - ture – he will guide us by his power - ful hand.
- bel - lion as his peo - ple did in time of old.

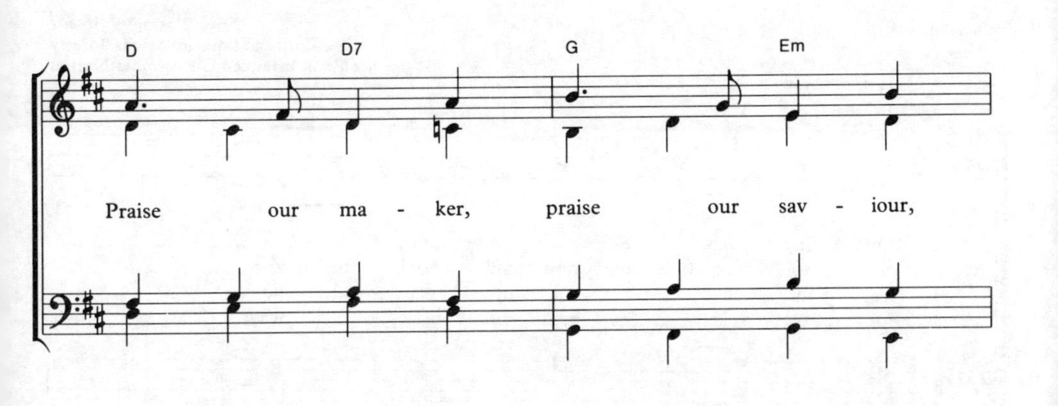
D
D7
G
Em
Praise our ma - ker, praise our sav - iour,

A
D
G
D
D
D7
praise the Lord our ev - er - last - ing king: ev - ery throne must

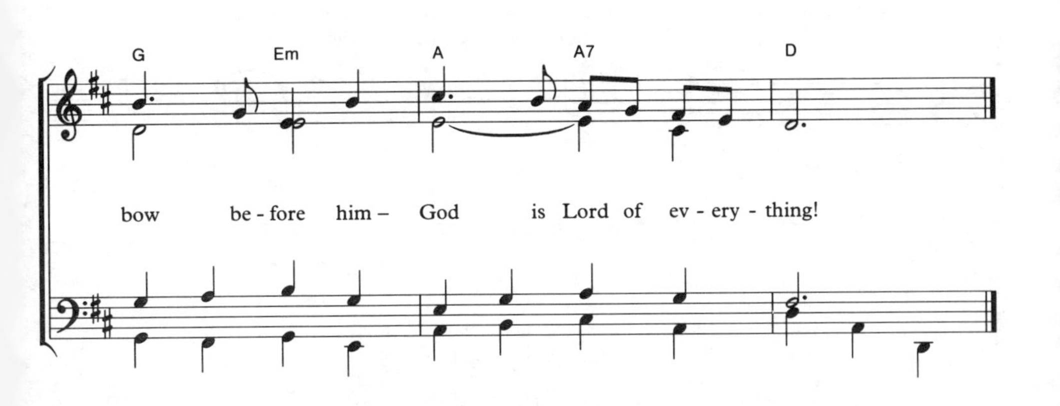
G
Em
A
A7
D
bow be - fore him – God is Lord of ev - ery - thing!

95F Come, sing praises to the Lord above

Calypso Carol
From Psalm 95, *Venite*
Words and music: Michael Perry
Music arranged Christopher Norton
Calypso style
D
B7
Em
A7
D
1 Come, sing prais - es to the Lord a - bove,
2 Come to wor - ship him and bow the knee,
3 Hear the sto - ry of his peo - ple now,
4 For - ty years he kept the prize a - way,
rock of our sal - va - tion, God of love;
for the shep - herd of the flock is he;
you with stub - born hearts who will not bow;
made them wan - der till they walked his way,
with de - light in - to his pres - ence move,
hum - ble crea - tures in his hand are we –
learn what hap - pened long a - go and how
ex - iled all of them un - til the day
for the Lord our God is king!
sing the praise of God the king!
God can show you he is king!
they should hon - our him as king:

G
D
He's the king a - bove the moun - tains high, the

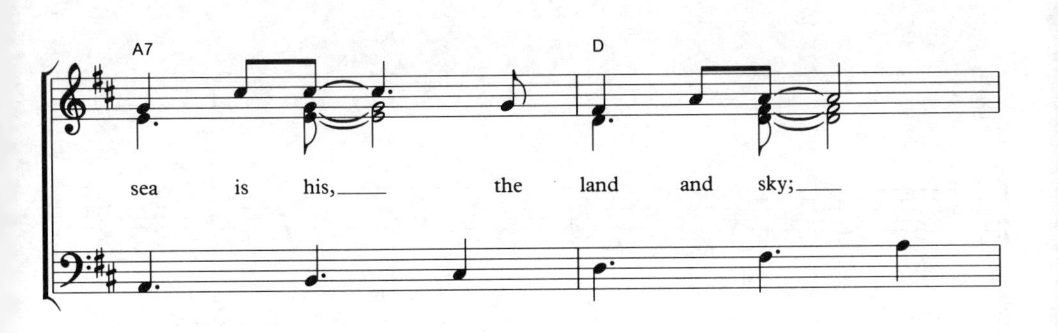
A7
D
sea is his, the land and sky;

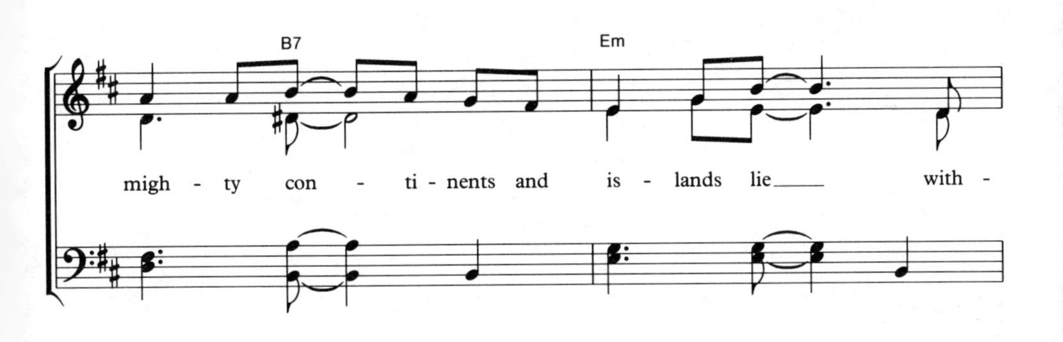
B7
Em
migh - ty con - ti - nents and is - lands lie with -

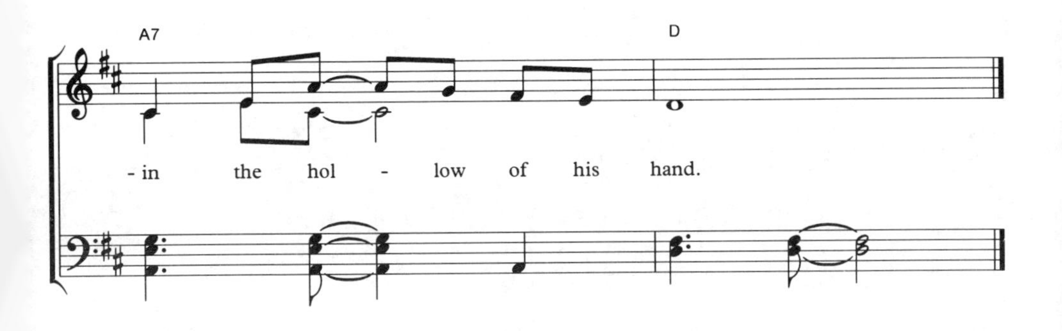
A7
D
- in the hol - low of his hand.

95G Come, let us praise the Lord

Words: from Psalm 95, *Venite*
Timothy Dudley-Smith
Music: Chilean folk song
adapted and arranged Michael Paget

Steadily 𝅗𝅥. = 54

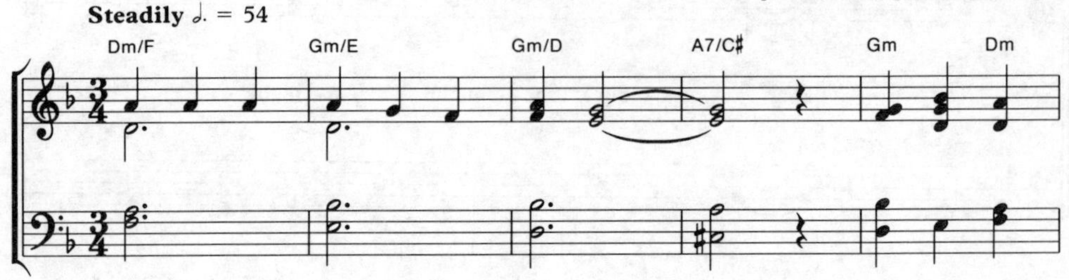

Dm/F
Gm/E
Gm/D
A7/C♯
Gm
Dm

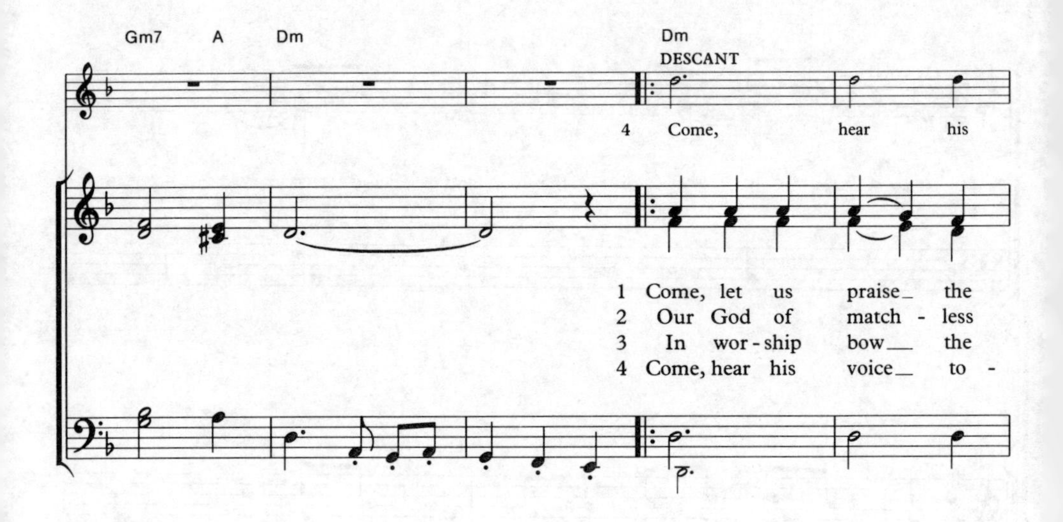

Gm7
A
Dm
Dm
DESCANT
4 Come, hear his
1 Come, let us praise_ the
2 Our God of match - less
3 In wor - ship bow_ the
4 Come, hear his voice_ to -

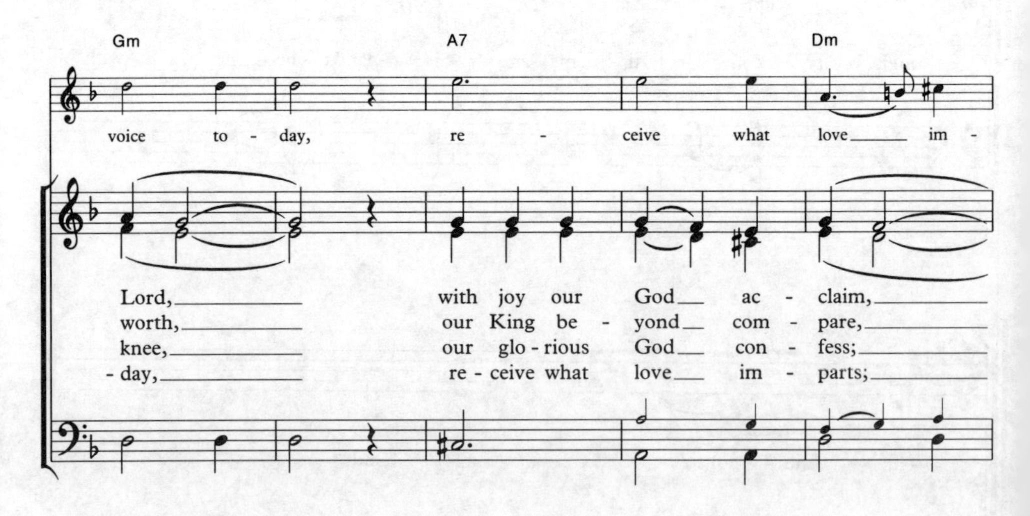

Gm
A7
Dm
voice to - day, re - ceive what love_ im -
Lord,_ with joy our God_ ac - claim,_
worth,_ our King be - yond_ com - pare,_
knee,_ our glo - rious God_ con - fess;_
- day,_ re - ceive what love_ im - parts;_

Sung in harmony, the words of the bass part are the same as for the tune, but sung to the bass rhythm one syllable to each note.

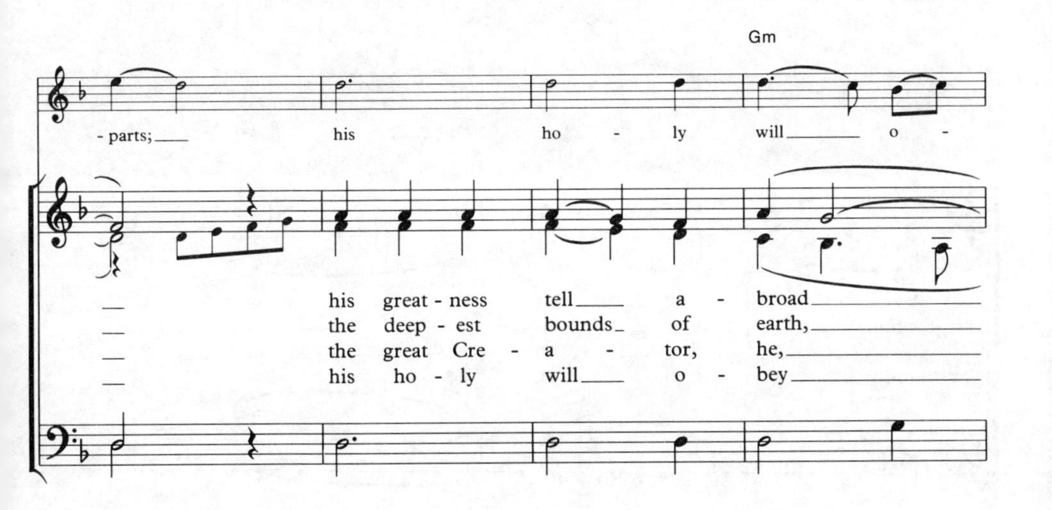
Gm
- parts; his ho - ly will o -
his great - ness tell a - broad
the deep - est bounds of earth,
the great Cre - a - tor, he,
his ho - ly will o - bey

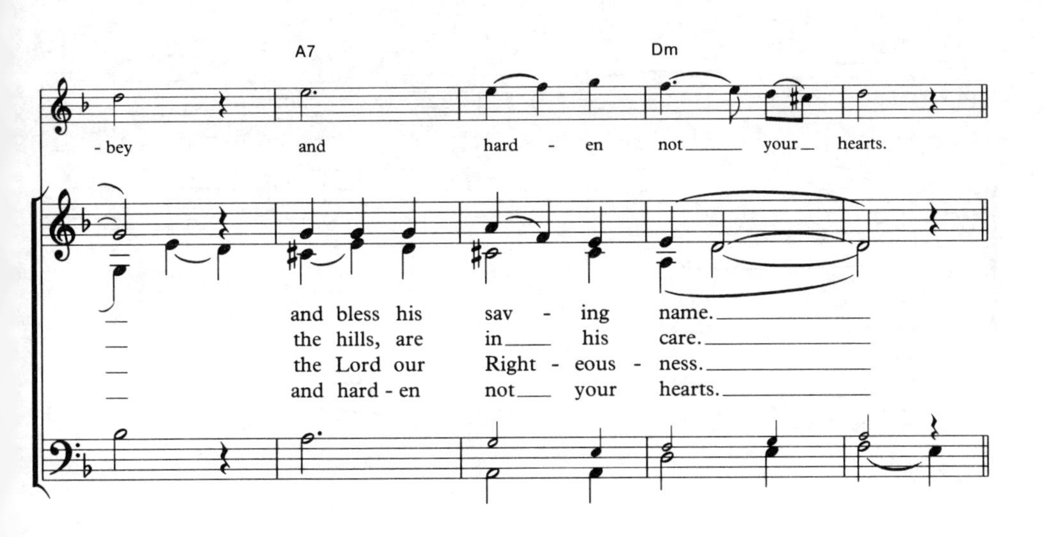
A7 Dm
- bey and hard - en not your hearts.
and bless his sav - ing name.
the hills, are in his care.
the Lord our Right - eous - ness.
and hard - en not your hearts.

Dm C F
His ways are
Lift high your songs
He all de - crees,
He reigns un - seen:
His ways are best;

95G Come, let us praise the Lord

Dm
C
F
G
A
best;
and
lead
at
last,
(at
be - fore his throne
who by his hand
his flock he feeds
and lead at last,
Dm
Gm
last,)
all
trou - bles
past,
to whom a - lone
pre - pared the land
and gent - ly leads
all trou - bles past,
A7
Gm7/A
A7
Dm
to per - fect rest.
A - men.
all praise be - longs.
and formed the seas.
in pas - tures green.
to per - fect rest.

Come, let us sing for joy 95H

From Psalm 95, *Venite*
Words and music: Brent Chambers
Music arranged Christopher Norton

Lively
G
(F)
mf
Come, let us sing for joy to the Lord,
come, let us sing for joy to the Lord,
cresc.
come, let us sing for joy to the Lord,
come, let us sing for joy to the Lord!

This may be played a tone lower in F major.

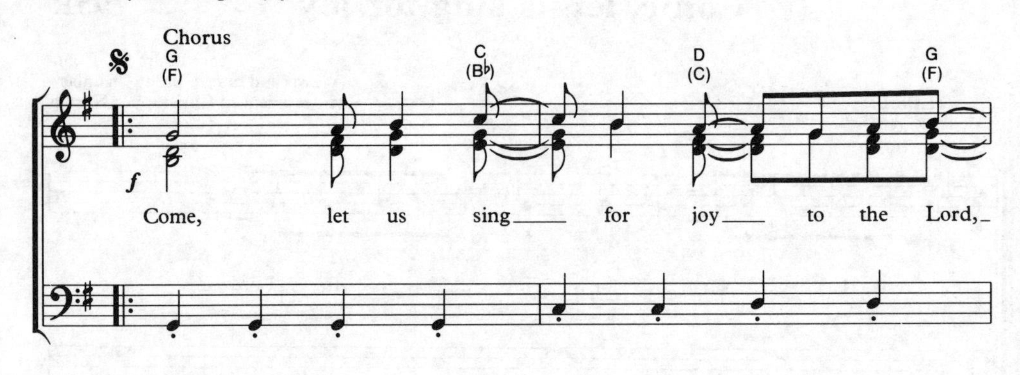
Chorus
G
(F)
C
(B♭)
D
(C)
G
(F)
f
Come, let us sing for joy to the Lord,

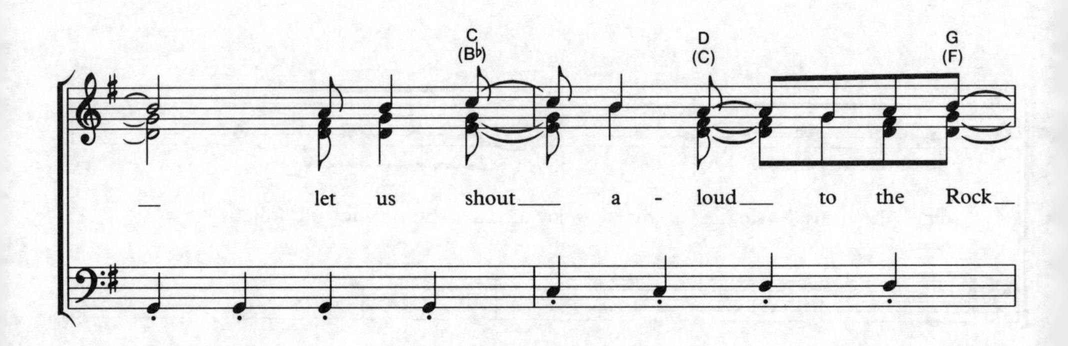
C
(B♭)
D
(C)
G
(F)
let us shout a - loud to the Rock

D
(C)
C
(B♭)
last time to Coda
of our sal - va - tion;

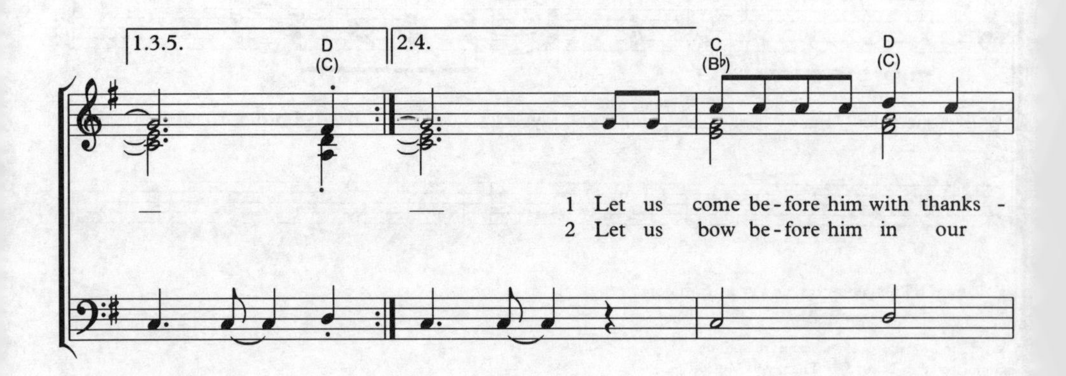
1.3.5.
2.4.
D
(C)
C
(B♭)
D
(C)
1 Let us come be - fore him with thanks -
2 Let us bow be - fore him in our

G
(F)
C
(B♭)
D
(C)
-giv - ing, and ex - tol him with mu - sic and
wor - ship, let us kneel be - fore God, our great
song: for the Lord, our Lord, is the
king; for he is our God, and
Verse 2
B
(A)
Em
(Dm)
A7
(G7)
C/D
(B♭)
great God, the great king a - bove all gods.
we are his peo - ple – that's why we shout and sing:
D7
(C7)
D.S.
CODA
D
(C)
G
(F)

951 Joy, joy, ring out your joy

From Psalm 95, *Venite*
Words and music: Paul Inwood

With exuberance ♩ = c.176
Capo 5(A)
Asus (Esus)
A7 (E7)
Chorus
D (A)
Em7 (Bm7)
Joy, joy, ring out your joy to the
C (G)
Lord, the sav-ing Lord;
sing, sing, praise him and sing of his
love in all his works!
1–3.
to Verses
last time
Fine
works!
dim. molto
cresc.
sffz

Verse 1
Gm7
(Dm7)
C
(G)
F
(C)
1 A migh - ty God is the Lord, a great King, who
Gm7
(Dm7)
A7
(E7)
Dm
(Am)
Dm7
(Am7)
holds the earth in his hands; to
G
(D)
F
(C)
him be - long all the seas and moun - tains, the
Em7
(Bm7)
Asus
(Esus)
A7
(E7)
D.𝄋
heights and the depths of the world.

Verse 2
Gm7
(Dm7)
C
(G)
F
(C)
2 Come, let us wor - ship the Lord, the God__ who made us;
Gm7
(Dm7)
A7
(E7)
Dm
(Am)
Dm7
(Am7)
let us bow down__ in his sight, for
G
(D)
C
(G)
A
(E)
D
(A)
we are his peo - ple, the sheep of his flock,__ and
Em7
(Bm7)
F
(C)
A
(E)
D.𝄋
he is our shep - herd and pas - tor.

Verse 3
Gm7
(Dm7)
C
(G)
F
(C)
3 Lis - ten to - day to the voice of the Lord, and
Gm7
(Dm7)
A7
(E7)
Dm
(Am)
Dm7
(Am7)
o - pen your hearts to his word; let your
G
(D)
F
(C)
minds be not like a bar - ren des - ert, but
Em7
(Bm7)
Asus
(Esus)
A7
(E7)
D.S.
fer - tile, and wa - tered by faith.
cresc.

96C Sing out to the Lord a new song

From Psalm 96
Words and music: Mick Ray
Music arranged Christopher Norton

Joyfully
G
C/G
G
Sing out to the Lord a new song, sing out to the

C
D
Em7 D/F♯
G
G/B
C
Lord, all the earth; sing to the Lord, bless his name – he is

Em
Bm
Am
D7
G/D D
G
great-ly to be praised! Sing out to the Lord a new song!

last time only
Am
D7
G/D
D
G
Sing out to the Lord a new song!

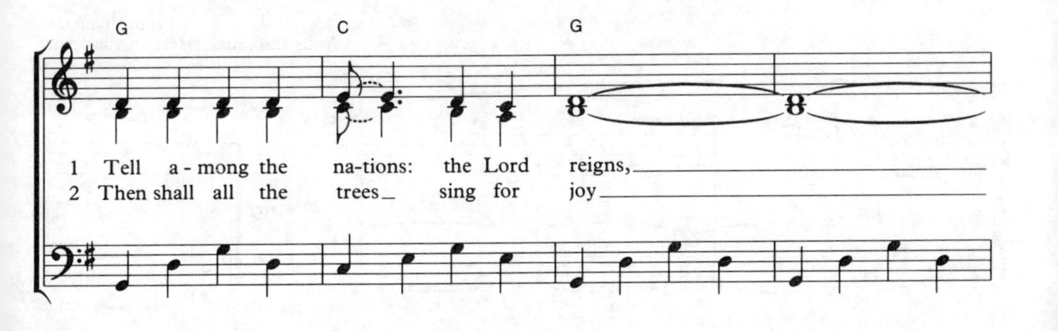
G C G
1 Tell a-mong the na-tions: the Lord reigns,
2 Then shall all the trees sing for joy

C D Em7 D/F♯
the world shall ne-ver be moved. Let the
be-fore the Lord – for he comes; he will

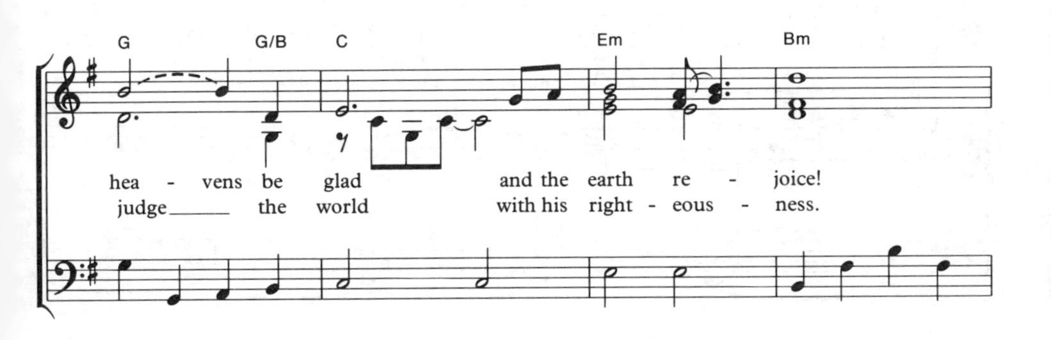
G G/B C Em Bm
hea-vens be glad and the earth re-joice!
judge the world with his right-eous-ness.

Am D7 G/D D G
D.C.
Sing out to the Lord a new song!

96D O sing out to the Lord

From Psalm 96
Words and music: Herbert Chappell

Capo 3(C)
𝅗𝅥 = 72
pp
mf
E♭ (C)
A♭/E♭ (F)
E♭ (C)
B♭7/E♭ (G7)
E♭ (C)
A♭/E♭ (F)
LEADER O sing out to the Lord a new song,
E♭ (C)
A♭/E♭ (F)
E♭ (C)
A♭/E♭ (F)
E♭ (C)
ALL O sing out to the Lord a new song!
E♭7 (C7)
A♭6 (F6)
E♭/G (C)
A♭6 (F6)
E♭/G (C)
LEADER Bless his name, ALL bless his name;

A♭6 (F6) E♭/G (C) Fm7 (Dm7) B♭9 (G9) B♭7 (G7)
LEADER sing of his glo - ry from day to day. De -
E♭ (C) A♭/E♭ (F) E♭ (C) A♭/E♭ (F) E♭ (C)
- clare his won-ders to all the world,
ALL de - clare his won-ders
A♭/E♭ (F) Dm7 (Bm7) Gdim (Edim) G7 (E7) A♭6 (F6) E♭/G (C)
to all the world.
LEADER Bless his name,
A♭6 (F6) E♭/G (C) A♭6 (F6) E♭/G (C) Fm9 (Dm9)
ALL bless his name:
LEADER hon - our and ma - jes - ty are in his place.

96D O sing out to the Lord

D♭7 (B♭7) G♭6 (E♭) G♭6/F E♭m7 (Cm7)
— O wor-ship the Lord in the
Fm7 (Dm7) B♭9 (G9) B♭7 (G7) Cm (Am)
beau - ty of ho - li - ness, let the
Cm/B E♭/B♭ (C) Am7 (F♯m7) A♭maj7 (Fmaj7)
heavens and the sea and the fields and the trees of the
E♭/G (C) Fm7 (Dm7) B♭ (G) B♭7 (G7) E♭ (C) A♭/E♭ (F)
wood re - joice. O sing out to the Lord a new song,

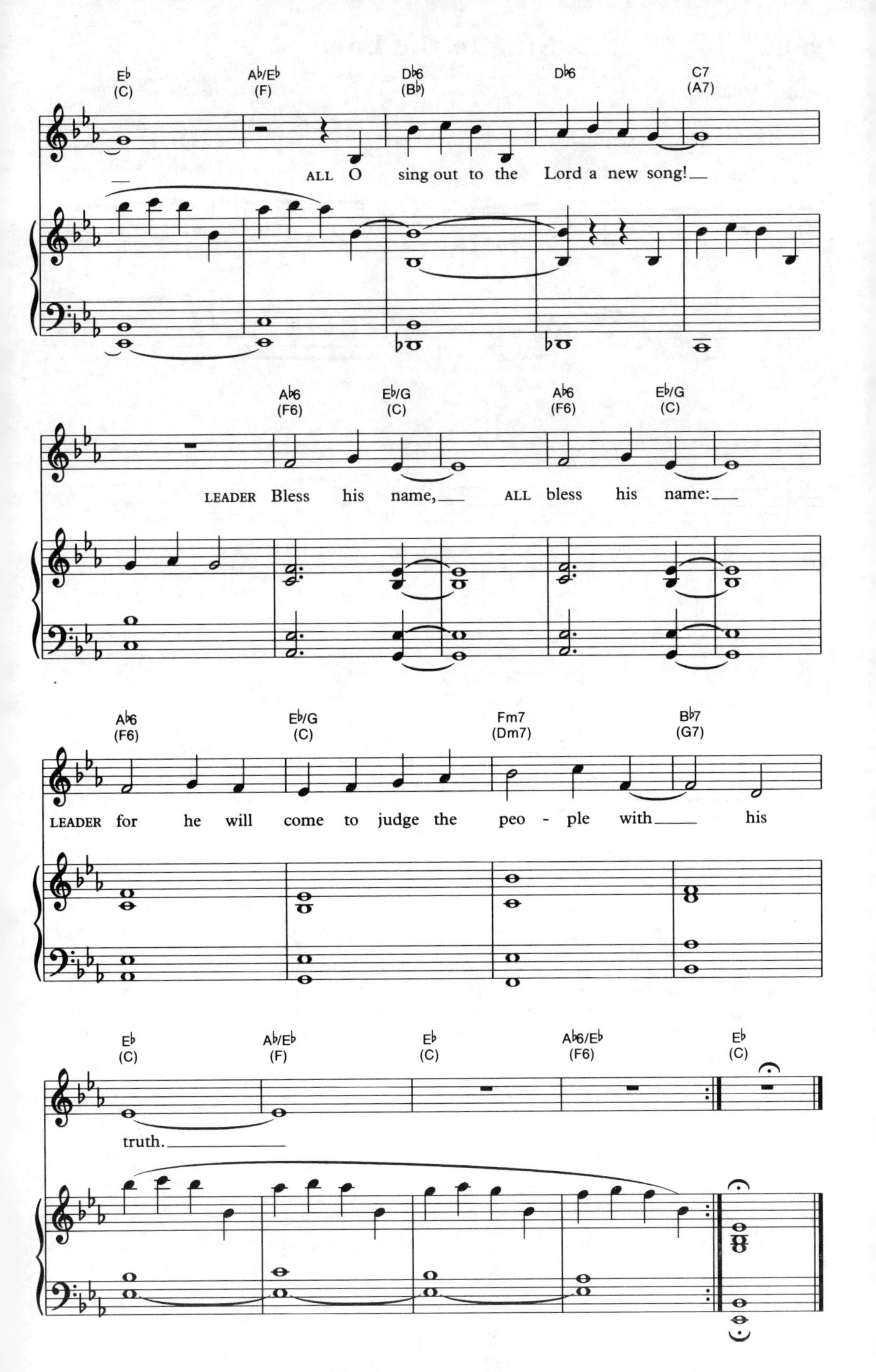

E♭
(C)
A♭/E♭
(F)
D♭6
(B♭)
D♭6
C7
(A7)
ALL O sing out to the Lord a new song!
A♭6
(F6)
E♭/G
(C)
A♭6
(F6)
E♭/G
(C)
LEADER Bless his name, ALL bless his name:
A♭6
(F6)
E♭/G
(C)
Fm7
(Dm7)
B♭7
(G7)
LEADER for he will come to judge the peo - ple with his
E♭
(C)
A♭/E♭
(F)
E♭
(C)
A♭6/E♭
(F6)
E♭
(C)
truth.

96E Sing to the Lord

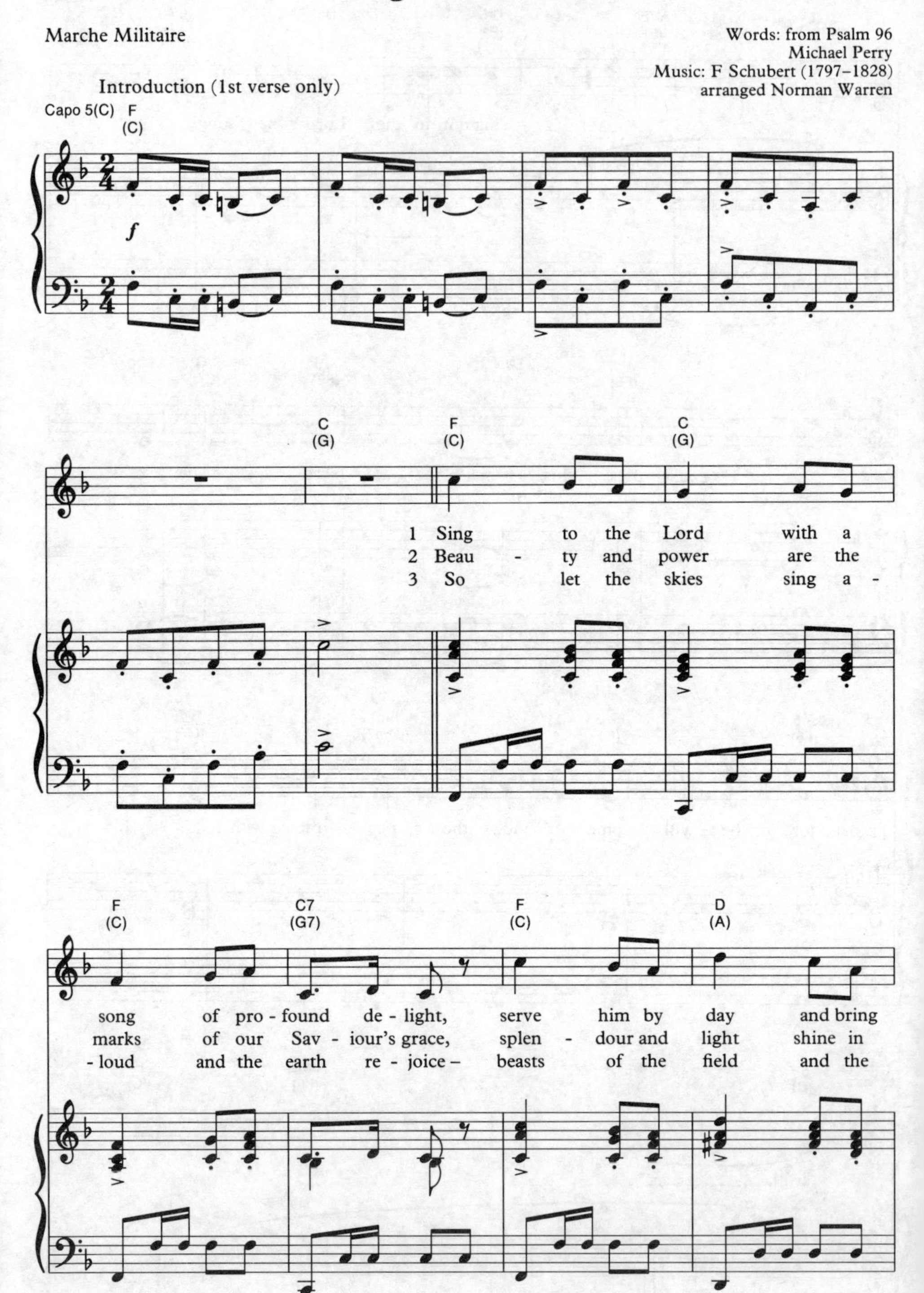
Marche Militaire
Words: from Psalm 96
Michael Perry
Music: F Schubert (1797–1828)
arranged Norman Warren
Introduction (1st verse only)
Capo 5(C) F (C)
C (G) F (C) C (G)
1 Sing to the Lord with a
2 Beau - ty and power are the
3 So let the skies sing a -
F (C) C7 (G7) F (C) D (A)
song of pro - found de - light, serve him by day and bring
marks of our Sav - iour's grace, splen - dour and light shine in
- loud and the earth re - joice – beasts of the field and the

Gm (Dm) D7 (A7) Gm (Dm) C (G) F (C)
MEN
prais - es__ in the__ night: tell of the bat - tles fought for us,
glo - ry__ from his__ face: wor - ship the Lord in ho - li - ness,
for - est__ lift their voice: firm - ly he set the so - lid ground,
C7 (G7) F (C) C (G) F (C)
GROUP A
GROUP B
WOMEN
mar - vel - lous, glo - ri - ous; tell of his won - ders done for us,
faith - ful - ness, god - li - ness – judg - ing the world with right-eous-ness
seas a - bound, skies re - sound; all we de - sire in God is found –
1.2.
3.
G7 (D7) C (G) C7 (G7) F (C)
ALL
wor - thy of ac - claim.
he will come to reign.
ALL
glo - ry to his name!

98A Sing to God new songs of worship

Ode to Joy 8 7 8 7 D

Words: from Psalm 98, *Cantate Domino*
Michael Baughen
Music: L van Beethoven (1770–1827)
Instrumental arrangements: Noël Tredinnick

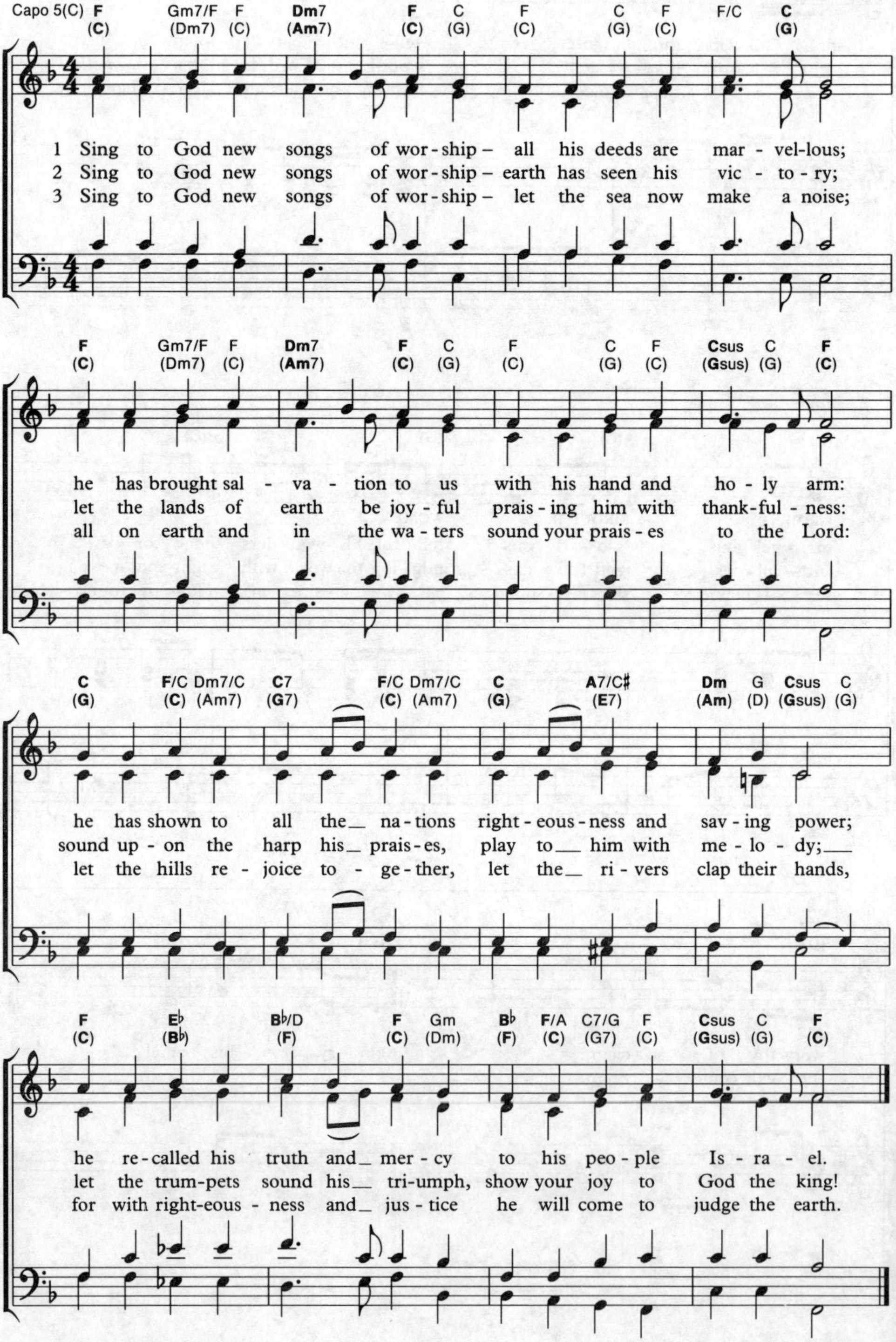

Capo 5(C)

1 Sing to God new songs of wor - ship – all his deeds are mar - vel-lous;
2 Sing to God new songs of wor - ship – earth has seen his vic - to - ry;
3 Sing to God new songs of wor - ship – let the sea now make a noise;

he has brought sal - va - tion to us with his hand and ho - ly arm:
let the lands of earth be joy - ful prais - ing him with thank-ful - ness:
all on earth and in the wa - ters sound your prais - es to the Lord:

he has shown to all the_ na - tions right - eous - ness and sav - ing power;
sound up - on the harp his_ prais - es, play to_ him with me - lo - dy;_
let the hills re - joice to - ge - ther, let the_ ri - vers clap their hands,

he re - called his truth and_ mer - cy to his peo - ple Is - ra - el.
let the trum-pets sound his_ tri - umph, show your joy to God the king!
for with right-eous - ness and_ jus - tice he will come to judge the earth.

Instrumental accompaniment

B♭ TRUMPETS

Verse 1

Verse 2

Solo

Verse 3

B♭ CLARINETS

Verses 1–3

98D Lift up your hearts to the Lord

Words: from Psalm 98, *Cantate Domino*
Michael Perry
Music: Christopher Norton

Moderato
D
G/D
1 Lift up your hearts to the
2 Bow down and wor - ship the
3 Tell out the word of the
D
C/E
D7/F♯
G
Asus
A/G
Lord, break in - to songs of
Lord, greet him who comes to
Lord, speak of his sav - ing
F♯sus
F♯
F♯/E
Bm/D
F♯7/C♯
Bm
Bm/A
joy; let the sea roar, let the
reign; share his tri - umph, hear his
power: sure his mer - cy, true his
Bm/G♯
C♯
F♯m
Bm
F♯m/C♯
C♯7
F♯
hills ring, shout his glo - rious name!
judge-ment, see his mar - vel - lous works:
pro - mise, great his won - der - ful love!

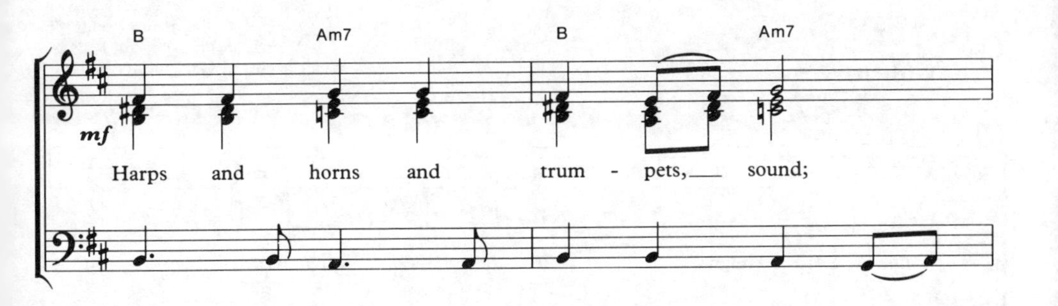
B
Am7
B
Am7
mf
Harps and horns and trum - pets, sound;

B/F♯
Em
Em7
D/A
G/A
A7/G
cresc.
praise him, all the world a - round! O

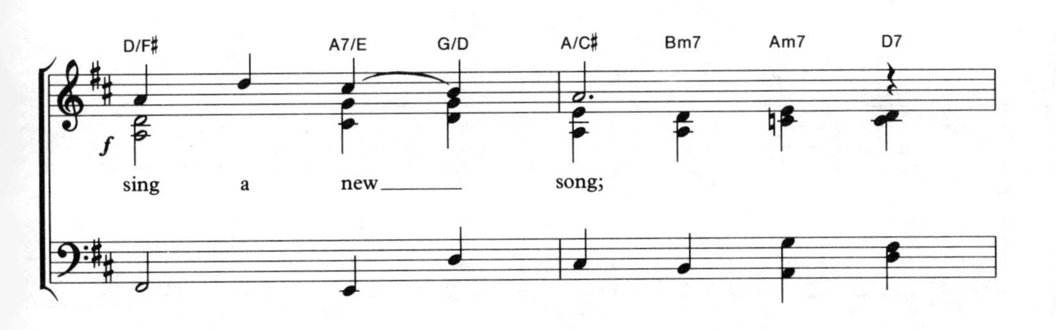
D/F♯
A7/E
G/D
A/C♯
Bm7
Am7
D7
f
sing a new song;

Gmaj7
Em7
Asus
A
D
Fine
to repeat
Em7
G/A
O sing a new song!

99B The Lord reigns

From Psalm 99
Words and music: Phil Rogers
Music arranged Christopher Norton

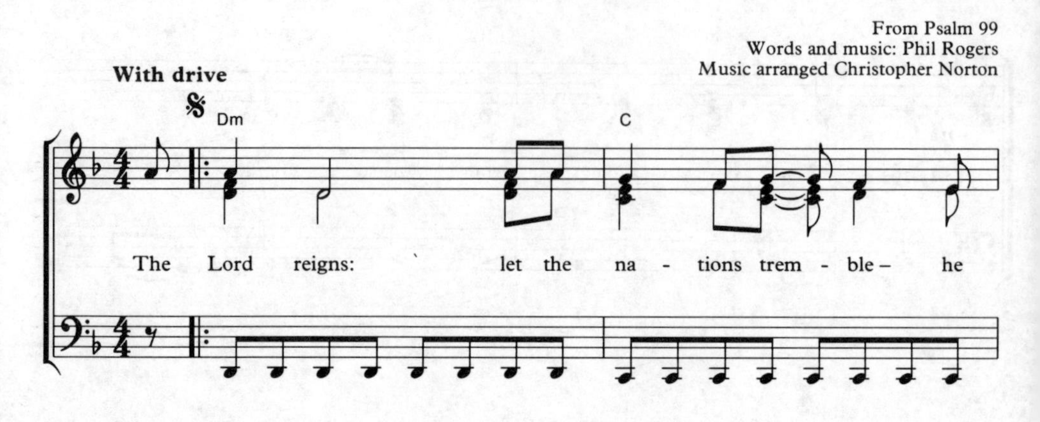
With drive
Dm
C
The Lord reigns: let the na - tions trem - ble – he

B♭
Asus
A
sits en - throned be - tween the che - ru - bim — let the

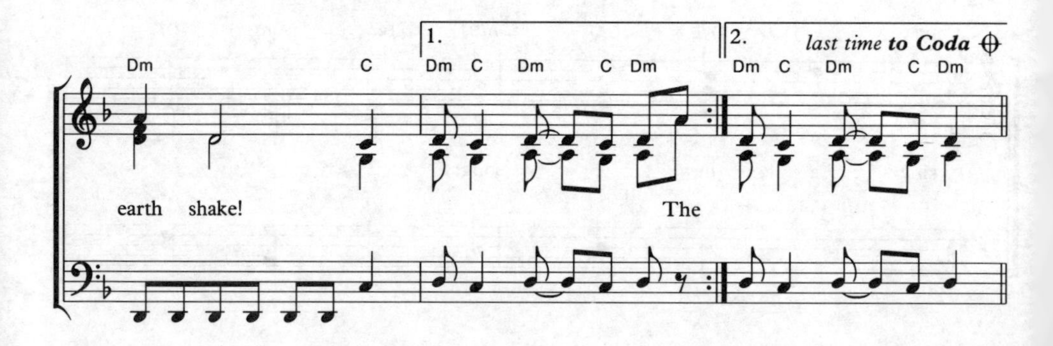
1.
2. last time to Coda
Dm
C
Dm C Dm C Dm
Dm C Dm C Dm
earth shake! The

B♭
F/A
Dm7
Gm7
Great is the Lord in Zi - on, ex - alt - ed a - bove all the na -

Dm
E♭ B♭/E♭ E♭ B♭/E♭ E♭ B♭/E♭ E♭ A7sus
- tions: let them praise his great and awe-some

A
D.𝄋 al Coda
name. The

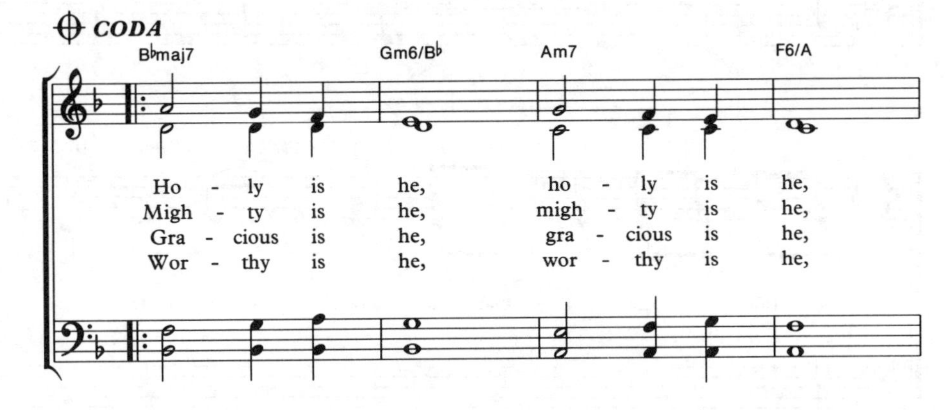

CODA
B♭maj7 Gm6/B♭ Am7 F6/A
Ho - ly is he, ho - ly is he,
Migh - ty is he, migh - ty is he,
Gra - cious is he, gra - cious is he,
Wor - thy is he, wor - thy is he,

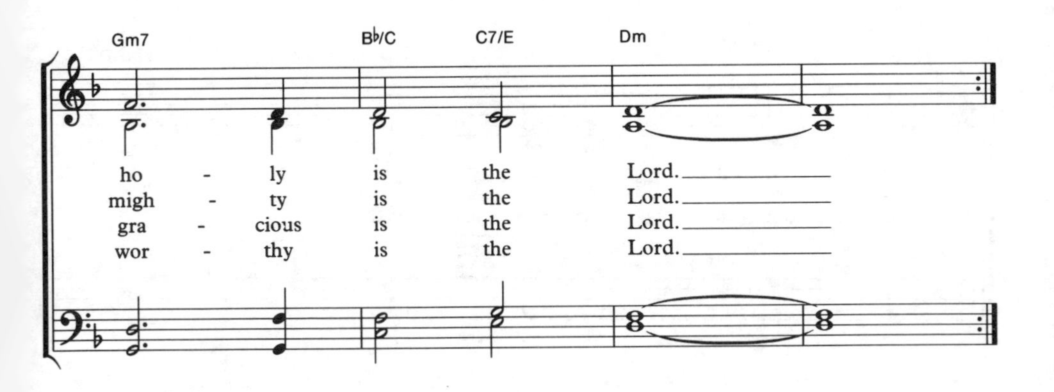

Gm7 B♭/C C7/E Dm
ho - ly is the Lord.
migh - ty is the Lord.
gra - cious is the Lord.
wor - thy is the Lord.

100E I will enter his gates

From Psalm 100, *Jubilate Deo*
Words and music: Unknown
Music arranged Christopher Norton

Rhythmically
D D/F♯ G G/B D D/C♯ Bm D/A
I will en - ter his gates with thanks - giv - ing in my heart, I will
D D/F♯ G G/B Asus A
en - ter his courts with praise; I will
D D/F♯ G G/B D F♯7/C♯ Bm D7/A
say this is the day that the Lord has made, I
G A7 D G/D D Em7/D
will re - joice for he has made me glad.

D D/F♯ G D D/C♯ Bm
He has made me glad, he has made me glad, I
Em7 A7 G/A A7 D Em7 Asus A
will re - joice for he has made me glad.
D D/F♯ G D D/C♯ Bm
He has made me glad, he has made me glad, I
Em7 A7 A7sus A7 D
will re - joice for he has made me glad.

100F O shout to the Lord

Jubilate

Words: from Psalm 100, *Jubilate Deo*
from *The Liturgical Psalter*
David Frost and others
Music: Chris Rolinson
arranged David Peacock

Triumphantly
D
A/D
G/D
A/D
GROUP A
O
Chorus 1
shout to the Lord in tri-umph all the earth,
GROUP B
O
shout to the Lord in tri-umph all the earth;

The singers divide at A and B.
Group A: could be men/soloist/group, Group B: could be women/congregation

G/A D G/A D
GROUP A
Serve the Lord with glad - ness,
GROUP B
serve the Lord with glad - ness, and
GROUP A
G D/F♯ Em7 G/A A7 D G/A D
come be - fore his face with songs of joy,
GROUP B
and
1.
G D/F♯ Em7 G/A A7 D G/A D
come be - fore his face with songs of joy!
GROUP A
O
2.3.
D G/A D
3rd time to Chorus 2
joy!
Verse 1
B♭/F C/G D/A B♭/F C/G
ALL
Know that the Lord, he is
D/A G D/F♯ Em7 D/E
God; it is he who has made us and we are

Asus A B♭/F C/G D/A B♭/F C/G D/A
his: we are his peo - ple and the
G D/F♯ Em D/F♯ Asus A
sheep of his pas - ture.
Chorus 2
D A/D G/A A/D
GROUP A
Come in - to his gates with thanks - giv - ing,
D A/D G/A A/D
GROUP B
come in - to his gates with thanks - giv - ing,
G/A D G/A D
GROUP A
and in - to his courts with praise,
GROUP B
and in - to his courts with praise; give
GROUP A

G D/F♯ Em7 G/A A7 D G/A D
thanks to him and bless his ho - ly name,
GROUP B
give
G D/F♯ Em7 G/A A7 D G/A D
Fine
thanks to him and bless his ho - ly name.
Verse 2
B♭/F C/G D/F♯ B♭/F C/G D/F♯ G
ALL
For the Lord, the Lord is good: his lov - ing
D/F♯ Em7 D/F♯ Asus A B♭/F C/G D/A
mer - cy is for ev - er, his faith - ful - ness
B♭/F C/G D/A G G/A
D.𝄋 al Fine
through-out all ge - ne - ra - tions.
GROUP A
O

100G Jubilate, everybody

Words: from Psalm 100, *Jubilate Deo*
after Michael Perry
Fred Dunn
Music: Fred Dunn
arranged Christopher Norton

Joyfully
Dm Gm A Dm A7 Dm A7
Ju - bi - la - te, ev - ery-bo - dy, serve the Lord in — all your ways, and
Dm Gm A Dm A7 Dm
come be-fore his pres-ence sing-ing; en - ter now his — courts with praise.
D Gm C F Gm A7 Dm/F A7/E Dm
For the Lord our God is gra-cious, and his mer-cy's ev - er - last - ing,
D Gm C F Gm A7 Dm/F A7/E Dm
Ju - bi - la - te, ju - bi - la - te, ju - bi - la - te De - o.

Come, rejoice before him

100H

(Jubilate Deo)

Words: from Psalm 100, *Jubilate Deo*
Music: M Praetorius (1571–1621)
arranged Jacques Berthier

Lively
C F G C F G C F G C F G
Come, re - joice be - fore him; sing to God your prais - es:
Ju - bi - la - te De - o, ju - bi - la - te De - o,
C F G C F G C F G C F G
Al - le - lu - ia! Come, re - joice be - fore him;
Al - le - lu - ia! Ju - bi - la - te De - o,
C F G C F G C F G C F G C
sing to God your prais - es: Al - le - lu - ia!
ju - bi - la - te De - o, Al - le - lu - ia!

To be sung as a 6-part canon. Each part begins in successive bars.
May also be combined with 100I (sung in C major).

100I Come, rejoice in God

Jubilate Servite

From Psalm 100, *Jubilate Deo*
Words and music: Taizé – Jacques Berthier

Joyfully ♩ = 84
D G A D G A D G A
Come, re - joice in God; praise him, all the
Ju - bi - la - te De - o om - nis ter -
earth. Serve your God, serve your God,
- ra, ser - vi - te Do - mi - no
glad - ly serve your God! Al - le - lu - ia,
in lae - ti - ti - a, al - le - lu - ia,

To be sung in canon. Part 2 to begin at bar 2.
When sung in C major, it may also be combined with 100H.

D G A D G A D G A
al - le - lu - ia, glad - ly serve your God;
al - le - lu - ia, in lae - ti - ti - a!
D G A D G A
al - le - lu - ia, al - le - lu - ia,
Al - le - lu - ia, al - le - lu - ia,

D G A D G A D
glad - ly serve your God!
in lae - ti - ti - a!

100J O be glad in the Lord

Jane (adapted) 9 9 9 9 D

Words: from Psalm 100, *Jubilate Deo*
Stephen Wilcockson
Music: David Peacock

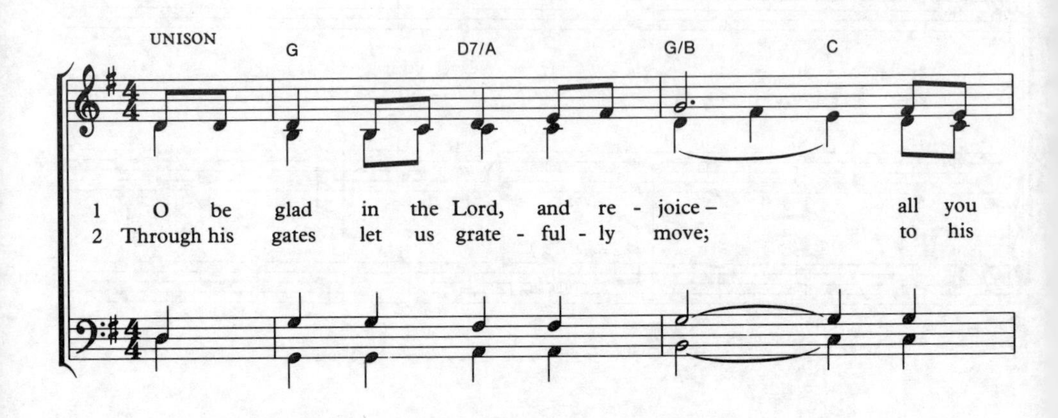

UNISON
G
D7/A
G/B
C
1 O be glad in the Lord, and re - joice – all you
2 Through his gates let us grate - ful - ly move; to his

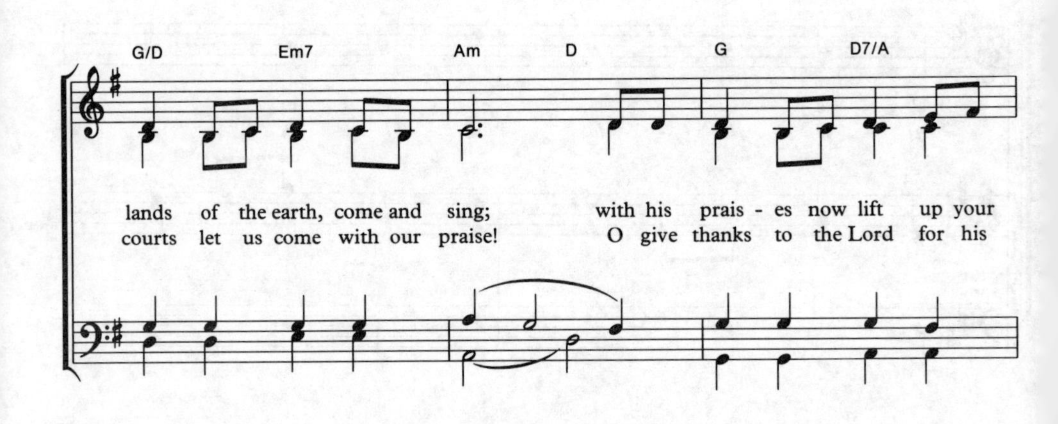

G/D
Em7
Am
D
G
D7/A
lands of the earth, come and sing; with his prais - es now lift up your
courts let us come with our praise! O give thanks to the Lord for his

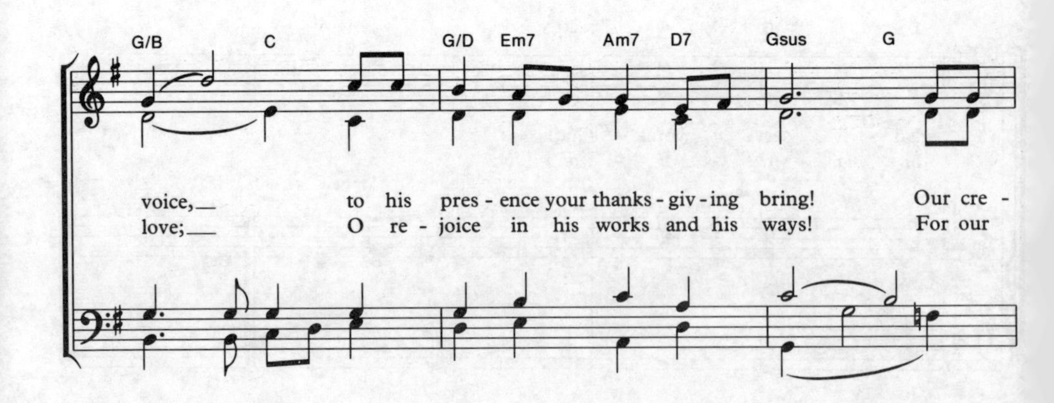

G/B
C
G/D
Em7
Am7
D7
Gsus
G
voice,— to his pres - ence your thanks - giv - ing bring! Our cre -
love;— O re - joice in his works and his ways! For our

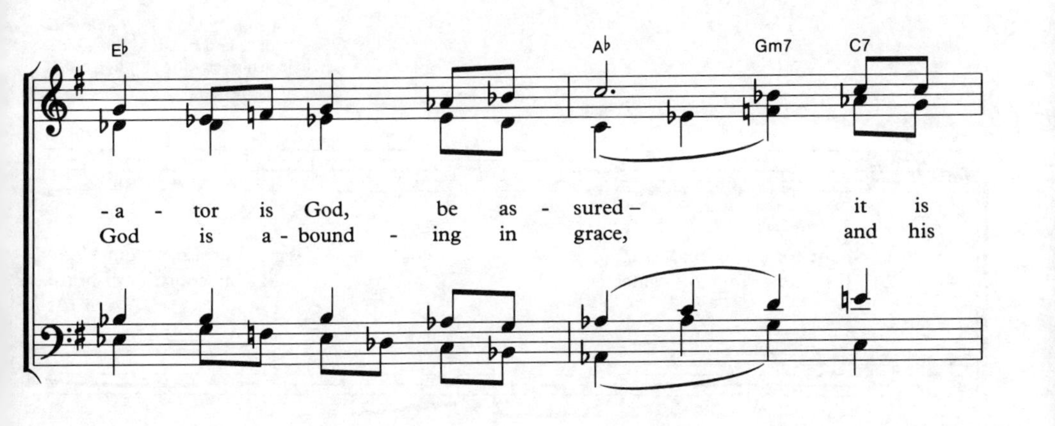

E♭
A♭
Gm7
C7
-a - tor is God, be as - sured – it is
God is a - bound - ing in grace, and his

Fm
Cm
Dsus
D
G
D7/A
not by our-selves we were made; God him - self is our Shep-herd and
mer - cy is faith - ful and sure: ge - ne - ra - tions to come, seek his

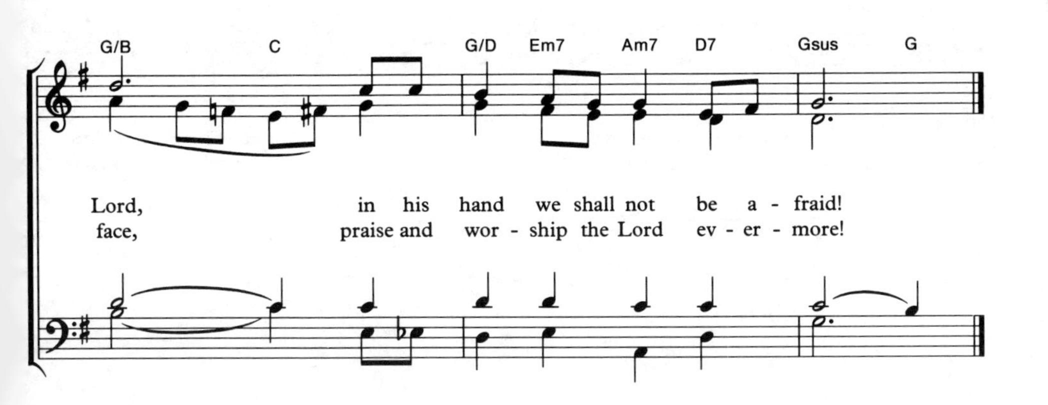

G/B
C
G/D
Em7
Am7
D7
Gsus
G
Lord, in his hand we shall not be a - fraid!
face, praise and wor - ship the Lord ev - er - more!

100K **Shout for joy and sing**

From Psalm 100, *Jubilate Deo*
Words and music: John Daniels
Music arranged Christopher Norton

Joyfully
E
B7/E
f
1 Shout for joy and sing,
2 En - ter in his gates
serve the Lord your king,
and his courts with praise,

E
com - ing be - fore him
giv - ing thanks to him

B7/E
G♯m7
mf
joy - ful - ly - and sing,
through-out all our days:
know-ing that the
for the Lord our

C♯m7
G♯m7
C♯m7
Lord is God; he has made us, we are his
God is good, and his love has ev - er stood;
G♯m7
C♯m7
F♯m7
1.3.
B7sus
B7
in his pas - ture we have food and in his pres-ence live
(repeat verse)
faith - ful - ly he keeps his word and his love to all
(repeat verse)
2.
B7sus
E
B7/E
D.C.
ev - er - more.
4.
B7sus
E
ge - ne - ra - tions.

100M Shout, shout joyfully

From Psalm 100, *Jubilate Deo*
Words and music: Tom Brooks

Joyfully
A A/C# D Esus E
Shout! Shout joy - ful - ly to your God, all the

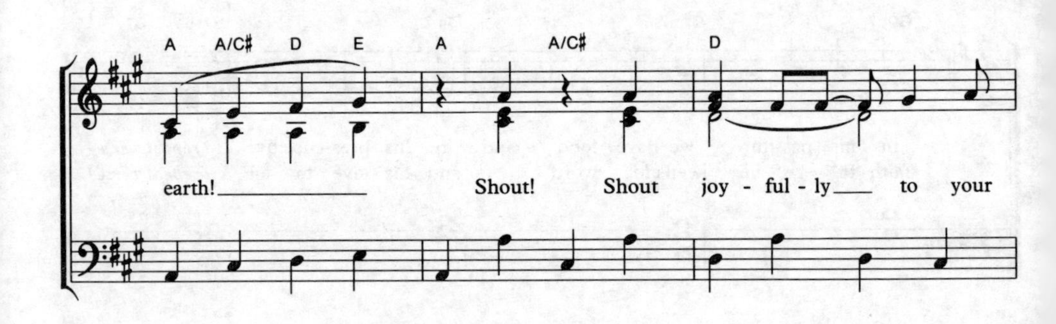
A A/C# D E A A/C# D
earth! Shout! Shout joy - ful - ly to your

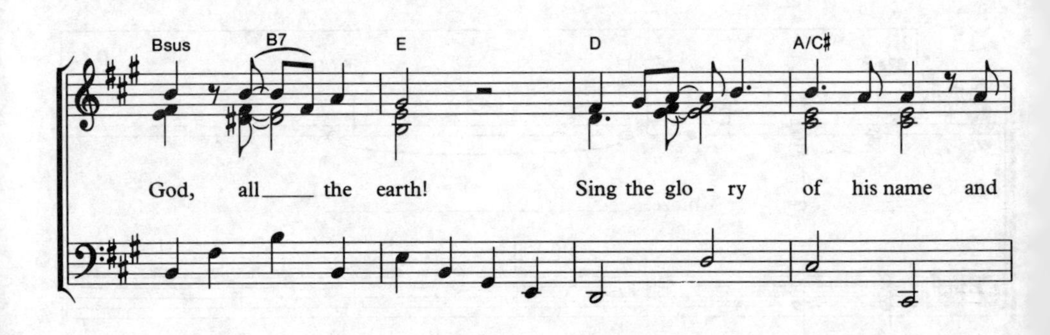
Bsus B7 E D A/C#
God, all the earth! Sing the glo - ry of his name and

Bm A/C# D Bm7 Dmaj7/E E A A/C#
make his prais - es glo - ri - ous. Shout! Shout

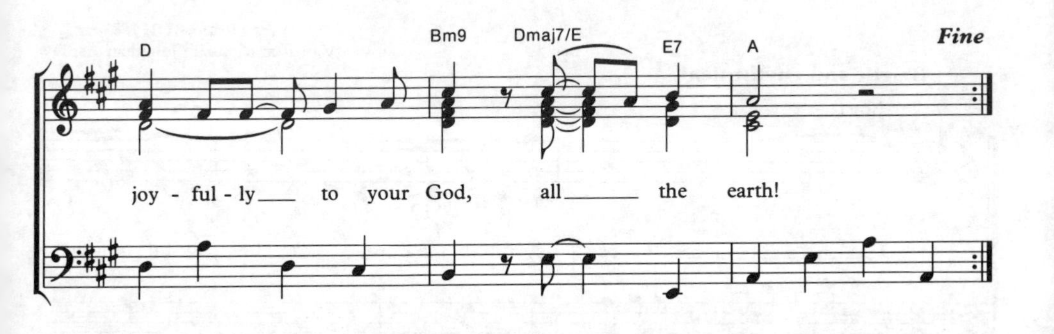
D Bm9 Dmaj7/E E7 A
Fine
joy - ful - ly to your God, all the earth!

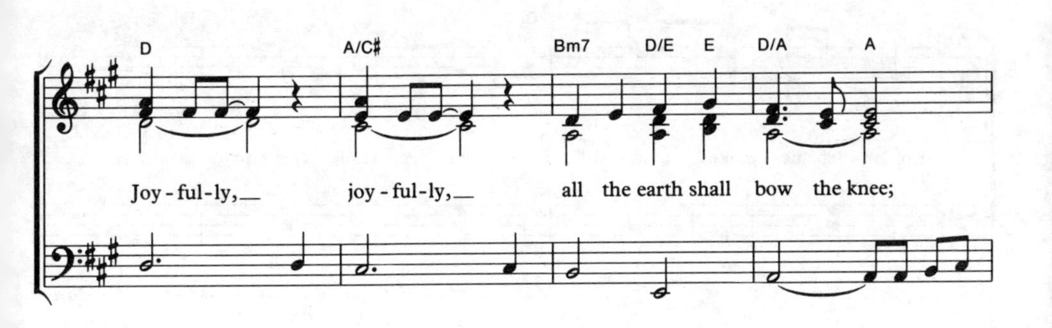
D A/C# Bm7 D/E E D/A A
Joy - ful-ly, joy - ful-ly, all the earth shall bow the knee;

D B Bm7 Dmaj7/E E
joy - ful-ly, joy - ful-ly, we will sing in har - mo-ny,

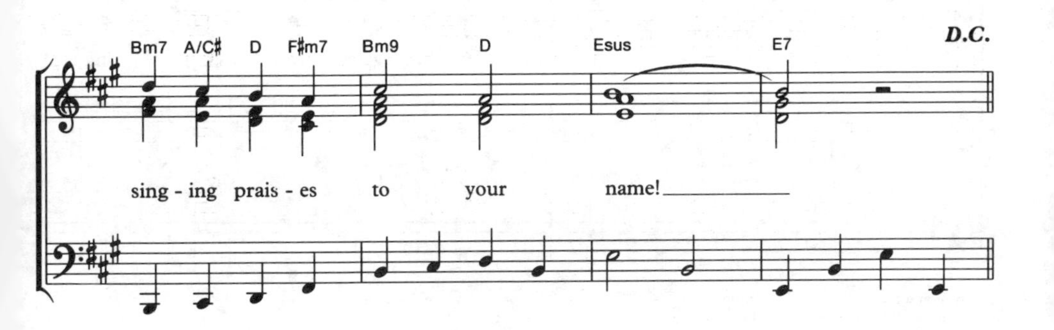
Bm7 A/C# D F#m7 Bm9 D Esus E7
D.C.
sing - ing prais - es to your name!

100N O be joyful in the Lord

From Psalm 100, *Jubilate Deo*
Words and music: Jonathan Asprey

Bright and rhythmical
Chorus
G D G C G Em Am D C G D G
O be joy-ful in the Lord, O be joy-ful in the
Lord, let us make a joy-ful noise, let the whole earth re-joice;
O be joy-ful in the Lord, all you lands!
Fine
Em G
1 Know that the Lord he is God:
3 Know that the Lord he is good:
2 En-ter his gates with thanks-giv-ing,

Em
G
— he has made us we are his; we are the
— his love lasts for ev - er; he's
— come in - to his courts with praise; be
C
G
sheep of his pas - ture, the
faith - ful and true through
thank - ful now to him, and
C
D
D.C.
peo - ple of his hand.
ev - ery ge - ne - ra - tion.
speak good of his name.

102B Hear my prayer

Kyebambe

From Psalm 102
Words and music: Christopher Hayward

With feeling

Chorus
Dm Em7 D2/F♯ E♭
Hear my prayer, O Lord, hear my prayer, O

Asus A D2 Em7 D/F♯ B♭7/F
Lord; let my cry for help

Em7 Gm/A A6 to verse D F♯sus F♯
come to you.

last time
D
Fine
Verse
Bm
A/B
Bm6
F♯/B
you. Do not hide your face from me
Em7
F♯m7
Gmaj7
A/G
when I am in dis-tress; turn your ear to
D/F♯
Dm/F
E7
A/E
me. When I call, ans-wer me quick-ly,
D.C. al Fine
E7
A/E
Em7
F♯m7
Gmaj7
G/A
ans-wer me quick-ly; turn your ear to me.

103D Bless the Lord, my soul

Ostinato Chorale

From Psalm 103
Words and music: Taizé – Jacques Berthier

♩ = 76
MIXED VOICES
Dm G Dm B♭ C F A
Bless the Lord, my soul, and bless his ho - ly name;
Dm G Dm B♭ C Dm
bless the Lord, my soul, he res - cues me from death.
DESCANT
Bless the Lord, my soul, and bless his ho - ly name;
bless the Lord, my soul, he res - cues me from death.

Verses (sung above the continuous response)
SOLO
Dm G Dm
1 It is he who for - gives all your guilt, who
B♭ C F A Dm G
heals ev - ery one of your ills, who re - deems your life from the
Dm B♭ C Dm
grave, who crowns you with love and com - pas - sion.

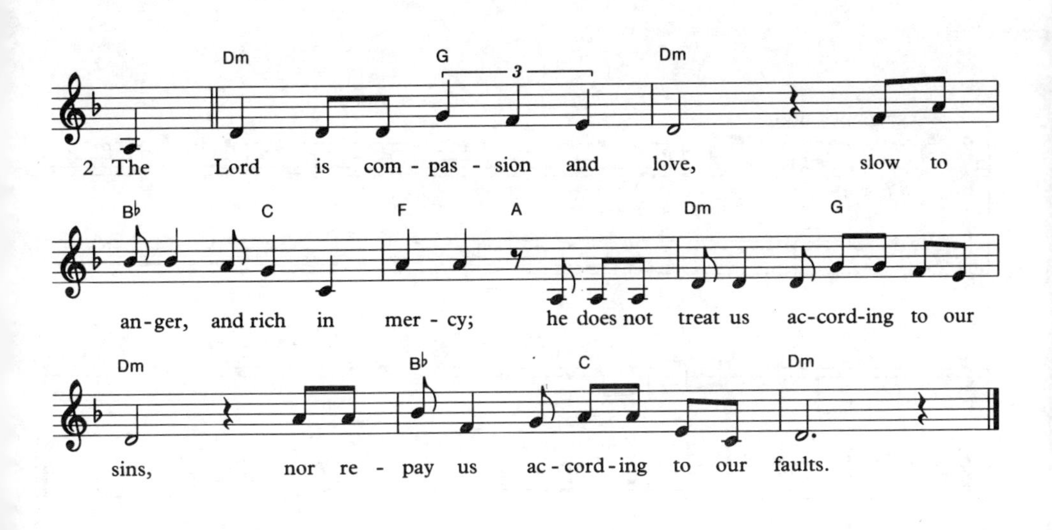
Dm G Dm
2 The Lord is com - pas - sion and love, slow to
B♭ C F A Dm G
an - ger, and rich in mer - cy; he does not treat us ac - cord - ing to our
Dm B♭ C Dm
sins, nor re - pay us ac - cord - ing to our faults.

Dm G Dm
3 As a fa - ther has com - pas - sion on his child - ren, the Lord has
B♭ C F A Dm G
pi - ty on those who fear him; for he knows of what we are
Dm B♭ C Dm
made, he re - mem - bers that we are but dust.

Instrumental parts overleaf

Varied Accompaniments and Solos

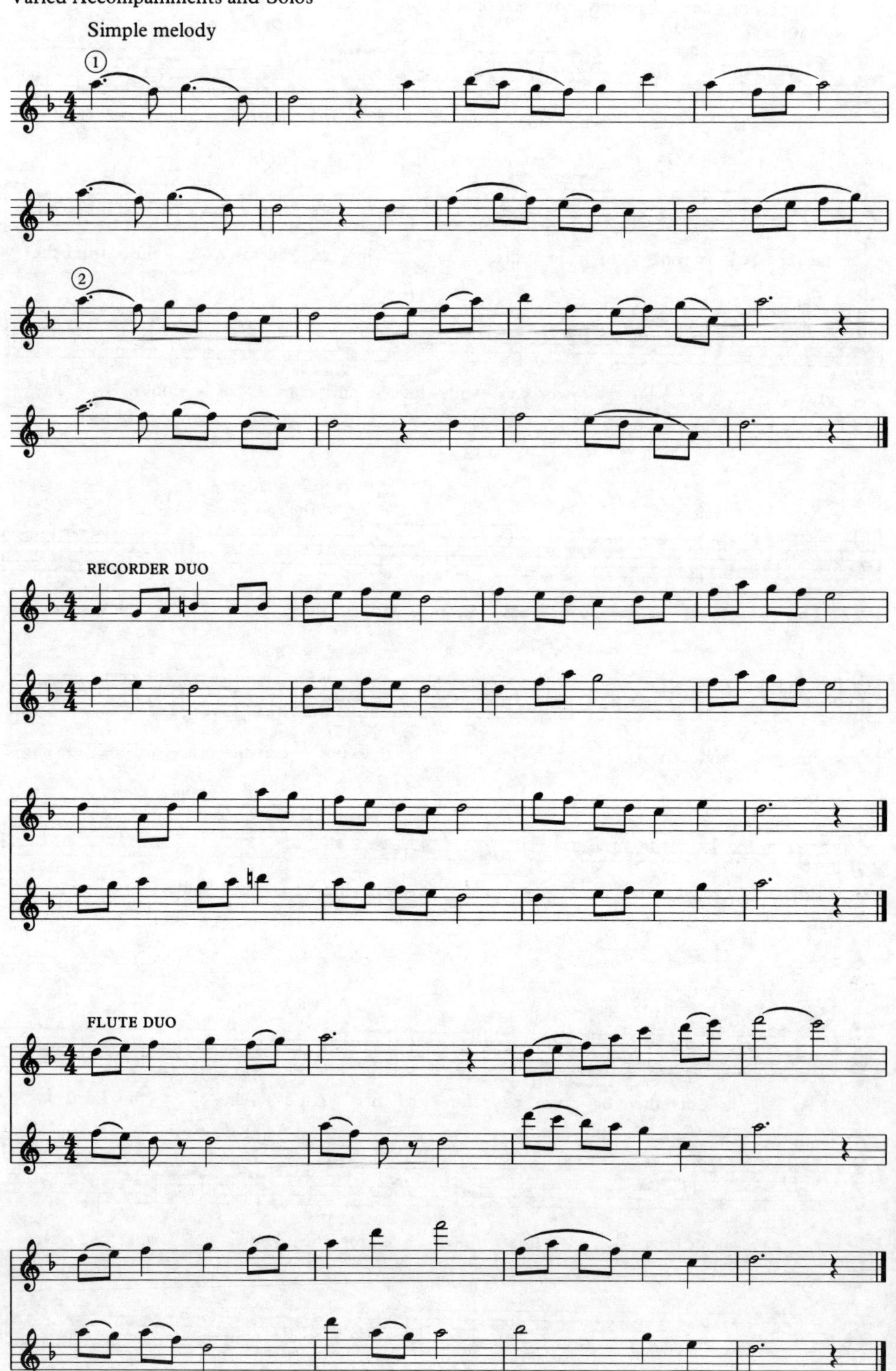
Simple melody
①
②
RECORDER DUO
FLUTE DUO

OBOE AND CLARINET DUO *
OBOE
B♭ CLARINET
HORN AND BASSOON DUO *
HORN
BASSOON
TRUMPET
①
3
②
BASSOON

* These two duos can be played together as a quartet

103E Bless the Lord, O my soul

From Psalm 103
Words and music: Unknown
Music arranged David Peacock

With majesty
G C E7 A
Bless the Lord, O my soul, bless the Lord, O my
D G C Am G/D Dsus
last time to Coda
soul, and all that is with - in me bless his ho - ly
1. G C G/B D7/A
2. G C D7 G C G C G
name; bless the name; King of kings (for ev-er and ev-er),
A D A D A B Em B Em B
Lord of lords (for ev-er and ev-er), King of kings (for ev-er and ev-er),
Am G/B Am/C C/E G/D D7 G C G/B D7/A
D.S. al Coda
King of kings and Lord of lords! Bless the
CODA
G
name;

O bless the Lord, O my soul 103F

From Psalm 103
Words and music: John Bell

Joyfully
D Gmaj7 Am7/G G D Gmaj7 Am7/G
O my soul, O my
O bless the Lord, O bless the Lord,
G D Gmaj7 D/F♯ Em Em/D Cmaj7 Cmaj7/A
soul, bless the Lord and ne - ver for - get his
O bless the Lord, bless the Lord and ne - ver for - get his
D7 Gmaj7 Am7/G G D Gmaj7 Am7/G
love; O my soul, O my
love; O bless the Lord, O bless the Lord,
G D Gmaj7 D/F♯ Em Em/D Cmaj7 Cmaj7/D G
soul, bless the Lord and ne-ver for-get his love!
O bless the Lord, bless the Lord and ne-ver for-get his love!

103G Bless the Lord, O my soul

From Psalm 103
Words and music: Michael Baughen
Music arranged Noël Tredinnick

With a swing
Chorus (vv. 1–4)
Capo 5(C) Dm7 (Am7) G7 (D7) B♭/C (F/G) C7 (G7) F (C) Am (Em)
Bless the
Gm7 (Dm7) B♭/C (F/G) C/B♭ (G/F) Am7 (Em7) Dm (Am) Gm7 (Dm7) B♭/C (F/G) B♭dim7 (Fdim7)
Lord, O my soul, and all with - in me, hon - our his name;
Am7 (Em7) D7 (A7) Gm7 (Dm7) A7 (E7) Am7/D (Em7/A) D7 (A7) G7 (D7) Gm7/C (Dm7/G) C7 (G7) F (C)
bless the Lord, O my soul, and ne - ver for - get all his bless - ings.
Verses 1–4
C7 (G7) F (C) Dm7 (Am7) Gm7 (Dm7) C7 (G7)
1 He for - gives all your sin and he heals all your ills; he re -
2 Jus-tice for the op-pressed with com - pas - sion and grace, slow to
3 As the hea - vens are high, so to those who fear God his com -
4 All our days are like grass or a flower of the field – as the

Fmaj7 (Cmaj7) F♯dim7 (C♯dim7) Gm7 (Dm7) C7 (G7) B♭dim7 (Fdim7) Am7 (Em7) Cm7/F (Gm7/C) F7 (C7)
- deems_ your life from the pit, he shows mer - cy up - on you and
an - ger, a-bound-ing in love: he is not al-ways chi-ding but
- pas - sion and mer - cy are great; he re - moves our sins from us and
wind pas-ses ov - er, it goes; but on those who o - bey him, with
D7/B♭ (A7/F) A7 (E7) Dm7 (Am7) G7 (C7) C7 (G7)
stead - fast love; he re - news your youth by good things.
in his love he does not re - mem-ber our sins.
all our guilt as far as the East from the West.
stead - fast love he be - stows his love ev - er - more.
Final chorus
F (C) F♯dim7 (C♯dim7) Gm7 (Dm7) B♭/C (F/G) C/B♭ (G/F) Am7 (Em7) Dm7 (Am7) G7 (D7) B♭/C (F/G) B♭dim7 (Fdim7)
Bless the Lord, king of all, all you his an - gels do-ing his word;
Am7 (Em7) D7 (A7) Gm7 (Dm7) A7 (E7) Am7/D (Em7/A) D7 (A7) G7 (D7) Gm7/C (Dm7/G) C7 (G7) F (C)
bless the Lord, all his hosts, and all of his works in cre - a - tion!
Grandioso
B♭m6 (Fm6) Am7 (Em7) Gm9 (Dm9) F♯9♭5 (C♯9♭5) F9 + 6 (C9 + 6)
Fine
Bless the Lord, O my soul!

103H Bless the Lord, O my soul

From Psalm 103
Words and music: Berj Topalian

With strength
Capo 3(C)
E♭ (C) B♭ (G) E♭ (C) A♭ (F) E♭/B♭ (C) B♭ (G) E♭ (C) A♭/B♭ (F) B♭ (G)
Bless the Lord, O my soul, bless his ho - ly name
(bless the Lord):
to verse
to end
Fine
E♭ (C) B♭ (G) E♭ (C) A♭ (F) E♭/B♭ (C) B♭ (G) E♭ (C) E♭ (C)
ev - er - last - ing is his love, from age to age the same! 1 For - same!
2 He
A♭ (F) B♭7 (G7) Gm (Em) Cm (Am) E♭7 (C7) A♭ (F) Cm/G (Am) B♭7/F (G7) E♭sus (Csus) E♭ (C)
get not all his be - ne - fits – he par - dons all your sin; he
crowns you with his stead - fast love, he fills you with good things; your
A♭ (F) E♭/B♭ (C) Csus (Asus) Gm/C (Em) F7 (D7) B♭sus (Gsus) B♭ (G)
heals your in - fir - mi - ties, re - deems you from death's sting.
vi - gour dai - ly he re - news – you rise on ea - gles' wings!

The majesty of mountains

104C

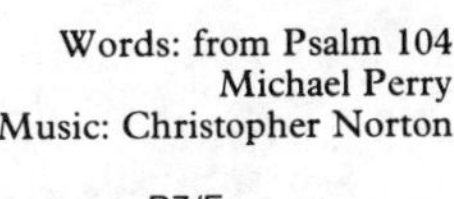

Words: from Psalm 104
Michael Perry
Music: Christopher Norton

Misterioso, with movement
Em B7/E Em B7/E
1 The ma - je - sty of moun-tains, the sov-ereign-ty of skies, the
2 The run-ning of the ri - ver, the sur - ging of the sea, the
3 The glo - ry of the God-head, the Spi - rit and the Son, the
Am7 D9 Gmaj7 Cmaj7 C7♭5 Bsus B7 Em
re - gal rocks that arch a - bove where veils of va - pour rise, are
grass that grows high on the hill, the flower and fruit - ing tree, our
Fa - ther, faith - ful down the days: to them, the Three-in - One, while
Am7 D9 Gmaj9 G6 F♯m7 B7 Em
gifts of God, the Lord of love, the
Sav - iour sends us, by whose will all
life shall last be per - fect praise and
Am B7sus B7 1.2. Em 3. Em
wor - ship - ful, the wise.
crea-tures came to be.
high - est hon - our done!

104D Bless the Lord

From Psalm 104
Words and music: Peter and Hanneke Jacobs
(from Colby's *Make a joyful noise*)
Music arranged Christopher Norton

Worshipfully
Capo 3(A) C (A) G/C (E) B♭/C (G) C7 (A7) F/C (D)
Bless the Lord, O my soul – O Lord, you are so
Fm6/C (Dm6) C (A) G/C (E) B♭/C (G) C7 (A7)
great! Bless the Lord, O my soul: I
F/C (D) D/E (B) E (C♯) Am (F♯m)
will be glad in him.
1 You made all things up -
2 For all your works I'll
G (E) F (D) C (A) Esus (C♯sus) E (C♯)
- on the earth, the o - ceans and the land;
praise you Lord, I will re - joice in you;

Am (F♯m) G (E) F (D) Dm7 (Bm7) C/F (A) B♭ (G)
and ev - ery crea - ture in this world was made by your com-mand.
and from my heart I'll sing this song so that I might bless you.
F/G (D) G7 (E7) C (A) G/C (E)
Bless the Lord,
B♭/C (G) C7 (A7) F/C (D) Fm6/C (Dm6)
O my soul - O Lord, you are so great!
C (A) G/C (E) B♭/C (G) C7 (A7) F/C (D)
Bless the Lord, O my soul: I will be glad in
Fm6/C (Dm6) rit. Fm (Dm) C (A)
him. I'll be glad in him.

104E I will sing out to the Lord

From Psalm 104
Words and music: Donya Brockway
Music arranged Christopher Norton
Easy waltz
D Dmaj7 D6 D D/E Am/F♯ G
mf
I will sing out to the Lord as
D A
long as I live, I will sing praise to my
D Dmaj7 D6 D
God while I have my be - ing;
Dmaj7 D6 D D/E Am/F♯ G
my me - di - ta - tion of him
D A
shall be sweet, I will be glad, I will be

A7
D
G/D
D
D7
glad in the Lord.
Bless the
G
A
D
Dmaj7
f
Lord, O my soul, praise the Lord;
D6
D
Em7
A
bless the Lord, O my soul,
1.
D
Dmaj7
D6
D7
praise the Lord!
Bless the
2.
A7
D
G/D
D
Fine
A7
D.C. al Fine
praise the Lord!

104F O praise the Lord, O my soul

From Psalm 104
Words and music: Paul Whitell

Relaxed swing
D F#m7 Em7 G/A A
MEN
O praise the Lord O my soul,
D F#m7 Em7 G/A A
WOMEN
O praise the Lord O my soul,
4th time to Coda
D B7/D# Em7 Em7/A A7
ALL
O praise the Lord O my
D Bsus B Em7 A
soul!
1 Lord, to you all
2 You have made the
3 All my life I'll

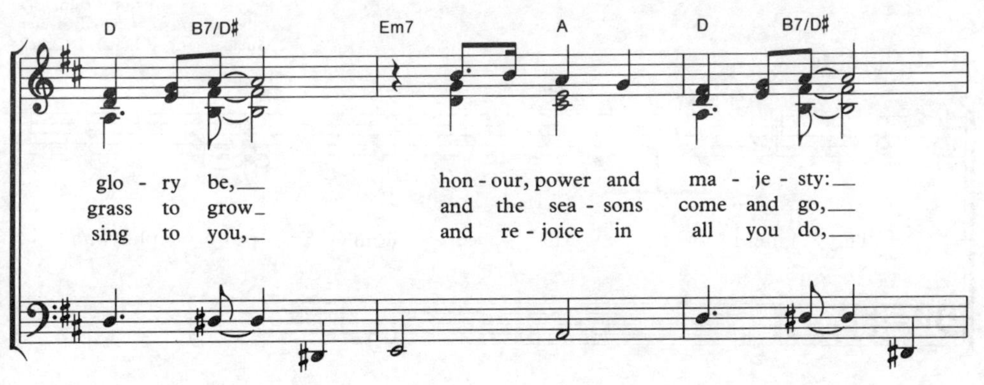
D
B7/D♯
Em7
A
D
B7/D♯
glo - ry be, hon - our, power and ma - je - sty:
grass to grow and the sea - sons come and go,
sing to you, and re - joice in all you do,

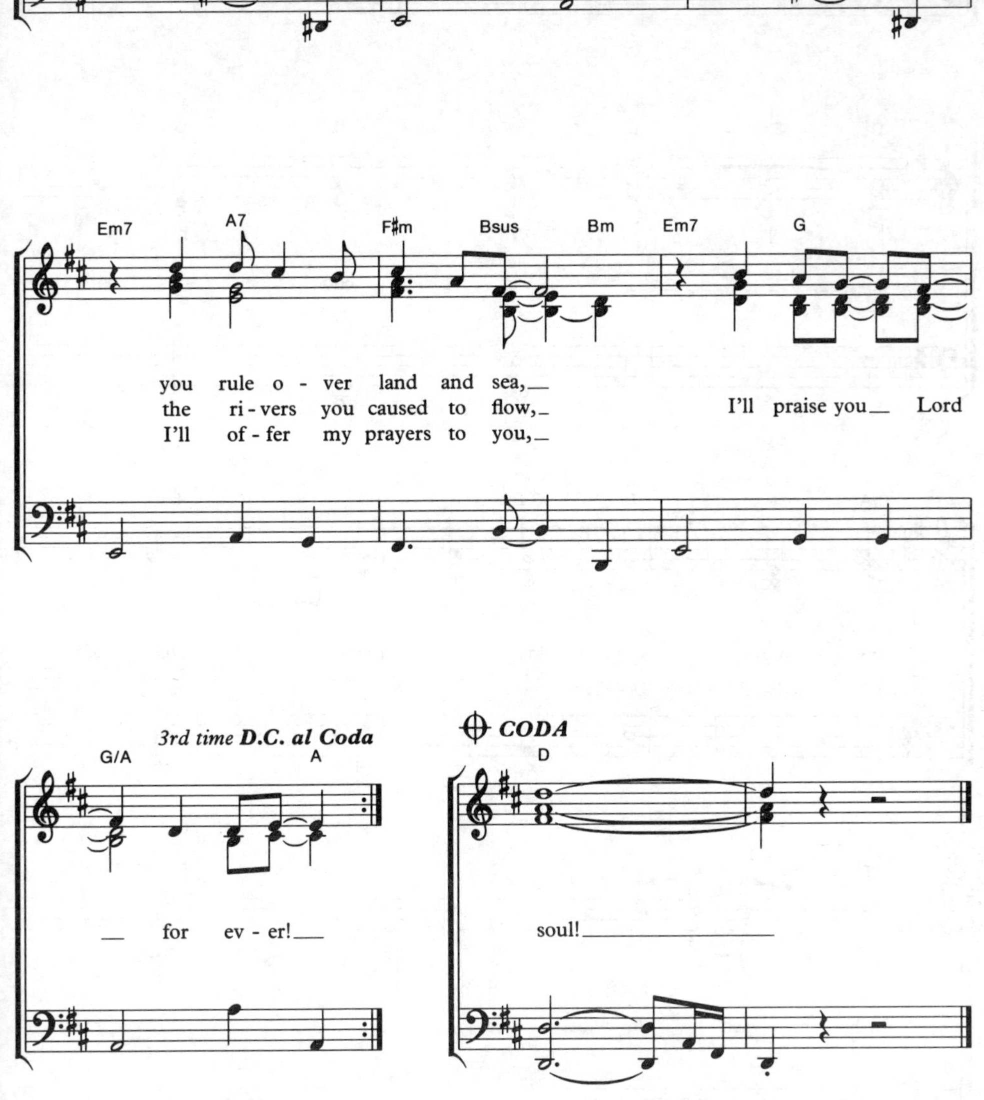
Em7
A7
F♯m
Bsus
Bm
Em7
G
you rule o - ver land and sea,
the ri - vers you caused to flow,
I'll of - fer my prayers to you,
I'll praise you Lord
3rd time D.C. al Coda
G/A
A
for ev - er!
CODA
D
soul!

105A The Lord has led forth

From Psalm 105
Words and music: Chris Bowater
Music arranged David Peacock
Joyfully
D Em7 D/F♯ G
The Lord has led forth his peo - ple with
D Em7 D Em7 D G
joy, and his cho - sen ones with
D/A A D G/D A D Em7
sing - ing, sing - ing; the Lord has led
D/F♯ G D Em7 D/F♯ Em7/G
forth his peo - ple with joy, and his

Fine
D/A
Bm
Em7
D/A
A
D
G/D
D
cho - sen ones with sing - ing.
Bm
F♯m
He has given to them the lands of the na -
Bm
F♯m
- tions, to pos - sess the fruit and keep his laws, and
D.𝄋 al Fine
G
G/A
A
praise, praise his name. The

105B Let the hearts of those who seek the Lord

From Psalm 105
Words and music: Christine Mitchell-Innes
Music arranged Richard Bowker

Joyfully
D
G/A
D
A
Let the hearts of those who seek the Lord re - joice, re -

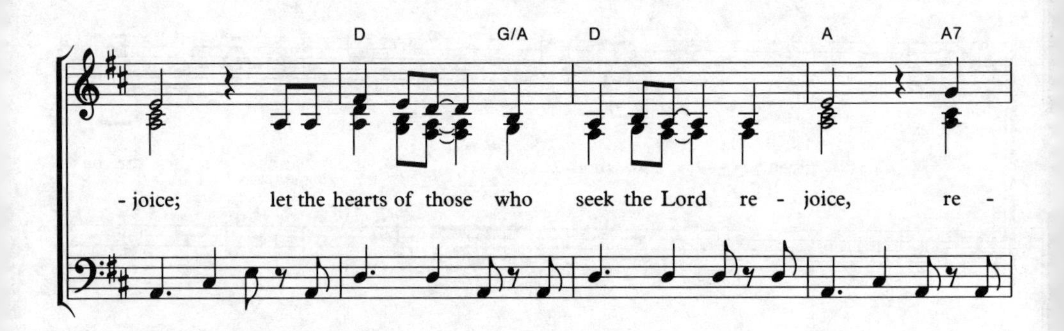
D
G/A
D
A
A7
- joice; let the hearts of those who seek the Lord re - joice, re -

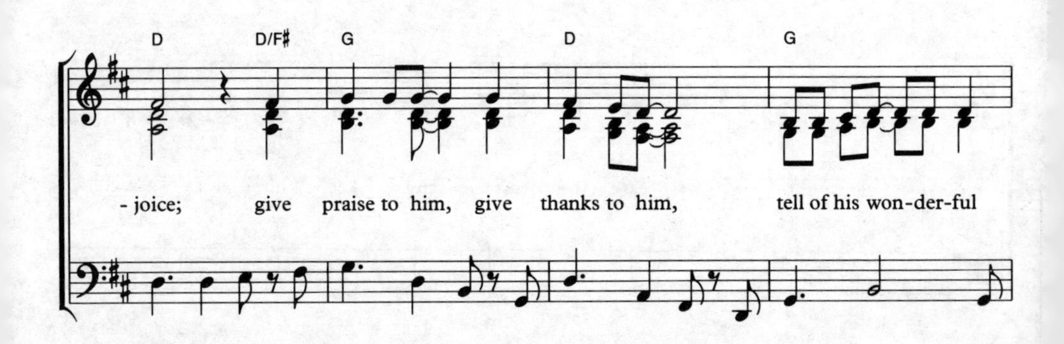
D
D/F#
G
D
G
- joice; give praise to him, give thanks to him, tell of his won-der-ful

A
D
G/A
D
works – let the hearts of those who love the Lord re -

1.
2.
A
D
A/G
B
- joice!
Let the
Let the
E
A/B
E
B
hearts of those who seek the Lord re - joice, re - joice; let the
E
A/B
E
B
B7
E
hearts of those who seek the Lord re - joice, re - joice; give
A
E
A
B
praise to him, give thanks to him, tell of his won-der-ful works – let the
poco rit.
E
A/B
E
B
E
hearts of those who love the Lord re - joice!

106B It is good to give thanks to the Lord

New 106th
From Psalm 106
Words and music: John Bell
Verse 1
N.C.
SOLO: It is good to give thanks to the Lord, to re - member all he has done; then God will re-mem - ber our prais - es when he looks with love on his peo - ple.
Chorus
Em Cmaj7 D Bm7 Em Am7 Bm B7
ALL O give thanks to the Lord, for his love en-dures for ev - er;
Em Cmaj7 D Bm7 Am7 Bm7 E
to Verses
O give thanks to the Lord, for the Lord a-lone is good.
Verse 2
Our sin is the sin of our fa - thers, we have done wrong, we all have been e - vil; like those who once lived in bond - age, we paid no heed to all you had done.
to Choru

Verse 3
Our fa - thers for - sook your love, at the Red
Sea, they ques - tioned their God; they fell from their faith in the
to Chorus
des - ert, and put God to the test in the wil - der - ness.
Verse 4
Time af - ter time he would res - cue them, yet in
mal - ice they dared to de - fy him; des - pite this he came to their
to Chorus
aid when he heard their cries of dis - tress.
Verse 5
Save us, O Lord, in your love, bring us
back from all that of - fends you; look not a - lone at our
to Chorus
sins, but re - mem - ber your pro - mise of mer - cy.
Verse 6
Blessed be the Lord God of Is - rael both
now and through all e - ter - ni - ty; let na - tions and peo - ple cry
to Chorus
out and sing, A - men! Al - le - lu - ia!

108B Through our God we shall do valiantly

Victory Song

From Psalm 108
Words and music: Dale Garratt
Music arranged Christopher Norton

Strongly
Capo 3(Am)
Cm
(Am)
G7
(E7)
Through our God we shall do val - iant - ly – it is
Cm
(Am)
he who will tread down our e - ne - mies; we'll
G7
(E7)
3rd time to Coda
sing and shout his vic - to - ry: Christ is
Cm
(Am)
B♭
(G)
E♭
(C)
king! For God has won the vic - to - ry and

Fm (Dm)
Cm (Am)
B♭ (G)
set his peo-ple free; his word has slain the

E♭ (C)
Fm (Dm)
G7 (E7) Fm/C (Dm) F7/A (D7) G7/B (E7)
e - ne - my, the earth shall stand and see that through our

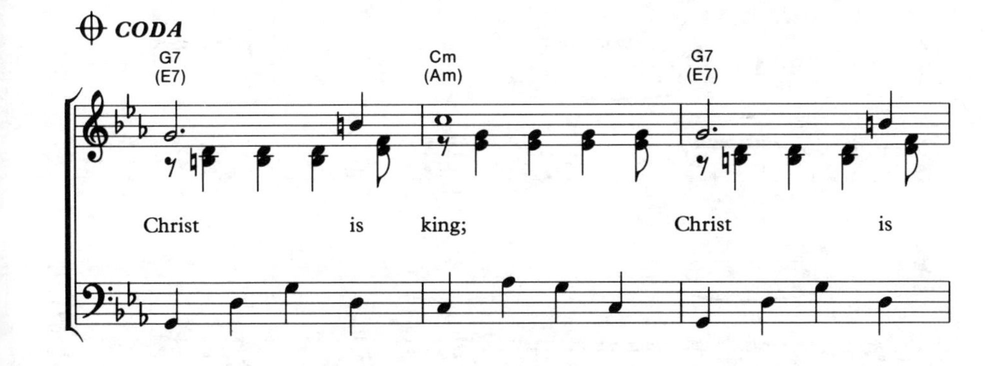
CODA
G7 (E7)
Cm (Am)
G7 (E7)
Christ is king; Christ is

Cm (Am)
G7 (E7)
Cm (Am)
king; Christ is king!

Instrumental parts overleaf

Instrumental arrangements

FLUTE
3rd time to Coda
CODA
B♭ CLARINET
3rd time to Coda
CODA

Hallelujah, praise the Lord

111B

Words: from Psalm 111
Christopher Idle
Music: Christopher Norton

Swing
D
A7 D
1 Hal - le - lu - jah, praise the Lord! Where the peo - ple love his name,
2 We re - call what he has done, ten - der mer - cies, firm and sure;
3 Rich in his re - deem - ing grace, keep - ing co - ve - nant he came:
A7 D
where my Sav - iour is a - dored, thanks and praise shall be my theme.
he is God, the ho - ly One, all his pro - mis - es en - dure.
see the glo - ry in his face – ho - ly, ho - ly is his name!
G D A7 D
All his works are just and great; here we find our chief de - light:
He pro - vides our dai - ly bread, he de - fends his peo - ple's cause,
Fear him – that is wis - dom's way; here be - gin our hap - piest days.
G D N.C.
good it is to me - di - tate_ all his ev - er - last - ing right.
life and home and all we need, by his ev - er - last - ing laws.
Trust him – thus we shall o - bey_ God our ev - er - last - ing praise.

113B From the rising of the sun

From Psalm 113
Words and music: Paul Deming
Music arranged Christopher Norton
With swing
E
From the ris-ing of the sun
to its go - ing down
F♯m7
the Lord's name
B7
E
is to be praised;
1.
from the ris-ing of the
2.
E7
A
Praise to the Lord;

E
G♯
praise him, all you ser - vants of the Lord,
A
B
E
praise the name_ of the Lord!
E7
A
Bless-ed be the name of the Lord_
E
G♯
A
from this time forth and for e -
B
E
- ver - more!_

117C Holy is God

From Psalm 117
Words and music: Paul Inwood

♩. = c.46
D G C Am Em
LEADER/ GROUP Ho-ly is God, ho-ly and strong, God ev-er-liv-ing,
Em/A A7 D G
al-le-lu-ia! ALL Ho-ly is God, ho-ly and
ALL Ho-ly is God,
C Am Em Em/A A7
strong, God ev-er-liv-ing, al-le-lu-ia!
ho-ly and strong, God ev-er-liv-ing, al-le-lu-

D
G
LEADER/GROUP 1 Sing the Lord's praise, ev - ery na - tion,
give him all
- ia!
ALL 1 Sing the Lord's praise, ev - ery na - tion,
C
Am
Em
hon-our and glo - ry:
strong is his love for his peo - ple;
give him all hon-our and glo - ry:
strong is his
Em/A
Asus
A7
his faith - ful - ness is e - ter - nal.
live for his peo - ple;
his faith - ful - ness is e -

117c Holy is God

D G C Am Em
ALL Ho - ly is God, ho - ly and strong, God ev - er - liv - ing,
- ter - nal. ALL Ho - ly is God, ho - ly and strong, God ev - er -
Em/A A7 D
al - le - lu - ia! LEADER/GROUP 2 Praise to the Fa - ther al - migh - ty,
- liv - ing, al - le - lu - ia! ALL 2 Praise to the
G C
praise to his Son, Christ the Lord,
Fa - ther al - migh - ty, praise to his Son, Christ the

Am Em Em/A
praise to the life - giv - ing Spi - rit, both now and for
Lord, praise to the life - giv - ing Spi - rit,
Asus A7 D
ev - er. A - men. ALL Ho - ly is God,
both now and for ev - er. A - men. ALL Ho - ly is
G C Am Em Em/A A7
ho - ly and strong, God ev - er - liv - ing, al - le - lu - ia;
God, ho - ly and strong, God ev - er - liv - ing, al - le - lu -

117C Holy is God

D
G
C
Am
più f
ho - ly is God, ho - ly and strong, God ev - er -
più f
- ia; ho - ly is God, ho - ly and strong,
Em
Em/A
A7
D
G
ff
- liv - ing, al - le - lu - ia! Ho - ly is God, ho - ly and
ff
God ev - er - liv - ing, al - le - lu - ia! Ho - ly is God,
C
Am
Em
Em/A
rit.
Asus
A
strong, God ev - er - liv - ing, al - le - lu - ia!
ho - ly and strong, God ev - er - liv - ing, al - le - lu - ia!

This is the day

118B

Words: from Psalm 118
Music: Fiji Island folk melody
arranged Christopher Norton

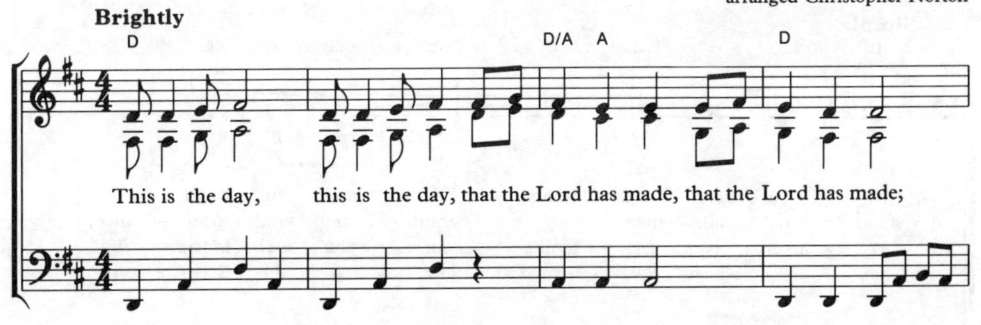
Brightly
D
D/A A
D
This is the day, this is the day, that the Lord has made, that the Lord has made;

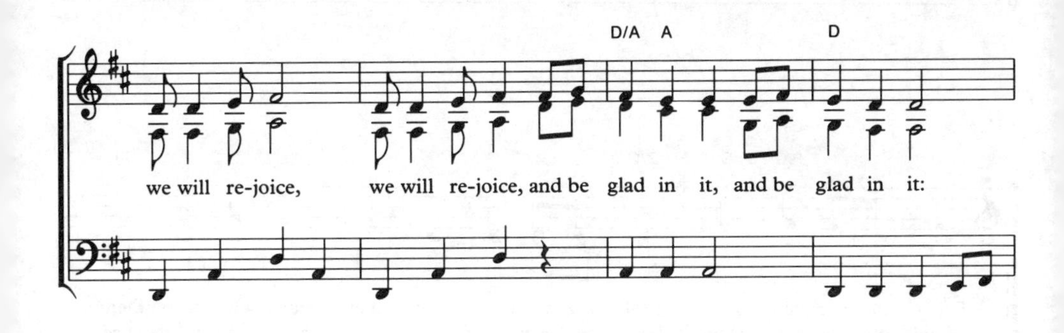
D/A A
D
we will re-joice, we will re-joice, and be glad in it, and be glad in it:

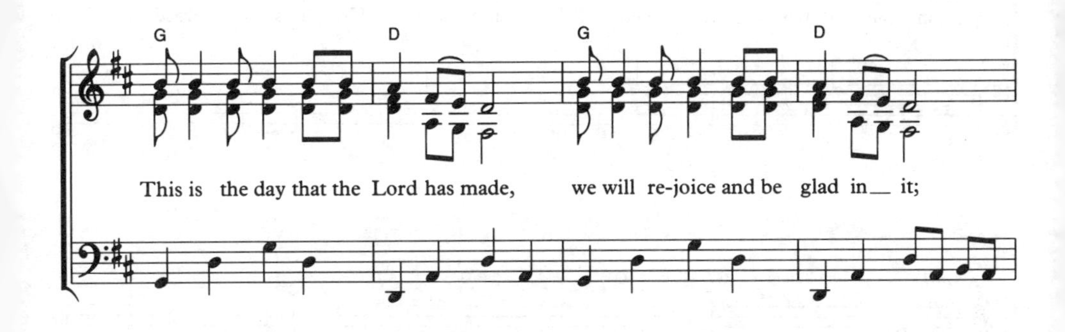
G
D
G
D
This is the day that the Lord has made, we will re-joice and be glad in it;

D/A
A7
D
this is the day, this is the day that the Lord has made.

119D All your commandments

Words: from Psalm 119
Christopher Idle
Music: Christopher Norton

Simply

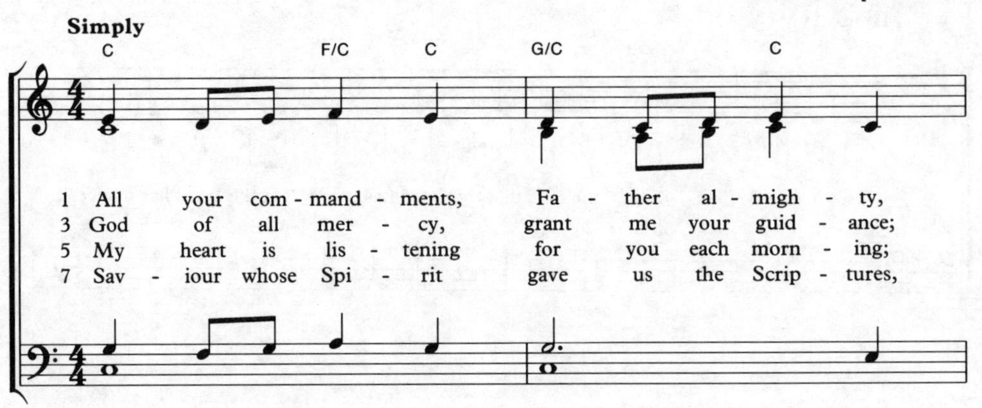
C F/C C G/C C
1 All your com - mand - ments, Fa - ther al - migh - ty,
3 God of all mer - cy, grant me your guid - ance;
5 My heart is lis - tening for you each morn - ing;
7 Sav - iour whose Spi - rit gave us the Scrip - tures,

F/C C G/C C C F C/E
Bring to your child - ren heal - ing and bless - ing; Chris - tians who keep them
How can a young man keep his way ho - ly? I have found trea - sure
Ne - ver des - ert me; speak in the night - time; O - pen my eyes, Lord,
Train me to trust them when I am temp - ted; Un - less you helped me,

Dm7 G7sus G7 C F/C C
find here their com - fort.
in your in - struc - tion.
then lead me on - wards.
I would go un - der.

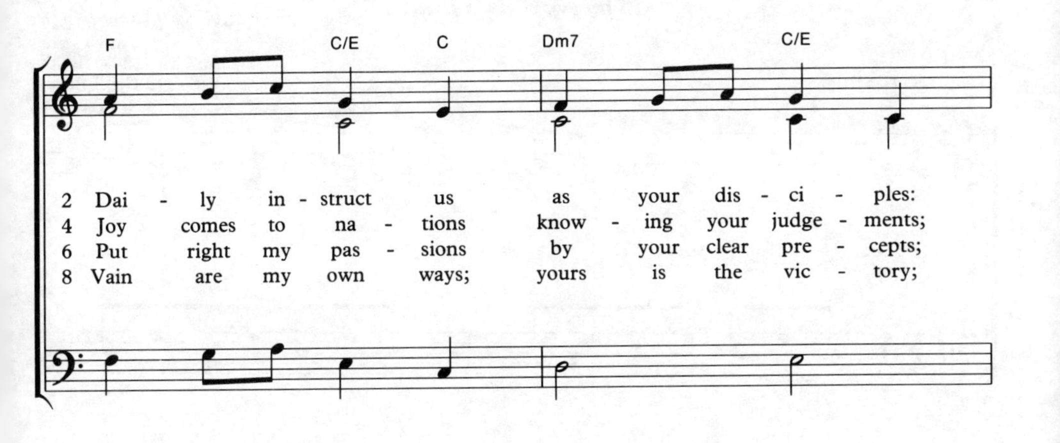
F C/E C Dm7 C/E
2 Dai - ly in - struct us as your dis - ci - ples:
4 Joy comes to na - tions know - ing your judge - ments;
6 Put right my pas - sions by your clear pre - cepts;
8 Vain are my own ways; yours is the vic - tory;

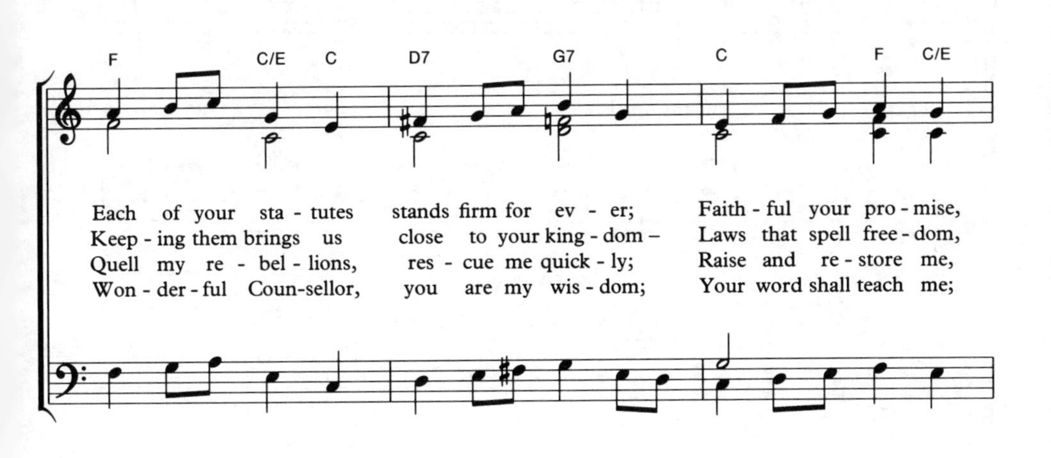
F C/E C D7 G7 C F C/E
Each of your sta - tutes stands firm for ev - er; Faith - ful your pro - mise,
Keep - ing them brings us close to your king - dom – Laws that spell free - dom,
Quell my re - bel - lions, res - cue me quick - ly; Raise and re - store me,
Won - der - ful Coun - sellor, you are my wis - dom; Your word shall teach me;

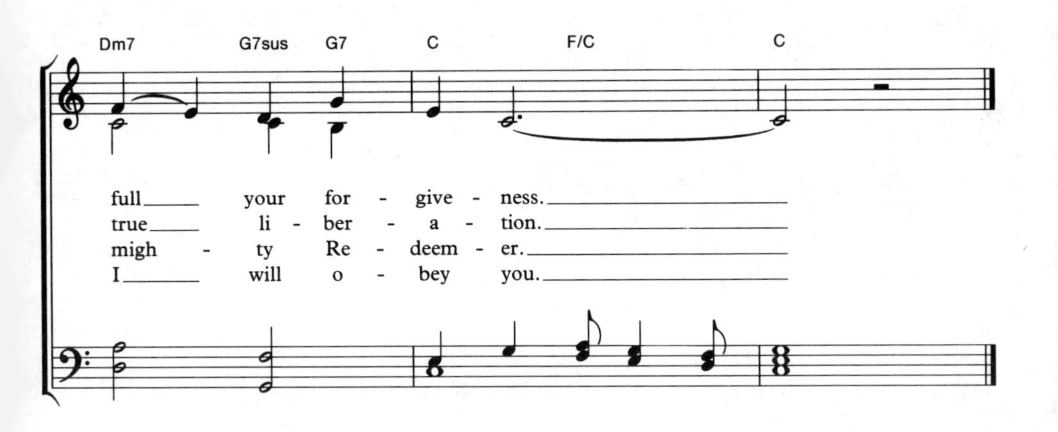
Dm7 G7sus G7 C F/C C
full your for - give - ness.
true li - ber - a - tion.
migh - ty Re - deem - er.
I will o - bey you.

119E Your word is a lamp

(Thy word is a lamp)

Words: from Psalm 119
Amy Grant
Music: Michael W Smith
arranged Geoff Baker

Smoothly
G D9 D G
Your word is a lamp __ un - to my feet and a __
Thy
C D G G
light un-to my path; your word is a lamp
thy
D9 D G C D G
__ un-to my feet and a __ light un-to my path.
D/F# Am Em Bm C D
1 When I feel _ a - fraid, __ think I've lost _ my way, ___ still you're there right be-side
2 I will not _ for-get your love for me – and yet my heart for ev - er is wan -

C/G G D/F♯ Am Em Bm
— me: and no-thing will — I fear as — long as you — are near. —
- dering: Je - sus, be — my guide and hold me to — your side. And
C D D/E Em D9 D
Please be near me to the end. —
I will love you to the end. —
G D9 D G
Your word is a lamp — un - to my feet and a —
Thy
C D G G
light un - to my path; your word is a lamp
thy
D9 D G C D G
— un - to my feet and a — light un - to my path.

119F Show me how much you love me, Lord

From Psalm 119
Words and music: Roger Mayor
Gently and prayerfully
Capo 3(D) B♭/C (G) C (A) B♭/C (G) C (A) F (D) F/A
pp
p
Show me how much you love me, Lord, and save me ac-cord-ing to your pro - mise;
show me how much you love me, Lord, and save me ac-cord-ing to your pro - mise.
to verses
last time
- mise.
B♭ (G) C (A) F (D) F/A B♭/F (G) B♭9 (G9) C (A) B♭/C (G)

SOLO
Verse 1
B♭/D (G)
C/E (A)
F (D)
B♭/D (G)
C7/E (A7)
F (D)
Teach me, Lord, the mean-ing of your laws
SOLO
Verse 2
I will live in per-fect free-dom
SOLO
Verse 3
Ev - en in my suf-fer-ing I was com-fort-ed
mf
E♭ (C)
B♭/D (G)
Gm7 (Em7)
C (A)
B♭/C (G)
C (A)
C7sus (A7sus)
and I will o-bey them at all times.
be-cause I try to o-bey your laws.
be-cause your pro - mise gave me life.
p

121E When I look towards the hills

Words: from Psalm 121
Pearl Beasley
Music: Christopher Norton

Moderately
E
A/E
mf
1 When I look to - wards_ the hills, I
(2) shield me from_ all harm each

B/E
E
E/D
know God's help is there;_ he will keep me from_ all
min - ute of the day;_ and the stress of life_ he'll

A/C♯
Am6/C♮
E/B
B7
1.
E
A/B
ills through his own lov - ing care. 2 He will
calm – for by my side he'll

2.
E
C7
Gm7/C
F
B♭/F
stay. 3 Day nor night no hurt will bring – his
f

C/F
F
F/E♭
help is al - ways here; he will guide through ev - ery -

B♭/D
B♭m6/D♭
F/C
C7
F
- thing, whose love is ev - er near.

121F I look up to the mountains

From Psalm 121
Words and music: Bill Batstone

Relaxed with a soul feel
Capo 2(D)
E (D)
A2 (G2)
E (D)
1 I look up to the moun-tains, to the hills I turn my eyes:
2 The One who watch-es Is - ra - el will his vi - gil keep,
B (A)
who will come to help me, can I find a place to hide? The
through the burn-ing sun-light and in the dark - ness deep;
E (D)
E/G♯ (D)
A2 (G2)
F♯m (Em)
One who made the hea - vens and the earth will hear my call, the
con-stant-ly be-side you - you need not fear at all, the
E/B (D)
B2 (A2)
A2 (G2)
E (D)
Lord will come to help me and he will not let me fall.
Lord is there to help you, and he will not let you fall.

E
(D)
A
(G)
E
(D)
He will not let_ you fall,___ he will not let_ you fall;_
B
(A)
A
(G)
E
(D)
he is ne-ver wea - ry, and he will not let__ you fall._
E
(D)
A2
(G2)
E
(D)
3 So when you are_ in dan-ger, when by trou-ble you are found, and your
B
(A)
ve-ry soul is threat-ened by_ the___ e - vil_ all a-round;

E
(D)
E/G♯
(D)
A2
(G2)
F♯m
(Em)
in all of ___ your ways and in your trou-bles great and small,
E/B
(D)
B2
(A2)
A2
(G2)
E
(D)
now and ev - er af - ter he will not let ___ you fall. ___
E
(D)
A
(G)
E
(D)
He will not let _ you fall, ___ he will not let _ you fall; _
B
(A)
A
(G)
E
(D)
Fine
he is ne-ver wea - ry, and he will not let ___ you fall. ___

I'll lift my eyes to the hills

From Psalm 121
Words and music: Phil Potter
Music arranged Christopher Norton

Worshipfully
C F C F
mp 1 I'll lift my eyes to the hills, I'll lift my eyes to the
mf 2 I'll bring my praise to the Lord, I'll bring my praise to the
mf 3 Lift up your voice to the Lord, Lift up your voice to the
G Am7 G/B C F E Am Am/G
hills; I'll lift my eyes to wor-ship God,
Lord; I'll bring my praise to wor-ship God,
Lord; Lift up your voice to wor-ship God,
Dm7 G7 1–4. C 5. C
I'll lift my eyes to the hills.
I'll bring my praise to the Lord.
Lift up your voice to the Lord.
king.

f 4 We lift our hands to the Lord . . .

ff 5 We lift our hearts to the King . . .

121H I will lift up my eyes

Words: from Psalm 121
Malcolm Scott
Music: Peter and Charlotte Wright
arranged Christopher Norton

Lively
A/B B7 Em A Em
mf
I will lift up my eyes, I will lift up my eyes, to the
Am D G B7 Em A
glo - ry and the ma - jes - ty of God. I will lift up my eyes, I will
Em F#m7 B7 Em Fine
lift up my eyes, to the glo - ry and the ma - jes - ty of God.
Am D G Am D
mp
I will lift up my eyes to see the moun - tains round a -

G
Am
F♯m7
-bout, to re - mind me of the ma - jes - ty of
B7sus
B7
Am
D
G
God: for the Lord who made the moun-tains and the
Am
D
G
Am
ri - vers in the val - leys is the Lord who leads his
D.𝄋 al Fine
F♯m7
Bsus
B
A/B
B7
peo - ple by his word. I will

122C I was glad

From Psalm 122
Words and music: Norman Warren
Music arranged Christopher Norton
Worshipfully
DESCANT (2nd time only)
Capo 1(A)
B♭ (A)
E♭maj7 (Dmaj7)
Cm7 (Bm7)
Pray for peace, pray for peace, pray for peace for the ci - ty of God: peace be with
I was glad when they said to me let us go to the house of the Lord: here we
F7 (E7)
D (C♯)
Gm (F♯m)
Gm/F
E♭ (D)
F (E)
D7/F♯ (C♯7)
Gm (F♯m)

Gm/F
C/E
(B)
you,
peace
be with
are
in the
pres - ence
of
F/E♭
(E)
D7
(C♯7)
Gm/E
(F♯m)
D/F♯
(C♯)
Gm
(F♯m)
Gm/F
E♭
(D)
you;
peace
be with
you,
God,
giv - ing
thanks
to our
1.
2.
F
(E)
E♭/F
(D)
B♭/F
(A)
F7
(E7)
B♭
(A)
B♭
(A)
peace
be
with
you!
migh - ty
Lord.
Lord.

122D Let us go to the house of the Lord

Words: from Psalm 122
adapted from the New International Version
by Ian White
Music: Ian White

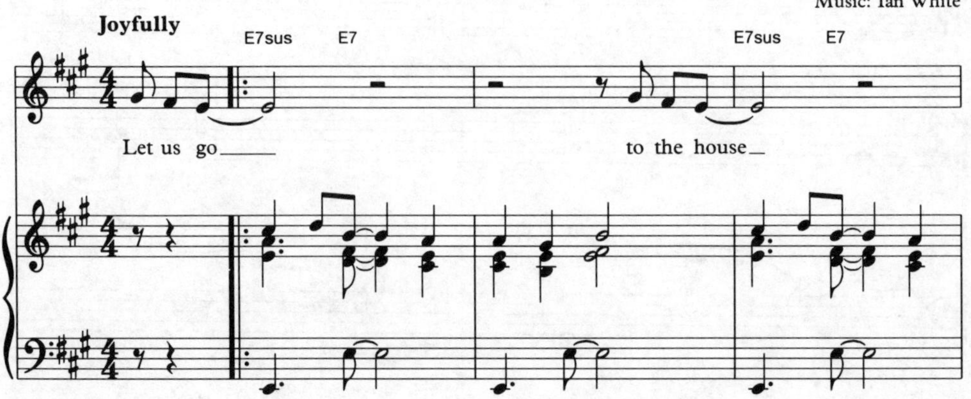
Joyfully
E7sus
E7
E7sus
E7
Let us go
to the house

E7sus
E7
F♯7sus
F♯7
of the Lord.

Bm7
Bm7/E
A
1 I re - joiced with those who
2 For peace for all Je -

C♯m
D
A
said to me,_ 'Let us go to the house of the Lord'. Our feet are stand-ing
-ru-sa-lem, and loved ones – this we_ pray: let peo-ple be se-
C♯m
E7sus
E7
A
C♯
in your gates, Je-ru-sa-lem, like a ci-ty built to-
-cure where they must live_ and to all my friends and
F♯m
D
A
Bm
-ge-ther, where the peo-ple of God go up, to_ praise the_
fa-mily – May God's peace be with-in you, for the sake of the
E7
A
1.
2.
name of the Lord. Let us go_
house of the Lord.

122E What joy to hear the pilgrims say

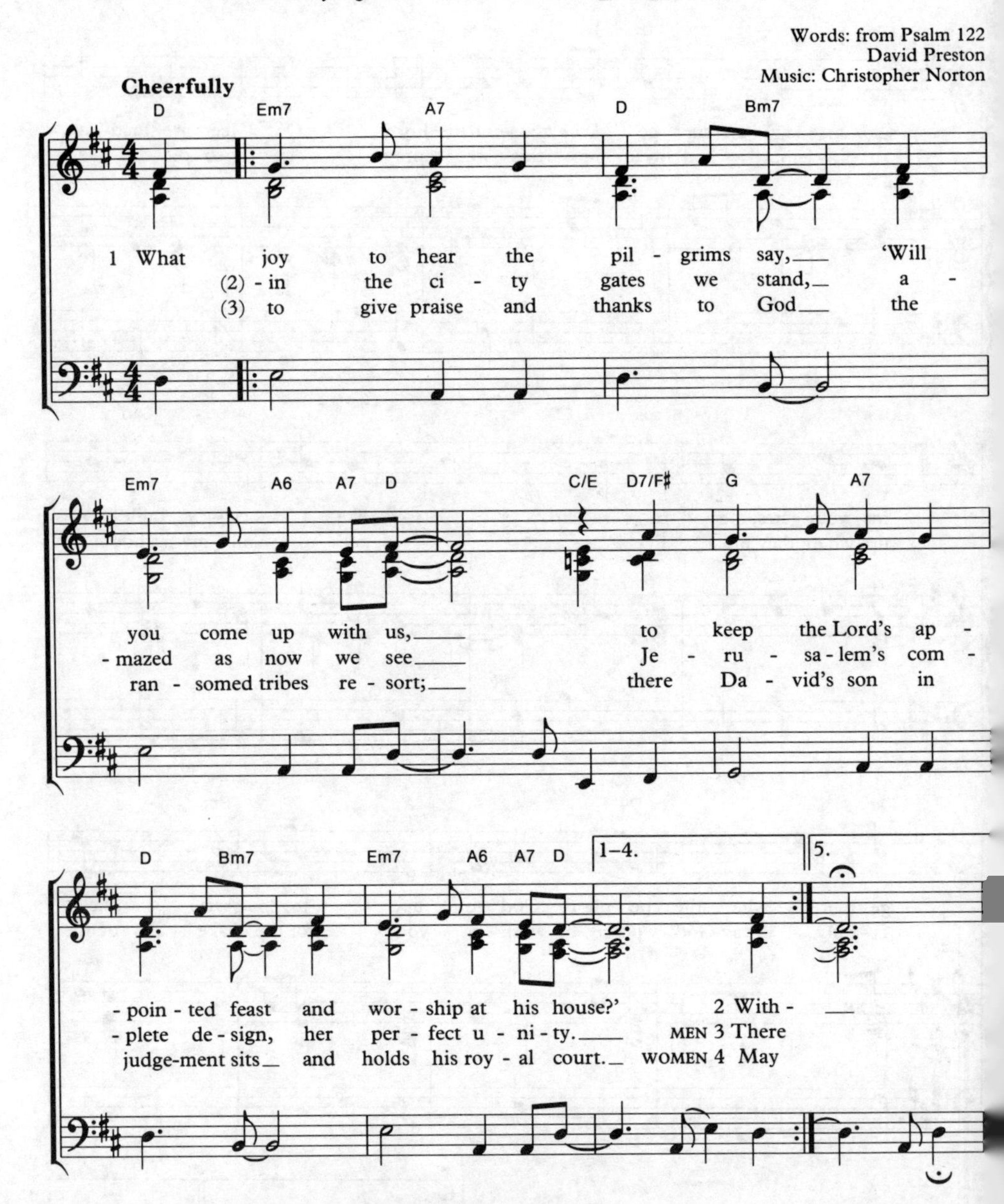

Words: from Psalm 122
David Preston
Music: Christopher Norton
Cheerfully
D Em7 A7 D Bm7
1 What joy to hear the pil - grims say, 'Will
(2) - in the ci - ty gates we stand, a -
(3) to give praise and thanks to God the
Em7 A6 A7 D C/E D7/F♯ G A7
you come up with us, to keep the Lord's ap -
- mazed as now we see Je - ru - sa - lem's com -
ran - somed tribes re - sort; there Da - vid's son in
D Bm7 Em7 A6 A7 D 1–4. 5.
- poin - ted feast and wor - ship at his house?' 2 With -
- plete de - sign, her per - fect u - ni - ty. MEN 3 There
judge-ment sits and holds his roy - al court. WOMEN 4 May

WOMEN

4 May peace abide within her walls,
prosperity abound,
with every good and perfect gift
her people all be crowned!

ALL

5 So for Jerusalem I'll pray
while life and breath remain,
since there my friends and kindred dwell
and God shall ever reign.

Holy Lord, have mercy on us all 123C

Miserere nobis

From Psalm 123
Words and music: Taizé – Jacques Berthier

Continuous Response
♩ = 69
E Am7 D G C Am B7 Em B
EQUAL VOICES
Ho-ly Lord, have mer-cy on us all, Lord have mer-cy on us;
Mi-se - re - re no-bis Do-mi-ne, mi - se - re - re no - bis;
MIXED VOICES AND KEYBOARD
p
Ho-ly Lord, have mer-cy on us all, Lord have mer-cy on us;
Mi-se - re - re no-bis Do-mi-ne, mi - se - re - re no - bis;
Verses
(sung above response)
SOLO
1 Be - hold, as the eyes of ser - vants
SOLO
2 Our eyes are fixed on the Lord our God
E Am7 D G C Am Em B Em
Ho - ly Lord, have mer-cy on us all, Lord have mer-cy on us.
mi - se - re - re no - bis Do - mi - ne, mi - se - re - re no - bis.
Ho - ly Lord, have mer-cy on us all, Lord have mer-cy on us.
mi - se - re - re no - bis Do - mi - ne, mi - se - re - re no - bis.
are on the hands of their mas - ters:
un - til he shows us his mer - cy.

Instrumental parts overleaf

123c Holy Lord, have mercy on us all

FLUTE
1
2
3
OBOE
1
legato
2
3
B♭ CLARINET

If the Lord had not been on our side 124B

Words: from Psalm 124
adapted from the New International Version
by Ian White
Music: Ian White

Flowing
A
D
Bm
Esus
If the Lord had not been on our side
would we still be here to -
A
A
D
- day;
and if the Lord had not been on our side,
Bm
Esus
A
would we not be swept a - way?
But like a

C
Fmaj7
C
bird, like a bird out from the net we have bro-ken free;

to Coda
Fmaj7
C
Fmaj7
C
but like a bird, like a bird out from the net we have

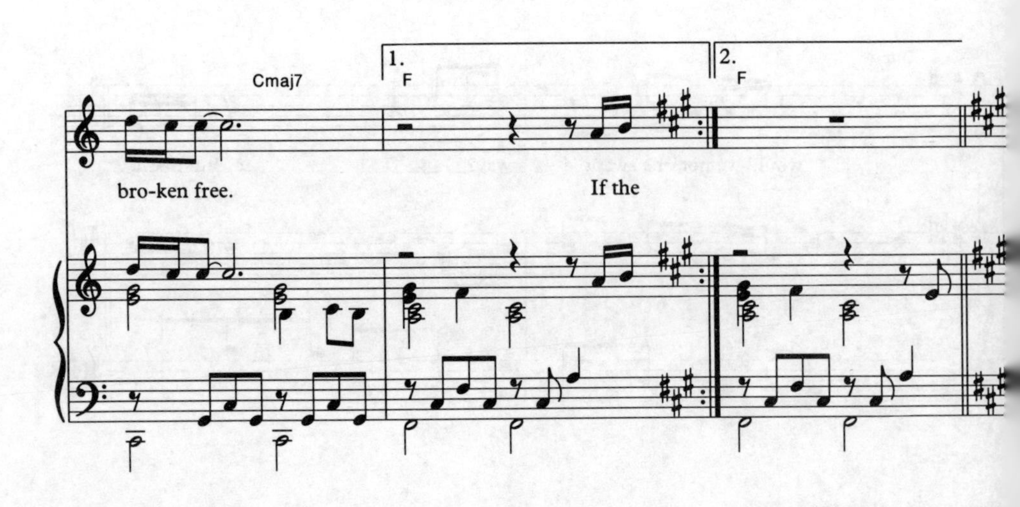
Cmaj7
1.
F
2.
F
bro-ken free. If the

A
D
Bm
E7sus
A
A
D
Bm
E7sus
A
D.𝄋 al Coda
𝄌 CODA
C
Cmaj7
Fmaj7
But like a
bro-ken free, we have bro-ken free, we have
C
Cmaj7
F
Cmaj7
bro-ken free, we have bro-ken free.

126C When God delivered Israel

Words: from Psalm 126
Michael Saward
Music: Christopher Norton
Strongly, rock-style
1 When God de - liv - ered Is - rael from
2 The god - less na - tions round them could
3 O God, re - store our na - tion; come
bond - age long a - go, they thought that they were dream -
not de - ny his power; they cried, 'O see this mar -
ir - ri - gate dry souls, that those who sow in sad -
- ing, but soon they turned to laugh - ing and
- vel!', 'God's work!', re - plied his peo - ple; and
- ness may reap their sheaves with glad - ness, and
sang the song of joy, and sang the song of joy.
so they sang for joy, and so they sang for joy.
sing the song of joy, and sing the song of joy!

Sound on the trumpet

126D

The Bridegroom Song

From Psalm 126
Words and music: John McNeil
Music arranged David Peacock

Strong and joyful
Increase in tempo with each repeat
Dm/B♭ Gm7 Asus A D Dmaj7/C♯
TRUMPETS
marcato
marcato
Chorus
Sound on the trum-pet,
Break out the ban-ners,
Bm7 Dmaj7/A Gm D
call to the peo - ple, sing your new song –
join in the danc - ing, no time for gloom –
last time to Coda
Gm D A7
1.
D Asus A
our Bride - groom's com - ing, it won't be long.
pre-pare the ban - quet, he's com - ing soon.

2.
D Asus A
a3
Dm
Verses
1 If you're one of God's
2 Go out with tears and
C
F
peo - ple, re - joice in praise and
weep - ing to bring the har - vest
A
Gm
song; come lift up your hearts be -
home: it's time for the joy of

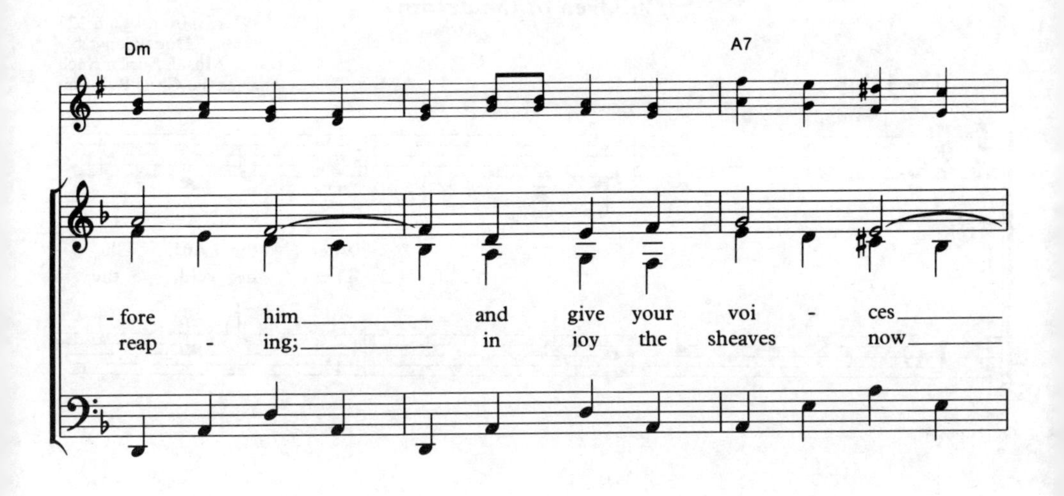
Dm
A7
- fore him and give your voi - ces
reap - ing; in joy the sheaves now

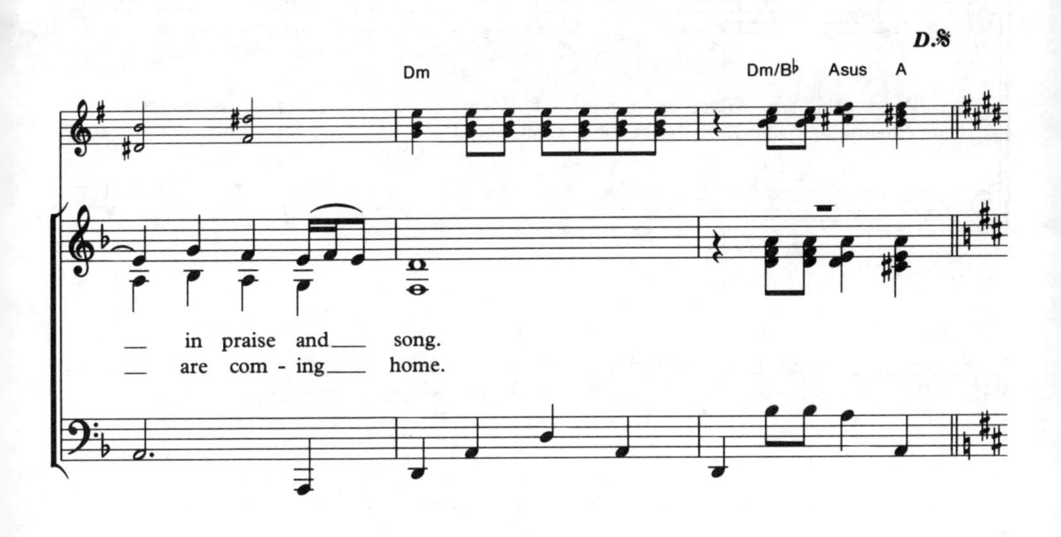
D.%
Dm
Dm/B♭
Asus
A
in praise and song.
are com - ing home.

CODA
D
A7
D
(Shout)
ban - quet, he's com - ing soon. Yes!

126E When the Lord, he turned again

(Children of the dream)

Words: from Psalm 126
Doug Constable
Music: Adrian Snell
arranged Chris Rolinson

Slow 4 time
F Gsus G F C
1 & 3 When the Lord, he
2 Then they said, the
F C F Gsus G C Am Cmaj7
turned a - gain the wretch-ed - ness of Zion; then we laughed and
hea - then said, 'The Lord has done great things!' Yes, he's done great
Fmaj7 C F C G7 C Gsus G
sang for joy as child - ren of the dream,
things for us – in him we now re - joice;
E Am Dm7 G C Fm6 Csus C
then we laughed and sang for joy as child - ren of the dream.
yes, he's done great things for us – in him we now re - joice.

Unless the Lord constructs the house

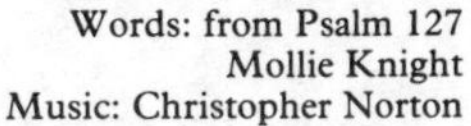
Words: from Psalm 127
Mollie Knight
Music: Christopher Norton

Rhythmically

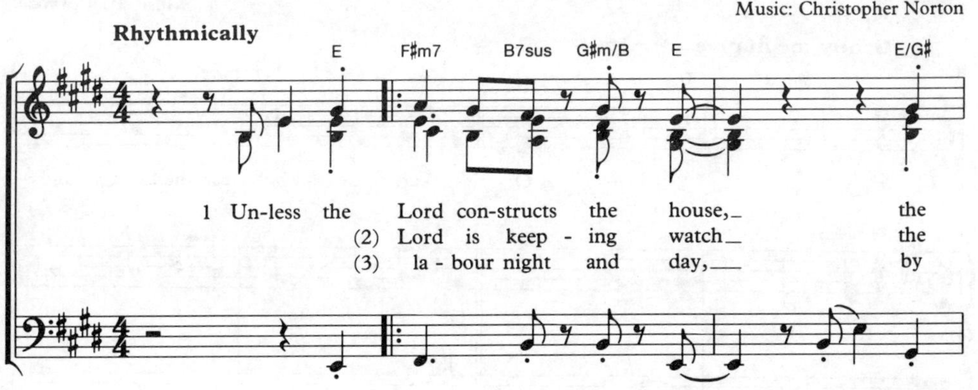
E F♯m7 B7sus G♯m/B E E/G♯
1 Un-less the Lord con-structs the house,_ the
(2) Lord is keep - ing watch_ the
(3) la - bour night and day,_ by

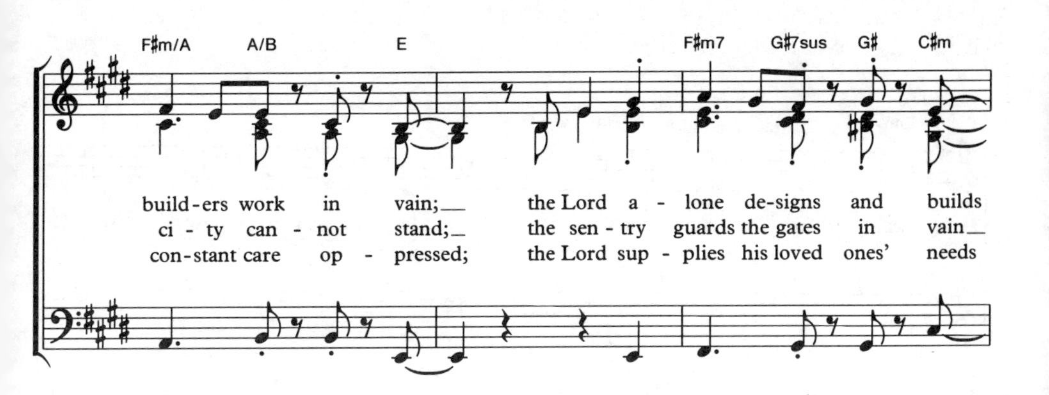
F♯m/A A/B E F♯m7 G♯7sus G♯ C♯m
build-ers work in vain;_ the Lord a - lone de-signs and builds
ci - ty can - not stand;_ the sen - try guards the gates in vain_
con-stant care op - pressed; the Lord sup - plies his loved ones' needs

N.C. F♯m/E E 1–4. 5.
_ foun - da - tions that re-main. 2 Un - less the
_ with-out God's migh-ty hand. 3 In vain you
_ and grants them sleep and rest. 4 The Lord de -

4 The Lord designed the family,
providing earthly love;
our children are his heritage –
a gift from heaven above.

5 Like weapons in a warrior's hand
are those who bear our name;
with them we face a hostile world
assured, and free from shame.

128c O blessed are those who fear the Lord

From Psalm 128
Words: from The Grail
Music: Paul Inwood

Gently meditative ♩ = c.66
D Em7/G D Em7/G D D/C♯
O blessed are those who fear the Lord and
Em7/B F♯m G D
walk in his ways; O blessed are those who
to continue
to end
D/C♯ Em7/B Dmaj7 Dmaj7
fear the Lord and walk in his ways!

G Em6 F#m7 Bm7 Em7 A7 Dadd9 D Dmaj7
1 O blessed are those who fear the Lord and walk in his ways! By the
2 Your wife like a fruit-ful vine in the heart of your house; your
3 In-deed, thus shall be blessed all those who fear — the Lord: may the

D.𝄋
G Em6 F#m7 Bm7 Em7 Asus A7
3
la - bour of your hands you shall eat – you will be hap - py and pros-per. O
3
child-ren like shoots of the o - live — a - round your ta - ble: O
Lord bless you from Zi-on all the days of your life! O

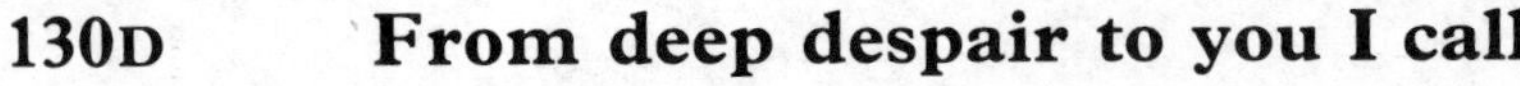

130D From deep despair to you I call

Words: from Psalm 130
David Preston
Music: Christopher Norton

Meditatively

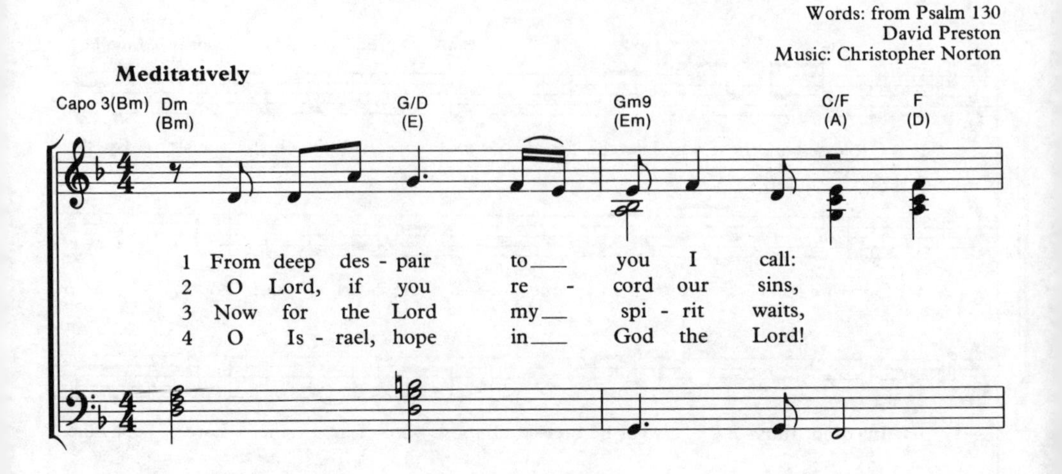
Capo 3(Bm) Dm (Bm) G/D (E) Gm9 (Em) C/F (A) F (D)
1 From deep des - pair to you I call:
2 O Lord, if you re - cord our sins,
3 Now for the Lord my spi - rit waits,
4 O Is - rael, hope in God the Lord!

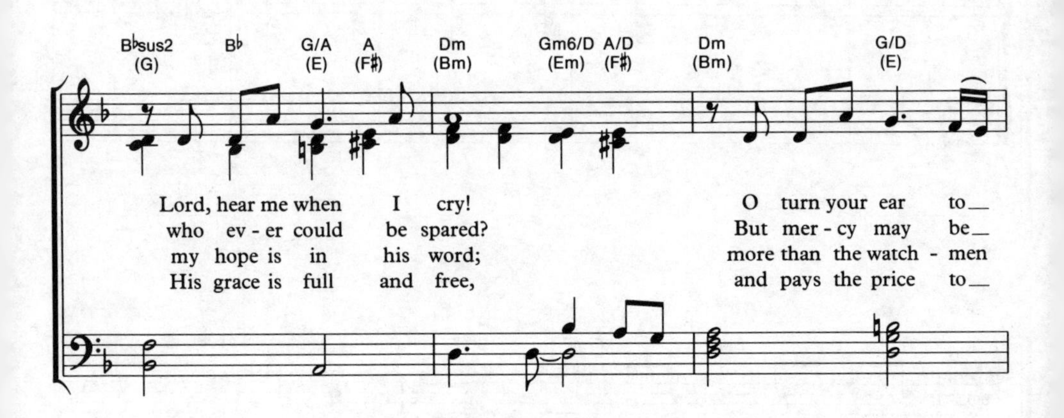
B♭sus2 (G) B♭ G/A (E) A (F♯) Dm (Bm) Gm6/D (Em) A/D (F♯) Dm (Bm) G/D (E)
Lord, hear me when I cry! O turn your ear to
who ev - er could be spared? But mer - cy may be
my hope is in his word; more than the watch - men
His grace is full and free, and pays the price to

Gm9 (Em) C/F (A) F (D) B♭sus2 (G) B♭ G/A (E) A7 (F♯7) Dm (Bm)
v.4
hear my voice which pleads with you on high!
found with you, that you may then be feared.
wait for dawn my soul waits for the Lord.
ran - som us from all i - ni - qui - ty.

From the very depths I cry 130E

Words: from Psalm 130
David Mowbray
Music: Christopher Norton

Rhythmically
A D Esus E A
1 From the ve - ry depths I cry: Lord, hear my voice,
2 In your word I put my trust: Lord, hear my voice,
D Esus E A
in your mer - cy, pass not by, Lord, hear my voice;
lift my spi - rit from the dust, Lord, hear my voice;
D E E/D C♯ C♯/D♯ C♯7/E♯
let your ears con-si - der well, Lord, the hope of Is - ra-el,
prayer a - wak - ens with the dawn - ing, from the watch be - fore the morn-ing:
F♯m F♯m/E B/D♯ A/E Esus E A
save my soul from ut - most hell. Lord, hear my voice!
al - ways pa - tient, ne - ver scorn - ing Lord, hear my voice!

130F I call to you

My soul waits

From Psalm 130
Words and music: Bill Batstone

With assurance ♩ = 80
B2/D♯
B/E
B2/D♯
B/E
A/C♯ E/B
Bm
F♯m/B
Em7
F♯m7
B2/D♯
1 I call to you_ from out of the deep, O Lord,_ most
B/E
Bm
A/B
Em7
F♯m7
high; a - ware of my sin and the_ dis - tance I keep from the
Chorus
Gmaj7
E/F♯
F♯/A♯
B
F♯/B
Light, O_ Lord. But_ there is_ for-give - ness with

E2/B
E/B F♯/B
B
F♯/B
E2/B
E/G♯ F♯/A♯
you! In wonder I fall on my knees; my soul

B
F♯/B
C♯m
G♯m7
waits for the Lord in the hope of his promise – in the

E
B/D♯
B
C♯m
E/G♯
F♯/A♯
hope of his promise de - liv - erance will come. My soul

B
F♯/B
C♯m
G♯m
waits for the Lord through the night to the morn-ing, like a

last time to Coda
1.
E
B/D♯
B
C♯m7
F♯7
B2/D♯
night-watch-man wait - ing for the com-ing of the dawn.
to Verse 2
B/E
B2/D♯
B/E
A/C♯
E/B
2.
to Verse 3
B2
C♯m7
A2/C♯
C♯m7
B2
C♯m7
A2/C♯
C♯m7
Verse 2
Bm
F♯m/B
Em7
F♯7
2 Look to the Lord all you peo - ple in need, for
B2/D♯
B/E
Bm
A/B
he is kind; he will break the chains of your

Chorus D.𝄋
Em7
F♯m
Gmaj7
E/F♯
F♯/A♯
soul's sla-ve-ry for all time, O Lord. But
Verse 3
F♯m
B
F♯m
B
3 Tell me who could stand in the Lord's right-eous reck-on-ing
F♯m
B
F♯m
B
if our lives faced his light?
G♯m
C♯
G♯m
C♯
Then, if all our deeds were re-vealed at God's beck-on-ing,
D.𝄋 al Coda
CODA
G♯m
F♯2
E2
C♯m7
F♯7
B
who could hold their head high? But
com-ing of the dawn.

130G O Lord, hear my prayer

Continuous Chorale
From Psalm 130
Words and music: Taizé – Jacques Berthier
MIXED VOICES
Em Em7/D Am/C D
O Lord, hear my prayer; O Lord, hear my prayer:
G/B C Am6 B Em Em7/D
when I call, ans - wer me – O Lord, hear my prayer; O
Am/C D Em/G Am B Em
Fine
Lord, hear my prayer; come and lis - ten to me. O
Accompaniment
Fine
Accompaniments and Solos
Simple melody
(end)

RECORDER DUO
DESCANT
TREBLE
1.
2.
FLUTE DUO
1
2
legato
OBOE
B♭ CLARINET

134D Come bless the Lord

From Psalm 134
Words and music: Philip Lawson-Johnston
Music arranged Christopher Norton

Moderato

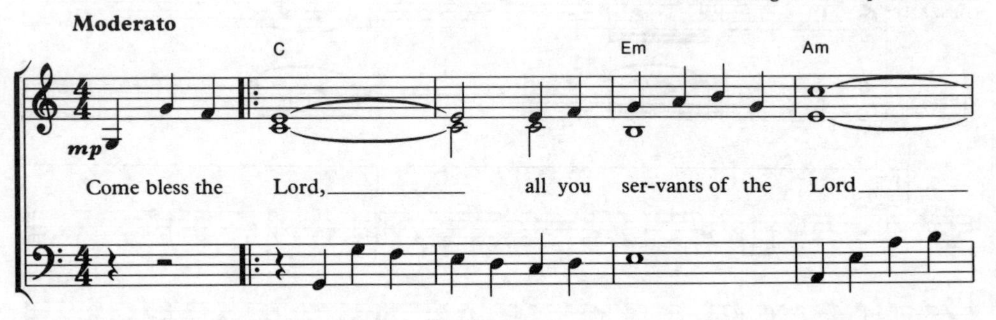
C
Em
Am
mp
Come bless the Lord, all you ser-vants of the Lord

F
G
C
G
Am7 G7/B
C
who stand by night in the house of the Lord; lift up your hands

Em
Am
F
to the ho-ly place and bless the Lord: come bless the

C/E
C
Gsus G
G7
1.
C
G
2.
C
Lord, come bless the Lord! Come bless the Lord!

Give thanks to God, for he is good 136B

I saw three ships

Words: from Psalm 136
Michael Perry
Music: English traditional melody
arranged David Iliff

G D G D7
1 Give thanks to God, for he is good, give
2 For God a - lone works mi - ra - cles; the
3 He made the stars to shine at night, he
4 He leads us on - ward by his grace, he
G Em G D D7 Em C D7/A G
thanks to him, the God of gods, give thanks to him, the
skies were made at his com-mand, he spread the seas up -
made the sun to shine by day; he brought us out from
saves us from our e - ne - mies – give thanks to God, for
D G Am G/D Em Am/C D G
Lord of lords:
- on the earth:
sla - ve - ry:
he is good:
his love shall last for ev - er!

136C O give thanks to the Lord

Steadfast love

From Psalm 136
Words and music: Bob Fraser
Music arranged Christopher Norton

Joyfully
D
A
Em
A7
mf
1 O give thanks to the Lord for he is good,
2 O give thanks to the God__ of__ gods
3 O give thanks to the King__ of__ kings
4 O give thanks to the Lord__ of__ lords
for his love en-dures_ for
ev-er;___
O give thanks to the Lord for he is good,
O give thanks to the God__ of__ gods
O give thanks to the King__ of__ kings
O give thanks to the Lord__ of__ lords
for his love en-dures for
F♯m
G
f
ev-er:___ for his stead-fast love, his stead-fast love, his love en-dures for
D.C.
ev-er;___ for his stead-fast love, his stead-fast love, his love en-dures for ev-er.___

By flowing waters of Babylon 137B

Solent Breezes

From Psalm 137
Words and music: Michael Perry
Music arranged Christian Strover

Em
B7
1 By flow - ing wa - ters of Ba - by - lon
2 They who op - press us and mock our grief
3 If we for - get you, Je - ru - sa - lem,
Em
B7
we hung our harps on the wil - lows:
tell us to sing and be mer - ry:
may we keep si - lence for ev - er!
Em
Am6
C
how shall we sing our Je - ho - vah's song in a
how can we wor - ship when spi - rits fail in an
Still we re - mem - ber our dis - tant home in a -
Em/B
Bm7
Em
for - eign land, far a - way?
a - lien land, far a - way?
- no - ther land, far a - way.

137C Babylon by the rivers of sorrow

Summertime

Words: from Psalm 137
Michael Perry
Music: G Gershwin (1898–1937)
arranged David Peacock

With expression

1 Ba-by -
8va
R.H.
L.H.
Em♯6 B7/F♯ Em♯6 B7/F♯ Em♯6 B7/F♯ Em♯6 B7/F♯ Em♯6
- lon by the ri - vers of sor - row! Hang your
(2) say, 'all the songs of your ci - ty!' How shall
(3) be to the name of the Fa - ther: glo - ry

Am Am7/C Am7/E
harps by the old wil-low tree.
we sing in an a - li - en land? –
be for the grace of the Son;

B/D♯
F♯7
B
B7/F
Em♯6
B7/F♯
All our joy is gone,
cap - tives brought a - way
glo - ry be
R.H.
Em♯6
B7/F♯
Em♯6
B7/F♯
Em
A7
there's no hope for to - mor - row.
We'll
with - out mer - cy or pi - ty!
We'll
in the joy of the Spi - rit:
we
G/D
Em/G
Em
A
C6/D
ne - ver for - get you,
O Je - ru - sa -
ne - ver for - get you,
O Je - ru - sa -
look for the mer - cy
of the Three - in -

1.2.
Em
B7
Em♯6
B7/E
Em♯6
B/E
- lem!
- lem!
2 'Sing', they
3 Glo - ry
8va
R.H.
L.H.

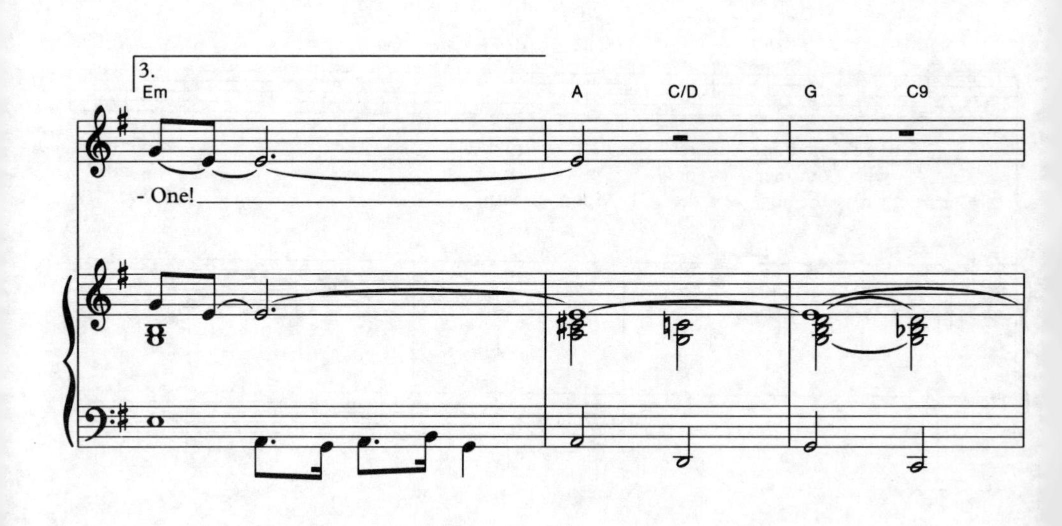
3.
Em
A
C/D
G
C9
- One!

F
B7
Em

B♭ melody version

4
1.2.
3.
5

E♭ melody version

4
1.2.
3.
5

138B **I will praise you Lord**

Words: from Psalm 138
adapted from the New International Version
by Ian White
Music: Ian White

Joyfully
D A/D G D
1 I will praise you Lord with all my heart, be -
(2) praise you for your faith and love – your
(3) kings of earth praise you, O Lord, when they
(4) Lord is high, he is near to the low; but the
G/D D Bm A D A/D
- fore the 'gods' I will sing your praise; I will bow down to your
name and your word are a - bove all things. When I called, you came and
hear the words of your mouth; and let them sing of the
proud he sees from far a - way: and though I walk in the
G D G A Bm A D
ho - ly place and praise your name! 2 I will
ans - wered me and made me bold and strong. 3 Let the
ways of the Lord, for the glo - ry of the Lord is great! 4 Though the
midst of trou - ble, you pre - serve my life! 5 You
D A G D G D
(5) stretch your hand a - gainst my foes, and you save me by

Bm A D A/D G/D D
your right hand. The Lord will see__ his__ pur - pose for me: your
G A Bm A D G A Bm A D
love will last for ev - er. Your love will last for ev - er!
G 3 A G 3 A G A Bm A D
Don't ev - er leave the works of your hand, your love will last for ev - er, your
G A Bm A D G A Bm A D
love will last for ev - er, your love will last for ev - er!

139C O Lord, you know my mind

From Psalm 139
Words and music: Colin Avery

Lively, with pace
Capo 3(Em)
D (B)
D7 (B7)
Gm (Em)
Gm/B♭
Cm (Am)
Cm/B♭
Asus (F♯sus)
A (F♯)
Verse
1 O
poco rubato
D (B)
D7 (B7)
Gm (Em)
Lord, you know my mind – each hid - den cor - ner there you
(2) morn - ing's wings I soar, or set - tle on some dis - tant
(3) no - where I can hide – you are a - round, in front, be -
(4) Lord, you know my heart for you cre - a - ted me, each
D (B)
Cm7 (Am7)
find; you know each se - cret thought and
shore, your hand will guide me ev - en
- side me; there is no - where I can
part: ex - am - ine me and know my

Dsus (Bsus)
D (B)
deed. You are ev - ery - where, all -
there. If I seek the depths of
flee. Though such know - ledge is too
ways. If I a - ny way of -
D7 (B7)
Gm (Em)
- see - ing, you have formed my in - ner be - ing, you per -
night, to you the dark - ness is as light: your hand will
grand for such as me to un - der - stand you stretched out
- fend then, Lord, as - sist me to a - mend that I may
D (B)
Cm7 (Am7)
Dsus (Bsus)
- ceive my ev - ery need.
hold me in your care.
your right hand to me.
of - fer wor - thy praise.
a tempo
Chorus
D (B)
B♭ (G)
B♭sus (Gsus)
F (D)
In your name I re - joice, I know

D7
(B7)
Gm
(Em)
Cm7
(Am7)
you hear my voice, I will put my
F
(D)
B♭
(G)
Dsus
(Bsus)
D
(B)
trust in you. You are
B♭
(G)
B♭sus
(Gsus)
F
(D)
D
(B)
Lord, you are King, set a - bove ev - ery -
Gm
(Em)
Cm7
(Am7)
D7
(B7)
- thing: I will praise you, for all your ways are

Gm
(Em)
D
(B)
true — Lord, — lead me in the
Cm7
(Am7)
Dsus
(Bsus)
way ev - er - last - ing. —
D
(B)
Gm
(Em)
Cm
(Am)
1–3.
Asus
(F♯sus)
A
(F♯)
4. rit.
Asus
(F♯sus)
A
(F♯)
D
(B)
2 If on
3 There is
4 O —

139D You are before me, Lord

Words: from Psalm 139
Ian Pitt-Watson
Music: Sarah Lacy
arranged Christopher Norton

Moderately
Capo 3(A)
Fmaj7
(Dmaj7)
E♭maj7/F
(Cmaj7)
p
1 You are be - fore me, Lord, you are be - hind,
2 Then where, Lord, from your pre - sence shall I go,
3 And if I take my flight in - to the dawn,
4 Search me, O God, search me and know my ways;

Fmaj7
(Dmaj7)
E♭maj7/F
(Cmaj7)
and ov - er me you have spread out your hand;
and from your Spi - rit where, Lord, shall I fly?
or if I dwell on o - cean's far - thest shore,
try me, O God, my mind and spi - rit try
Fmaj7
(Dmaj7)
E♭maj7/F
(Cmaj7)
B♭maj7
(Gmaj7)
B♭m9
(Gm9)
such know-ledge is too won - der - ful for me,
If I as - cend to hea - ven you are there,
your migh - ty hand will rest up - on me still,
keep me from a - ny path that gives you pain,

A♭(add B♭)
(F)
F/G
(D)
too high to grasp, too great to
and still are with me if in
and your right hand will guard me
and lead me in the ev - er -

Cmaj7
(Amaj7)
B♭/C
(G)
Cmaj7
(Amaj7)
un-der - stand.
hell I lie:
ev - er - more.
- last-ing way,

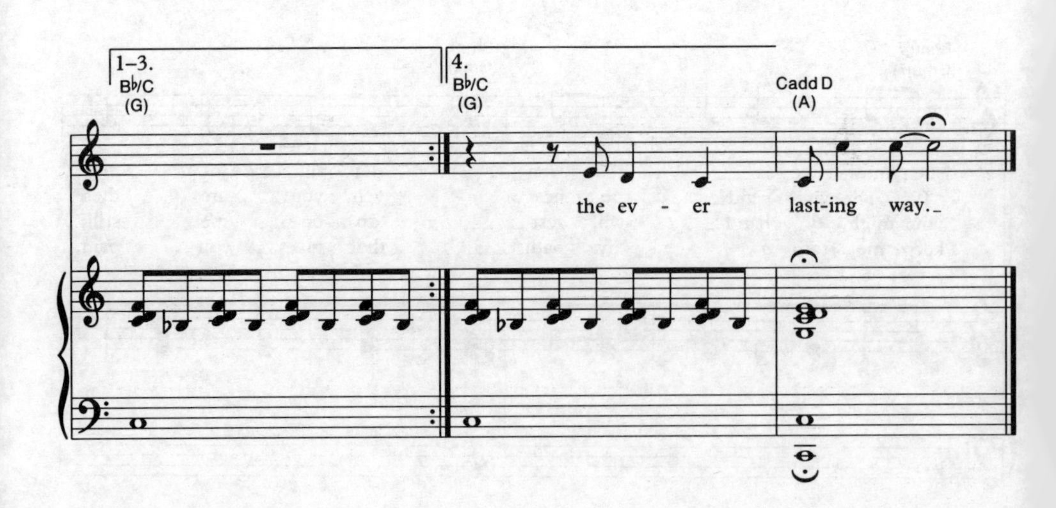
1–3.
B♭/C
(G)
4.
B♭/C
(G)
Cadd D
(A)
the ev - er last-ing way.

Search me, O God

139E

From Psalm 139
Words and music: Bob Fraser
Music arranged Christopher Norton

Simply
Em
B7/D♯
Em/D
A9/C♯
Cmaj7
D
Em
B7
Em
Em/D♯
Em/D
Search me, O God, and know my heart, and deal with a -
Em/C♯
Cmaj7
D
Em
- ny wick-ed part; re-veal the dark - ness and the sin,

B7
Em
Em/D♯
Em/D
3
ex-pose the se - crets of my soul, press to my
Em/C♯
Cmaj7
D
to Coda
Em
lips the heat-ed coal, and pu - ri-fy my life with - in.
E
Am
D
G
C/G
1 But if I real - ly start to pray
2 Your cross, a burn-ing bush a-head;
mf
G
Am7
D
Em
and from all e-vil turn a - way,
the ground is ho-ly where I tread:

E E7 Am D
then you are rea-dy to for-give
and all the guilt and all the shame
G Bm7/F♯ Em C Am7
and you will make the dry bones
will lift as I look to you a-
B D.𝄋 al Coda
live.
- gain.
CODA
Em G/D
- in.
Am7 D Em
and pu - ri-fy my life with - in.

142A(i) When I lift up my voice

Words: from Psalm 142
Michael Perry
Music: Christopher Norton

Solid rock-style
F/G C F/C C F/C C7 F/C C
1 When I lift up my voice, and I cry to the Lord,
2 When I see no-one cares, and I walk all a-lone,
3 When he comes to my side and he ans - wers my prayers,
B♭/D C/E F C/G Dm7/A Gsus
and I pour out my trou - bles be - fore him:
and my spi - rit grows wea - ry with - in me:
and he sets my soul free from its pri - son:
G F/G G Am Em/G C/G F C/F F6 C/F
I say You are my re - fuge, I will praise your name;
C/E Dm7 F/C C F/C C F/C C Csus C
you are good to me, O Lord!

Alternative tune: You are my refuge, *Psalms for Today* 142A

When I lift up my voice 142A(ii)

From Psalm 142
Words and music: Michael Perry
Music arranged David Peacock

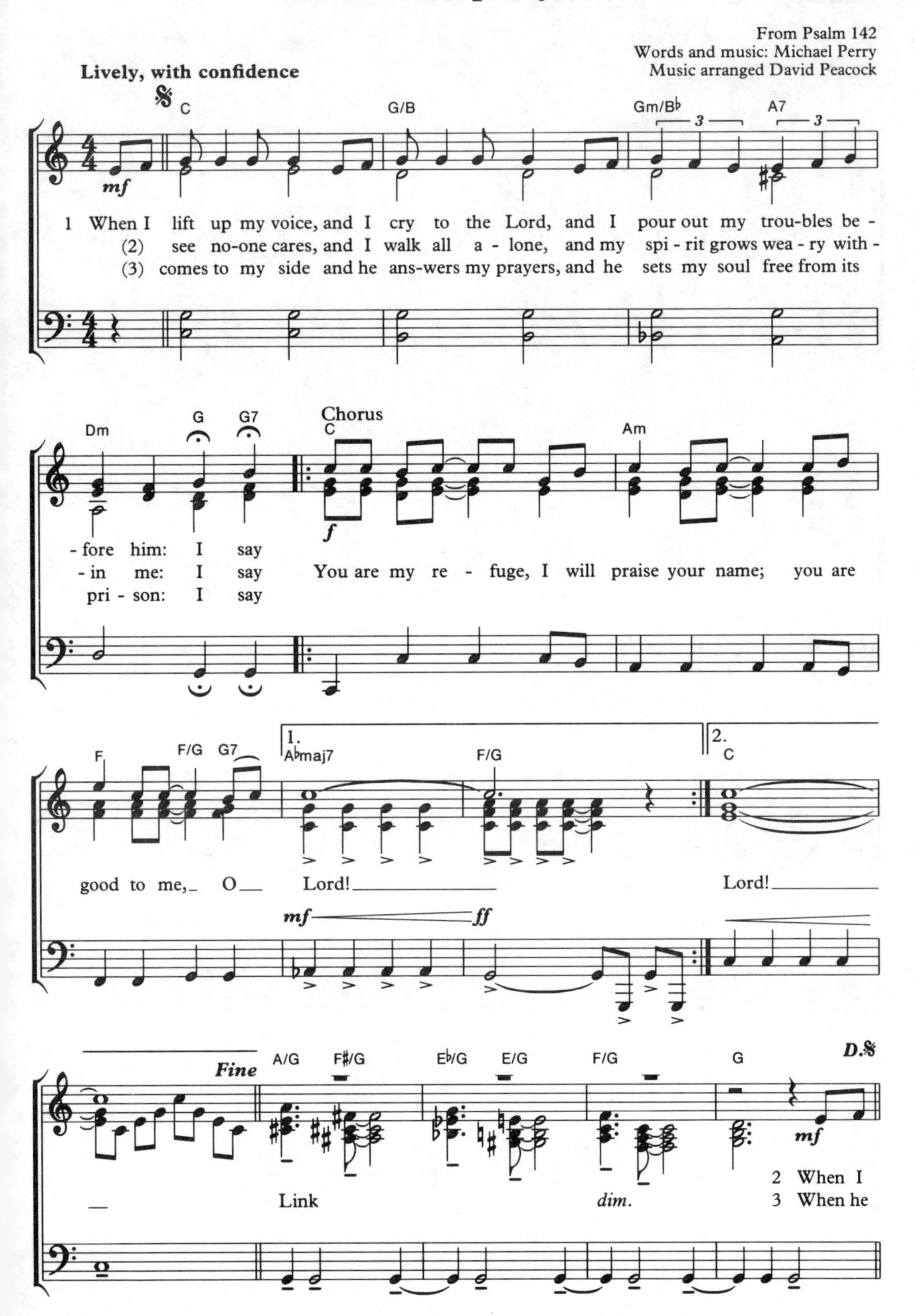

Lively, with confidence
C G/B Gm/B♭ A7
mf
1 When I lift up my voice, and I cry to the Lord, and I pour out my trou-bles be-
(2) see no-one cares, and I walk all a-lone, and my spi-rit grows wea-ry with-
(3) comes to my side and he ans-wers my prayers, and he sets my soul free from its
Dm G G7
-fore him: I say
-in me: I say
pri-son: I say
Chorus
C Am
f
You are my re-fuge, I will praise your name; you are
F F/G G7
good to me, O Lord!
1. A♭maj7 F/G
2. C
Lord!
mf ff
Fine
A/G F♯/G E♭/G E/G F/G G
D.𝄋
Link
dim.
mf
2 When I
3 When he

The phrase 'you are good to me, O Lord' may be repeated ad lib. on final chorus.

142B When I lift up my voice

Words: from Psalm 142
Michael Perry
Music: Chris Rolinson

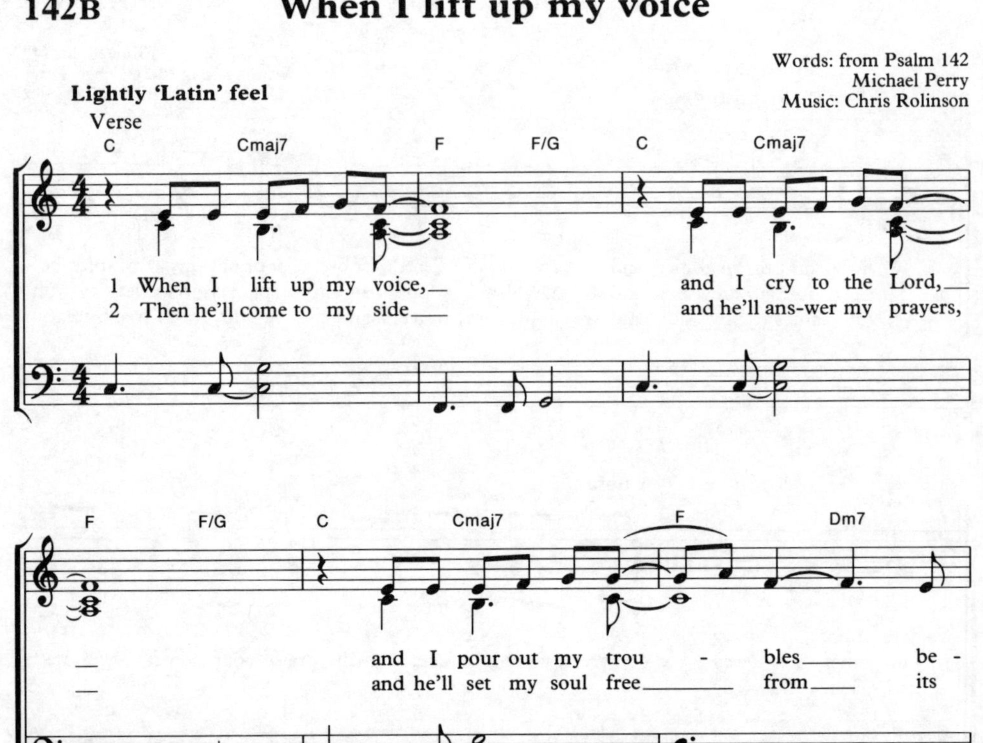
Lightly 'Latin' feel
Verse
C Cmaj7 F F/G C Cmaj7
1 When I lift up my voice,__ and I cry to the Lord,__
2 Then he'll come to my side__ and he'll ans-wer my prayers,
F F/G C Cmaj7 F Dm7
__ and I pour out my trou - bles__ be -
__ and he'll set my soul free__ from__ its

C/G G F/G G C Cmaj7
-fore__ him;__ when I see no - one cares,
pri - son;__ then the right-eous will see,__

F F/G C Cmaj7 F F/G
__ and I walk all a - lone,__
__ and they'll ga - ther a - round__

C Cmaj7 F Dm7 C/G G F/G G
and my spi-rit grows wea - ry___ with-in___ me,_______ then I sing:
all be-cause of his good - ness__ to-wards_ me,_______ then they'll sing:

Chorus
C Em7 Dm7 G F/G G
'You are my re - fuge,__ I will praise your
'You are our re - fuge__ we will praise your

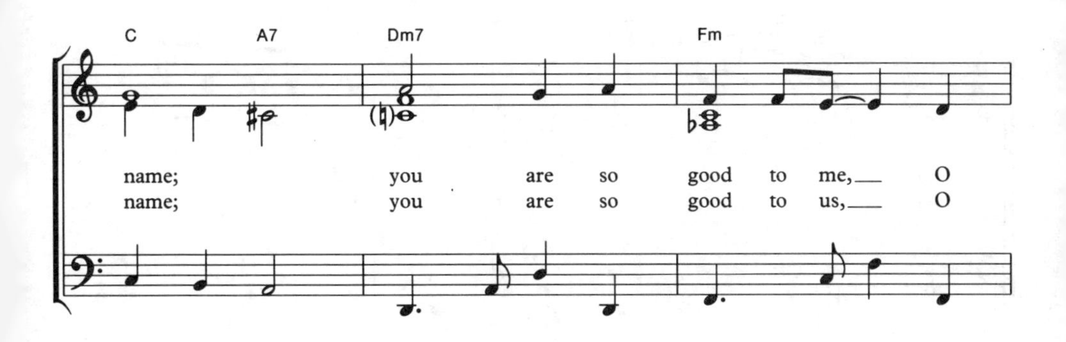
C A7 Dm7 Fm
name; you are so good to me,___ O
name; you are so good to us,___ O

F/G G C Em7
Lord!'_______________ Then I sing: 'You are my re -
Lord!'_______________ Then they'll sing 'You are our re -

Dm7
G
F/G
G
C
A7
- fuge, I will praise your name;
- fuge we will praise your name;

Dm
G
G/F
Em
you are so good to me, you are so
you are so good to us, you are so

Am
Am/G
Dm
G
good to me, you are so good to me, O
good to us, you are so good to us, O

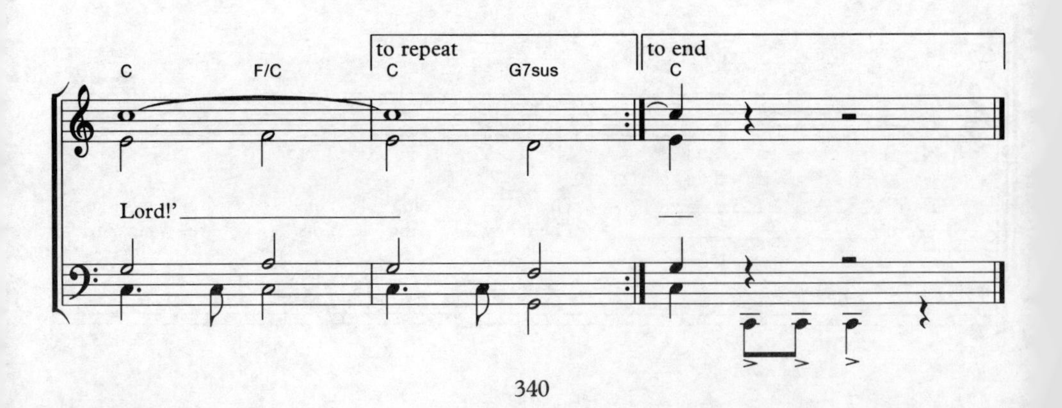

to repeat
to end
C
F/C
C
G7sus
C
Lord!'

O Lord, I bring myself to you **143B**

Words: from Psalm 143
Barbara Woollett
Music: Sarah Lacy
arranged Christopher Norton
Worshipfully
Capo 3(Bm)
Dm (Bm) Dm♯7 Dm7 D6 (B6)
1 O Lord, I bring my - self to you, Christ
2 O Lord, I bring my - self to you, your
3 O Lord, I bring my - self to you and
Gm9 (Em) C7sus (A7) C7 Fmaj7 (Dmaj7) Em7 (C♯m7) A7 (F♯7) Dm (Bm) Dm♯7
bears my guilt and shame; be - cause you are a
mer - cy to re - ceive; each morn - ing keep me
give you all my days; but need your strength to
Dm7 D6 (B6) Gm9 (Em9) C7sus (A7) C7 Asus (F♯sus) A (F♯)
faith - ful God I call up - on your name: when
in your love and all my sins for - give: your
ov - er - come the fail - ure of my ways: so,
B♭maj7 (Gmaj7) C/B♭ (A) Am7 (F♯m7) Dm7 (Bm7) Gm7 (Em7) Am7 (F♯m7) Dm (Bm)
dark-ness ov - er - whelms my soul your pro-mised grace I claim.
Ho - ly Spi - rit fill my soul and guide me how to live.
as your light shines in my soul, let o - thers learn your praise.

145c Worthy, the Lord is worthy

Words: from Psalm 145
adapted from the New International Version
by Ian White
Music: Ian White

Lively
G
C/G
Am7
D7
C6/G
G
1&6 Wor - thy, the Lord is wor - thy,
4 Faith - ful, the Lord is faith - ful
E7
Am7
D7
and no - one un - der-stands the great - ness of his
to all his pro - mis-es, and loves all he has
G
Fine
C/D
G
C/G
name.
made.
2 Gra - cious,
(3) mouth will speak
5 Right - eous,
Am7
D7
C6/G
G
E7
so kind and gra - cious, and slow to
in praise of my Lord: let ev - ery
in all ways, right - eous - and he is

Am7 Cm6 D7 G
an - ger and rich, so rich in love:
crea - ture praise his ho - ly name;
near to all who call on him in truth:
1. 2.3.
A E/A
3 My for ev - er and
A E/A D Am7 Em7/A
ev - er - more, for ev - er and
Am G/A D
1. 2. C/D D.C.
ev - er - more. For

145D We come to praise you, Father

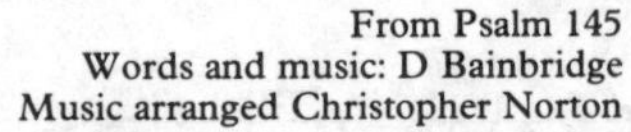
From Psalm 145
Words and music: D Bainbridge
Music arranged Christopher Norton

Solid rock style
A C♯m7 A/C♯ D A/C♯ D E Bm7 E7 A D/A
f

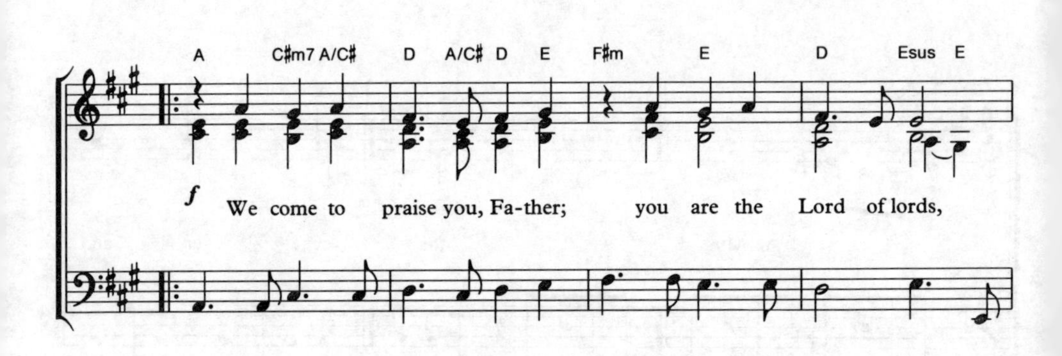
A C♯m7 A/C♯ D A/C♯ D E F♯m E D Esus E
f
We come to praise you, Fa-ther; you are the Lord of lords,

A C♯m7 A/C♯ D A/C♯ D E Bm7 E7 A D/A
you are the King of glo-ry, Lord of all.

A E/A D/A A F♯m E
mf
1 I will pro - claim your great - ness, ev - ery day I will praise your
2 The Lord is faith - ful, he will save those who

D A/C♯ E7/B A
name – now and for ev - er peo-ple will know of your
fall; all liv-ing things can look_ to him_ for_
G Esus E A E/A
glo - ry and ma - jes - ty: your crea - tures,
he will_ sa - tis - fy, for he is
D/A A F♯m E D
Lord, will praise you, so that peo - ple_ might know
right - eous,_ he is near those_ who call:
Repeat chorus to fade
A/C♯ E7/B A G Esus E
that your rule is e - ter - nal_ and you will be king for ev - er.
hon-our him, sing_ prais - es,_ pro - claim with me his great - ness.

147C Great is the Lord

From Psalm 147
Words and music: Dale Garratt

With strength
Capo 3(Am)
Cm
(Am)
F/C
(D)
Fm/C
(Dm)
Cm7
(Am7)
G
(E)
Fm
Fm6
Great is the Lord and migh - ty in pow - er; his un-der -
- stand - ing has no li - mit. The Lord de - lights in those who
fear him, who put their hope in his un-fail-ing love. He
strength-ens the bars of your gates, he grants you peace in your

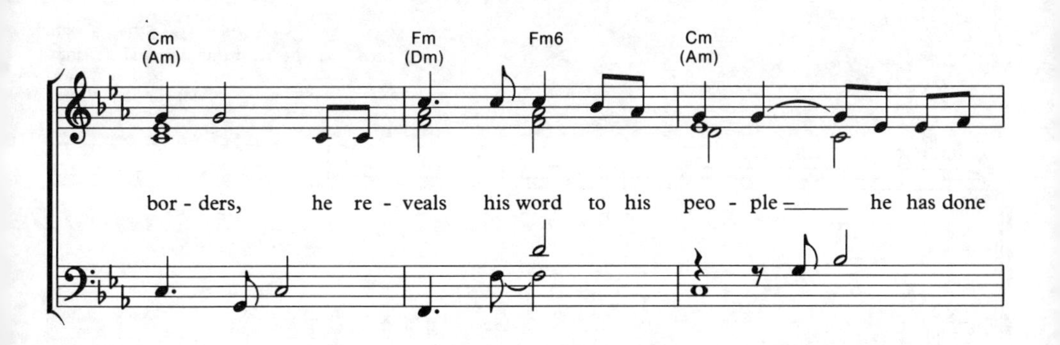
Cm
(Am)
Fm
(Dm)
Fm6
Cm
(Am)
bor - ders, he re - veals his word to his peo - ple — he has done

G
(E)
Fm7
(Dm7)
G
(E)
Cm
(Am)
F/C
(D)
Fm/C
(Dm)
this for no o - ther na - tion. Great is the Lord and migh - ty in

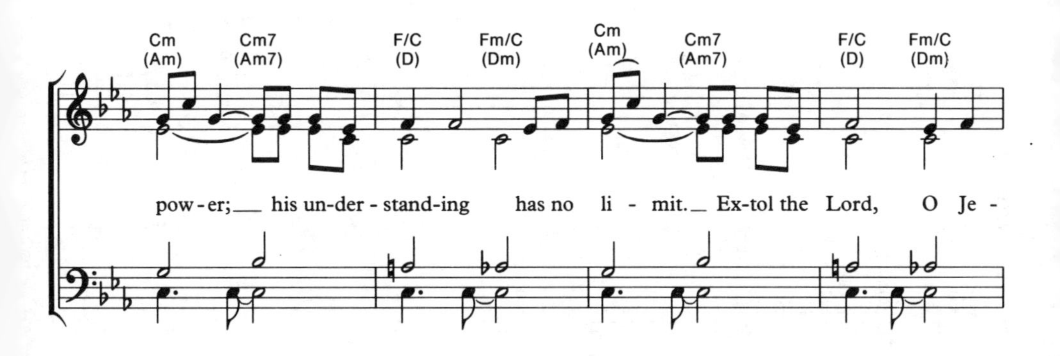
Cm
(Am)
Cm7
(Am7)
F/C
(D)
Fm/C
(Dm)
Cm
(Am)
Cm7
(Am7)
F/C
(D)
Fm/C
(Dm)
pow - er; his un - der - stand - ing has no li - mit. Ex - tol the Lord, O Je -

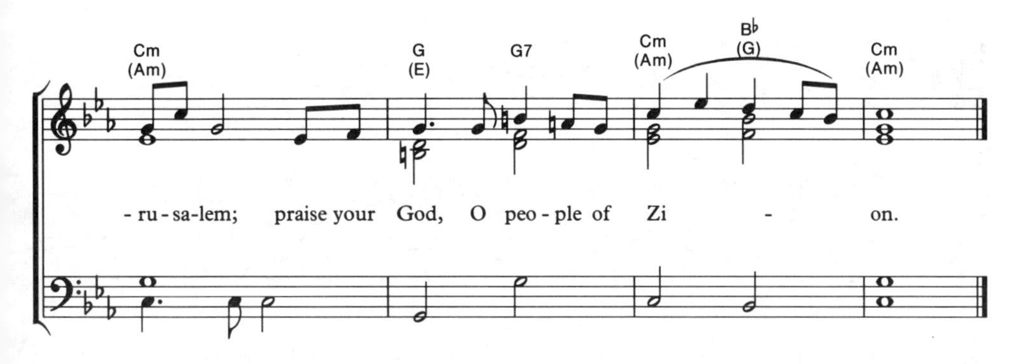
Cm
(Am)
G
(E)
G7
Cm
(Am)
B♭
(G)
Cm
(Am)
- ru - sa - lem; praise your God, O peo - ple of Zi - on.

147D How good it is to sing

Words: from Psalm 147
adapted from the New International Version
by Ian White
Music: Ian White

Boldly
E
A
B
1 How good it is to sing praise to our God – the right and pleasant thing to praise his name!
2 The Lord is build-ing up Je-ru-sa-lem; he ga-thers all the lost of Is-ra-el.
E
E
A
F♯m
B
E
Asus
A
3 He is heal-ing the bro-ken-heart-ed, he is bind-ing all their wounds;
E
Asus
A
E

Asus
A
E
he de - ter - mines the stars in the hea - vens
Asus
A
B
E
and he calls them_ each by___ name. 4 Great is the
A
B
E
E
Lord in power; all things he__ knows. He casts the
A
F♯m
B
E
wick - ed down but lifts the low!

147E The Lord is building Jerusalem

SATB version

From Psalm 147
Words and music: Rich Cook

Lively ♩ = 144
Dm
Gm
The Lord is build-ing Je-ru-sa-lem, the
A
Dm
D
C/E
D/F♯
Lord is build-ing Je-ru-sa-lem, ga-ther-ing to-ge-ther the
Gm
C
Dm
out-casts of Is-ra-el, heal-ing bro-ken hearts, bind-ing up their wounds. The
D
C/E
D/F♯
Gm
Asus
A7
Dm
Lord is build-ing, the Lord is build-ing up Je-ru-sa-lem.

Praise the Lord

148D

From Psalm 148
Words and music: Bill Batstone
and Tom Howard

In four, with a beat ♩ = 96
E B/E E
A
Praise the Lord,__ praise the Lord from the
E
A E/G♯ F♯m7 B7sus
hea - vens;__ all the an - gels sing, 'Praise the Lord!'
E
E B/E E
__ Praise the Lord – from the

A
E
heights of cre - a - tion___ they shall

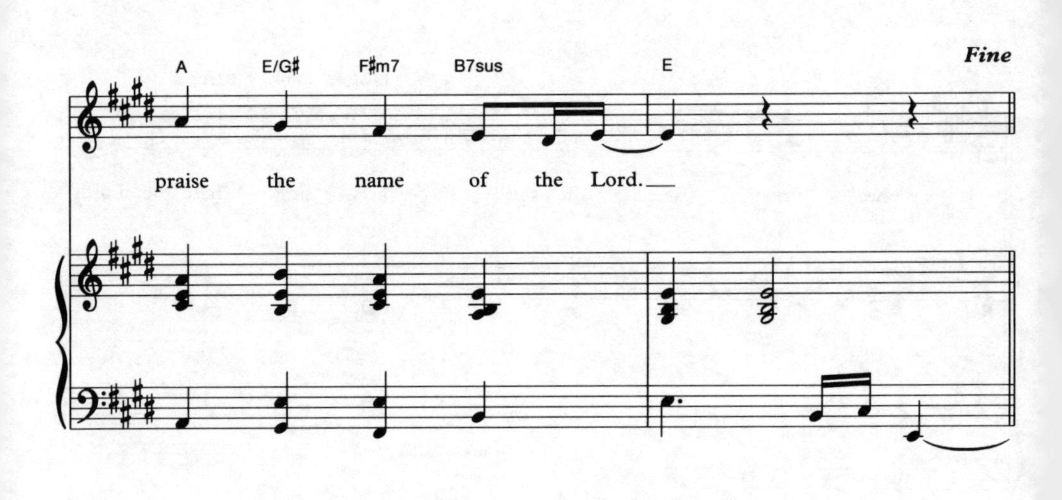
A
E/G♯
F♯m7
B7sus
E
Fine
praise the name of the Lord.___

Verses
B
A
E/G♯
1 He com-mand - ed them and the hea - vens were made; he es -
2 And___ on the earth let all na - ture a - gree – from the
3 All the peo - ple who in - ha - bit the world, from the

B
A
E
- tab - lished them, and they won't pass a - way: the
moun - tain - tops to the depths of the sea: the
rul - ing kings to the boys and the girls; the
B
C#m7
F#
sun and moon praise the Lord with their light; all the
winds and rain and the fie - ry light, all the
young and old join in praise to his name: God a -
B
F#m7
A/B
B
stars up a - bove, they keep shin - ing through the night.
beasts of the field, all the birds in their flight. Praise the Lord
- lone is su - preme let cre - a - tion pro - claim!

148E Praise the Lord, dark and light

From Psalm 148
Words and music: Colin Avery

Lively Latin feel
Em
Em7/D
Am/C
Am6 F♯m7
Bsus
B
(- more.)
Verse
1 Praise the Lord, dark and light, day and night,
2 Praise the Lord, fruit and seeds, plants and trees,
3 Praise the Lord, young and old, men and wo - men,
4 Praise the Lord, grass and ri - vers, hills and moun - tains,
B/D♯
Am6/C
praise him (praise him)! Praise the Lord,
space and sky,
fish and birds,
ru - lers, jud - ges,
fire and hail,
G
land and sea,
beasts and cat - tle,
kings and prin - ces,
wind and rain,
praise him (praise him)! Praise the Lord,

Bm
Fdim
F♯7/E
sun and moon; stars and pla-nets,
liv-ing crea-tures, all that breathes,
heaven-ly hosts, all his an-gels,
all the earth, all of hea-ven,
praise him (praise him);
Cdim/D♯
Am6/C
B
A/B
B
all cre-a-tion, join to sing his glo-ry!
Chorus
Am
D
G
I will praise the Lord with a song of thanks,
Am6/F♯
B
E
I will praise the Lord with a song of joy;

D/E
E
Am
D
G
I will praise his name for ev - er, praise his glo - rious
C
Am6/F♯
B
E
name for ev - er; I will praise the Lord for ev - er - more.
Am6/E
E
Am
D
G
I will praise his name for ev - er, praise his glo - rious
to end
Em
C
Am6/F♯
B
name for ev - er; I will praise the Lord for ev - er - more.

Instrumental arrangements

FLUTE

6 Verse

Chorus

1.2.3 4.

5

B♭ CLARINETS

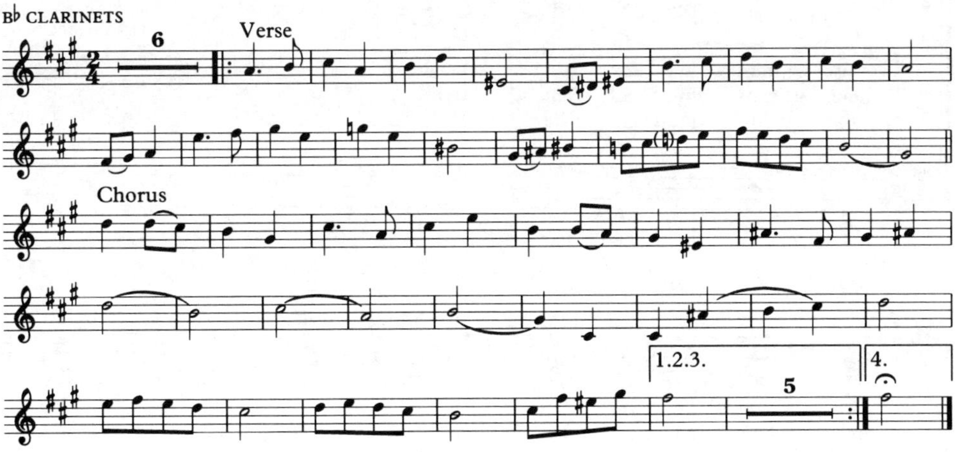

6 Verse

Chorus

1.2.3. 4.

5

B♭ TRUMPETS

tr Verse 4

4 4 2 Chorus

1.2.3. 4.

tr

148F Praise the Lord of heaven

Lord of heaven

Words: from Psalm 148
Timothy Dudley-Smith
Music: Christopher Norton

Firmly
D G/D A/D D
1 Praise the Lord of hea - ven,
2 Earth and o - cean, praise him;
3 Now by prince and peo - ple
G/D D G/D A/D D
praise him in the height;
moun - tains, hills and trees,
let his praise be told;
G/D A/D D
praise him, all his an - gels,
fire and hail and tem - pest,
praise him, men and maid - ens,
Em7 D/E Em7 D/E A7sus A7 C/E C/F♯ G G/B D
praise him, hosts of light.
wind and storm and seas.
praise him, young and old.
Sun and moon to - ge -
Praise him, fields and for -
He, the Lord of glo -

G A A7 D
- ther, shin - ing stars a - flame,
- ests, birds on flash - ing wings,
- ry! We, his praise pro - claim!
C/E C/F♯ G G/B D
plan - ets in their cour -
praise him, beasts and cat -
High a - bove all hea -
Em7 D/E G/A F♯m/A D D♯dim
- ses, mag - ni - fy his name (O
- tle, all cre - at - ed things (yes,
- vens mag - ni - fy his name (O
Em7 D/E G/A F♯m/A D
1.2. G/A A7
3.
mag - ni - fy his name)!
all cre - at - ed things)!
mag - ni - fy his name)!

148G Praise the Lord our God

Kum ba yah 8 8 8 5

Words: from Psalm 148
Richard Bewes
Music: traditional melody
arranged David Peacock
Verse 4 arranged Noël Tredinnick

Relaxed tempo
D G D D/F# G A D G D G/B D/A A7 D
1 Praise the Lord our God, praise the Lord; praise him from the heights, praise the Lord; praise him, angel throngs, praise the Lord – praise God, all his host!
2 Praise him, sun and moon, all the stars; praise him, sky and clouds, rain and snow; let them praise his name, works of God – all creatures, praise the Lord!
3 Praise him, wind and storm, mountains steep; praise him, fruitful trees, cedars tall; beasts and cattle herds, birds that fly – all creatures, praise the Lord!
(4) Kings of earth, give praise, rulers all; all young men and girls, praise the Lord; old men, children small, praise the Lord – all people, praise the Lord!

Verse 4 Choral arrangement ♪ = ♩
D
G
D
4 Kings of earth, give praise,
ru - lers all;
Em
Asus
praise the Lord;
all young men and girls,
praise the Lord; praise the
praise the Lord, praise the
A D
G
D
praise the Lord –
old men, child - ren small,
praise the Lord –
Lord;
praise the
old men, child - ren small,
Lord;
praise the Lord, praise the
G/B
D
A7
D
Lord – all peo - ple, praise the Lord!
Lord – all peo - ple praise the, praise the Lord!

149A Bring to the Lord

Jerusalem 8 8 8 8 D (DLM)

Words: from Psalms 149 and 150
Michael Perry
Music: C H H Parry (1848–1918)
simplified keyboard part arranged Christopher Norton

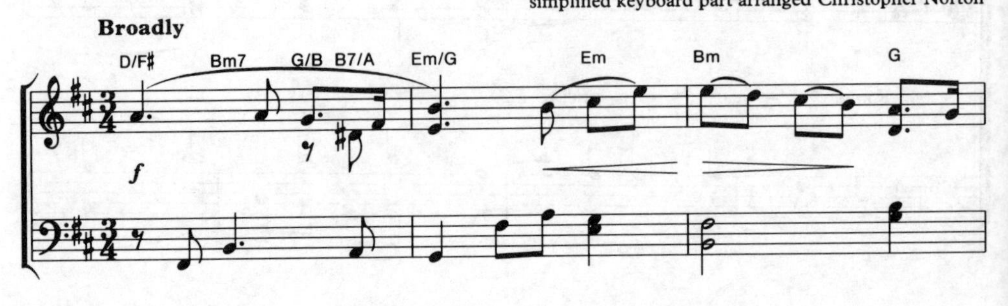

Broadly
D/F♯ Bm7 G/B B7/A Em/G Em Bm G
f

D A/C♯ Bm G D G
1 Bring to the Lord a glad new song, child-ren of
(2) - in these hal - lowed walls, wor - ship be -

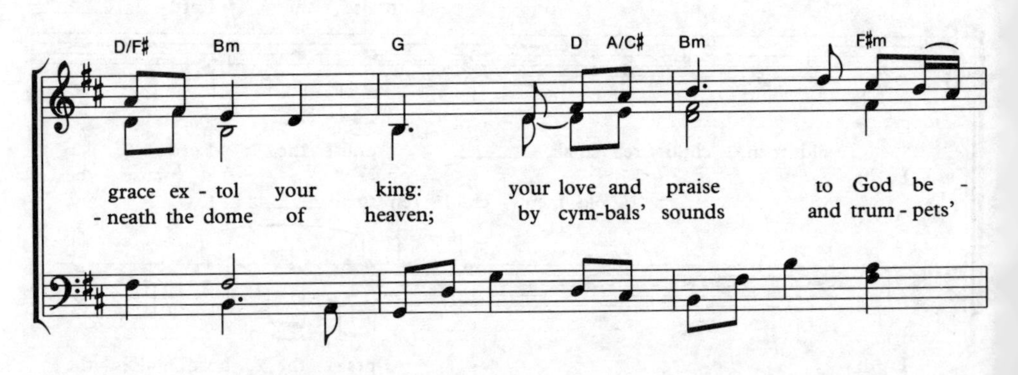

D/F♯ Bm G D A/C♯ Bm F♯m
grace ex - tol your king: your love and praise to God be -
- neath the dome of heaven; by cym-bals' sounds and trum - pets'

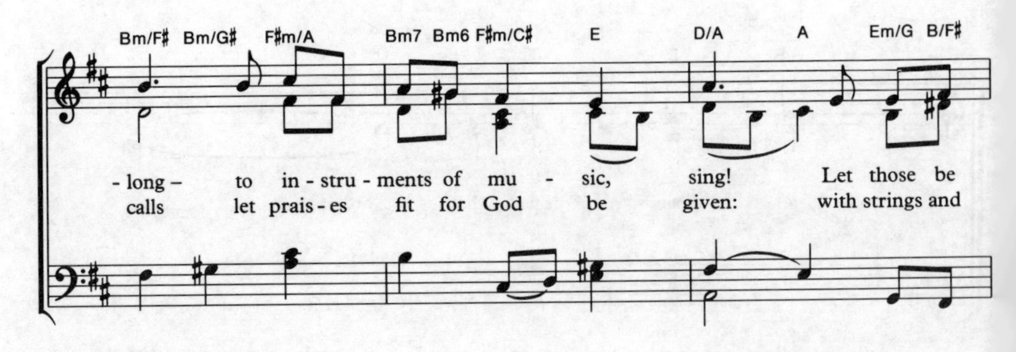

Bm/F♯ Bm/G♯ F♯m/A Bm7 Bm6 F♯m/C♯ E D/A A Em/G B/F♯
- long - to in - stru - ments of mu - sic, sing! Let those be
calls let prais - es fit for God be given: with strings and

Em
Am
Em
A7/E
G/D
C/D
D
G
D/F♯
warned who spurn God's name, let ru-lers all o - bey God's word: whose jus-tice
brass and wind re - joice – then, join our song in full ac - cord all liv-ing
Em
A
A/G
D/F♯
D
A/C♯
Bm
G
D/F♯
Gmaj7
A7
shall bring ty - rants shame – let ev - ery crea-ture praise the
things with breath and voice; let ev - ery crea-ture praise the
1.
D
Bm7
G/B
B7/A
Em/G
Em
Bm
G
D
A/C♯
Lord!
2 Sing praise with -
2.
D
A/C♯
Bm
Bm/A
G
D
Lord!

149B Sing a new song

Words: from Psalm 149
J E Seddon (1915–1983)
Music: Christopher Norton

Disco tempo
Asus
D
mf
f
Sing a new song – Al - le -

G/D
D
A
- lu - ia! Sing a - loud to God the king; –
sim.

Asus2 A
D
C/E
D7/F♯
D7/G G
D7/G G
— let the saints of God a - dore — him, let their

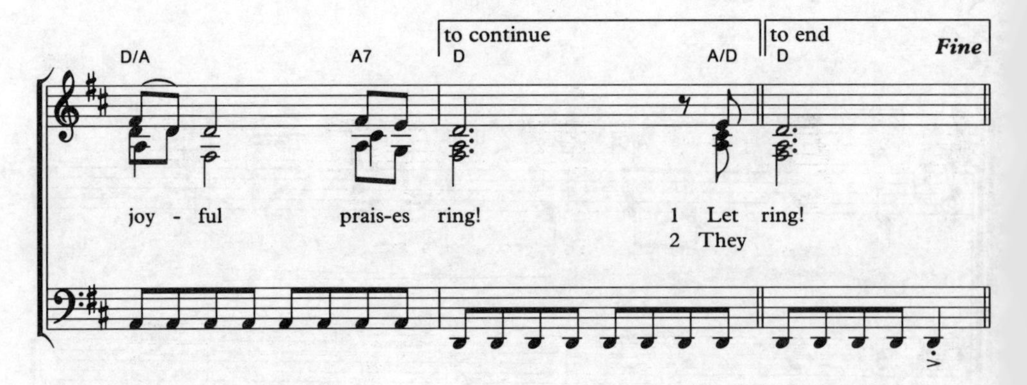
D/A
A7
to continue
D
A/D
to end
D
Fine
joy - ful prais-es ring!
1 Let ring!
2 They

D
G
D/G
A
D
A/D
in - stru - ments and voi - ces make mu - sic to the Lord; be
wield the sword of jus - tice, for God their hands are strong; they
D
D/G
A
Asus
D
glad, O ran - somed peo - ple, re - joice with one ac - cord! The
chal - lenge kings and na - tions, and fight all forms of wrong: they
F
B♭/F
F
C/F
F
C/F
Lord ac - cepts the ser - vice of those who love his name; he
work for truth and good-ness, the no - ble and the right; and
D.S.
F
B♭/F
F
C/F
Asus2
A
leads them on in tri-umph his great-ness to pro - claim.
this will be their glo - ry – to tri-umph in the fight.

150D Praise God within his holy place

Words: from Psalm 150
Stephen Horsfall
Music: Christopher Norton
Briskly
F/G C F/C C F G C F/G
1 Praise God with-in his ho - ly place, come, praise the Lord; praise
2 Praise him with tam-bour-ine and dance, come, praise the Lord; with
C F/C C F G7 C
God for all his acts of grace, come, praise the Lord. Praise
strings and wood-wind in - stru-ments, come, praise the Lord! Let
F B♭/F F B♭ C F N.C.
God for all his acts of pow - er, come, praise the Lord; praise
cym-bals' crash pro - claim his love, come, praise the Lord; praise
Dm7 G7 C/G G7 C 1. 2.
him with trum-pet, harp and lyre, come, praise the Lord!
him be-cause you live and move, come, praise the Lord!

Praise him in his sanctuary

150E

From Psalm 150
Words and music: Unknown
Music arranged Christopher Norton

Moderato
Em
1 Praise him in his sanc - tu - a - ry, praise him in the skies a - bove, praise him
2 Praise him with the clash-ing cym-bals – let them hear it far and near: with the
G C/G G D Em
for the acts of pow - er that he does; praise him
strings and flute we'll praise the Lord our God, who with
for sur - pass - ing great-ness, with the trum - pet, harp and lyre, with the
ma - jes - ty is reign - ing. He has pow - er o - ver all: give him
G C/G G D Em
tam - bour - ine and danc - ing praise him now!
glo - ry, and be thank - ful for his love!
Come and
G D G Cmaj7 Dsus D Em
praise him, for the Lord is good, and his mer-cy's ev - er - last-ing;

150F Praise the Lord

From Psalm 150
Words and music: Bob Fraser
Music arranged Christopher Norton

Joyfully
D
A/D
G/D
A/D
D
A/D
mp
Praise the Lord, sing him a new song –
praise the Lord, sing him a new song –
G/D
A/D
D
A/D
G/D
A/D
Zi - on, a - wake and
Zi - on, re - joice in your
1.
D
A/D
G/D
A/D
sing;
R.H.
2.
D
G/D
D
Fine
King!
R.H.

C G C G
1 Praise the Lord with ev - ery breath that you
2 Praise the Lord for all his migh - ty
3 Praise the Lord, with tam - bour - ine and
D
breathe;
power;
string;
C G C G
praise the Lord, re - joice all you that be -
praise the Lord ev - ery day and
praise the Lord, let ev - ery cym - bal
Asus A
D.C.
- lieve.
hour.
ring.

150G Praise him on the trumpet

From Psalm 150
Words and music: John Kennett
Music arranged Christopher Norton

Rock 'n' roll
E
A
Praise him on the trum-pet, the psal-tery and harp, praise him on the tim - brel
E
and the dance,___ praise him with stringed in - stru-ments too;
B
E
praise him on the loud cym-bals,
A
E
praise him on the loud cym - bals – let ev - ery - thing that has

B7
E
breath praise the Lord!
Al - le - lu - ia –
praise the Lord,
A
al - le - lu - ia – praise the Lord – let
E
B7
ev - ery - thing that has breath praise the Lord!
E
A
Al - le - lu - ia – praise the Lord,
al - le - lu - ia – praise the Lord – let
E
B7
E
ev - ery - thing that has breath praise the Lord!

153A O bless the God of Israel

Roewen

Words: from Luke 1
The Song of Zechariah/Benedictus
Michael Perry
Music: Roger Mayor

Flowing smoothly
Cmaj7 Dm7/C Em7/C Dm7 Em7 F Dm/F
F/G G7 C/E Am7 Dm7 G/B
1 O bless the God of Is - rael, who
(2) from the house of Da - vid a
(3) once were fear and dark - ness the
F/A Dm7 Gsus G7 C/E Am7
comes to set us free, who vis - its and re -
child of grace is given; a Sav - iour comes a -
sun be - gins to rise – the dawn - ing of for -
G♯dim7 Am D D7 Gsus Dm A7/E
- deems us and grants us li - ber - ty. The
- mong us to raise us up to heaven. Be -
- give - ness up - on the sin - ner's eyes, to

Alternative tune: Morning Light, *Psalms for Today* 153A

Dm C/E F D Gm Cm7 F7
pro - phets spoke of mer - cy, of free - dom and re -
- fore him goes the her - ald – fore - run - ner in the
guide the feet of pil - grims a - long the paths of
B♭ G7/B Csus C/E F G6 G♯dim7
- lease; God shall ful - fil the prom - ise to
way – the pro - phet of sal - va - tion, the
peace: O bless our God and Sav - iour, with
D7/A G7
1.2.
C Dm7/C Em7/C Dm7 Em7
bring our peo - ple peace.
mes - sen - ger of Day.
songs that ne - ver
F Dm/F F/G G7
3.
C
2 Now
3 Where cease!

153D Blessed be the God of Israel

Words: from Luke 1
The Song of Zechariah/Benedictus
David Mowbray
Music: Sarah Lacy
arranged Christopher Norton
Rhythmically
Capo 3(D)
F (D) C/F (A) B♭/F (G) F (D)
Gm/F (Em) F (D) Gm/F (Em) F (D)
Cm/A (Am) B♭ (G) F/A (D) Gm7add C (Em7)
1 Blessed be the God of Is - ra - el who sets his peo - ple free; the migh - ty sav - iour has ap - peared
2 This news ful - fils God's word which came to pro - phets long be - fore: the prom - ise made to Ab - ra - ham,
3 A - mong us walks the Lord Most High! How fa - voured is the child who bids God's peo - ple turn from sin,
4 Earth's sha - dows shall be swept a - way and dark - ness shall de - crease, and God's com - pas - sion bright - ly shine

F
(D)
Gm7add C
(Em7)
B♭/C
(G)
F
(D)
to bring us li - ber - ty.
the sol - emn oath God swore.
and so be re - con - ciled!
to guide our feet in peace.
F/A
Gm7
(Em7)
F
(D)
F/A
Gm7
(Em7)
F
(D)

153E O praise the Lord

Wharfdale
Words: from Luke 1
The Song of Zechariah/Benedictus
Michael Perry
Music: Norman Warren
Capo 3(Dm)
UNISON
Fm (Dm) B♭/F (G) Fm7 (Dm7) B♭m (Gm)
1 O praise the Lord, the migh-ty god of Is-rael, re-
2 Sal-va-tion from the hands of those who hate us! His
3 And you will be the pro-phet of the High-est, to
4 The Lord our God has shown his ten-der mer-cy, his
Fm (Dm) B♭m (Gm) Cm (Am)
-deem-er of his peo-ple he has come; he
co-ve-nant with Ab-ra-ham ful-filled! He
go be-fore him and pre-pare his way; to
shin-ing sun will come to us from heaven to
Fm (Dm) B♭m (Gm) E♭7 (C7) A♭maj7 (Fmaj7) D♭maj7 (B♭maj7) Fm7/C (Dm7)
rais-es up the dy-nas-ty of Da-vid as
res-cues us that, fear-less, we might serve him in
give his peo-ple know-ledge of sal-va-tion, the
dawn on those who live in death's dark sha-dow, and
B♭m (Gm) Cm7 (Am7) Fm (Dm) B♭m/F (Gm) Fm[F] (Dm[D])
prom-ised by his pro-phets long a-go.
hon-our and in good-ness all our days.
bless-ing of for-give-ness for their sins.
guide our foot-steps in the path of peace.
v.4

Angels, praise him

154B(i)

Song of Creation
With a swing
Words: from A Song of Creation/Benedicite
Michael Perry
Music: Norman Warren
Capo 5(A)
D (A) Em7 (Bm7) A7 (E7) D (A) G (D) A7 (E7)
1 An-gels, praise him, hea - vens, praise him, wa-ters, praise him, Al - le-lu-ia!
WOMEN 3 Wind, praise him, fire, praise him, heat, praise him, Al - le-lu-ia!
WOMEN 5 Earth, praise him, moun-tains, praise him, hills, praise him, Al - le-lu-ia!
7 Na-tions, praise him, church - es, praise him, saints, praise him, Al - le-lu-ia!
Bm (F♯m) F♯m (C♯m) G6 (D6) Em (Bm) Em7/A (Bm7) A7 (E7) D (A)
Fine
crea - tures of the Lord, all praise him for ev - er - more:
win - ter, praise him, sum - mer, praise him for ev - er - more:
green things, praise him, wells, praise him for ev - er - more:
all his peo - ple, join to praise him for ev - er - more!
B♭ (F) Cm7 (Gm7) F7 (C7) B♭ (F) Cm7 (Gm7) F7 (C7)
2 Sun, praise him, moon, praise him, stars, praise him, Al-le-lu - ia!
MEN 4 Nights, praise him, days, praise him, light, praise him, Al-le-lu - ia!
MEN 6 Seas, praise him, ri - vers, praise him, fish, praise him, Al-le-lu - ia!
B♭ (F) D7 (A7) Gm (Dm) D7 (A7) Gm6 (Dm6) C7 (G7) A7 (E7)
D.C.
show - ers, praise him, dews, praise him for ev - er - more:
light-nings, praise him, clouds, praise him for ev - er - more:
birds, praise him, beasts, praise him for ev - er - more:

154B(ii) **Angels, praise him**

From *A Song of Creation/Benedicite*
Words and music: Michael Perry

With gathering speed

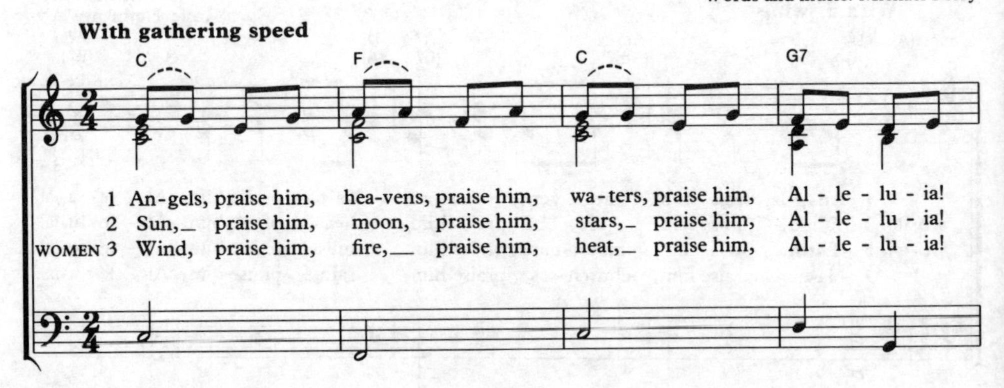
C
F
C
G7
1 An-gels, praise him, hea-vens, praise him, wa-ters, praise him, Al - le - lu - ia!
2 Sun,_ praise him, moon, praise him, stars,_ praise him, Al - le - lu - ia!
WOMEN 3 Wind, praise him, fire,_ praise him, heat,_ praise him, Al - le - lu - ia!

C
F
G7
C
crea - tures of the Lord, all praise him for ev - er - more:
showers, praise him, dews,_ praise him for ev - er - more:
win - ter, praise him, sum - mer, praise him for ev - er - more:

MEN
4 Nights, praise him,
days, praise him,
light, praise him,
Alleluia!
lightnings, praise him,
clouds, praise him
for evermore:

WOMEN
5 Earth, praise him,
mountains, praise him,
hills, praise him,
Alleluia!
green things, praise him,
wells, praise him
for evermore:

MEN
6 Seas, praise him,
rivers, praise him,
fish, praise him,
Alleluia!
birds, praise him,
beasts, praise him
for evermore:

ALL
7 Nations, praise him,
churches, praise him,
saints, praise him,
Alleluia!
all his people,
join to praise him
for evermore!

Alternative tune: Little Barrington, *Psalms for Today* 154B

Great and wonderful are your deeds 155D

Words: from Revelation 15
Great and Wonderful
derived from the Daily Office
of the Joint Liturgical Group
Music: Chris Rolinson
arranged David Peacock

Bouncy
D
F♯m7
Em7
A7
Great and won - der - ful are your deeds, Lord
F♯m7
Bm7
Em7
A7
F♯m7
God the al - migh - ty; just and
3rd time to Coda
Bm7
Em7
A7
D
G/A
true are your ways, O King of the
Dsus
D
Em7
Bm7
Em7
na - tions!
1 Who shall not re - vere and
2 All na - tions shall come and wor - ship

155D Great and wonderful are your deeds

Bm7
G
Asus
A
praise your name, O Lord? for
in your pres - ence, for
G
D/F♯
Em7
Asus
A
you a - lone are ho - ly.
your just deal - ings have been re - vealed.
CODA
Dsus
D
F♯m
na - tions! To him who sits on the
Em7
A
F♯m
Bm7
throne and to the Lamb, to the

Em7
A
F♯m7
Bm7
Lamb be praise and hon - our,
Em7
A7
D
G/A
glo - ry and might for ev - er and
Dsus
D
Em7/D
Dmaj7
Em7/D
ev - er. A - men, a -
Dmaj7
G6/D
D
- men, a - men.

156D Great is the Lord we now acclaim

Acclamation

Words: from *Te Deum*
David Mowbray
Music: Andrew Maries

Strongly
F♯m
D/E
1 Great is the Lord we now_ ac-claim – God ev - er-last - ing is__
2 Let pro - phets and_ a - pos - tles join_ with mar-tyrs in__ tri - um -
3 We praise God's true_ and on - ly Son, for ev - er with_ the Fa -
E/D
C♯m
A7
D
Gmaj7
Cmaj7
__ his name: let heaven and earth with mu - sic ring,_
- phant line__ to e - cho the an - gel - ic cry__
- ther one;__ we praise the Spi - rit at__ their side,_
F♯m
E
F♯m
v 6
E/F♯
and 'Ho - ly, ho - ly, ho - ly' sing!
and ce - le - brate God's mys - te - ry.
the Chur-ch's ad - vo - cate and guide.

This simpler rhythm may be substituted for bars 3 and 4:

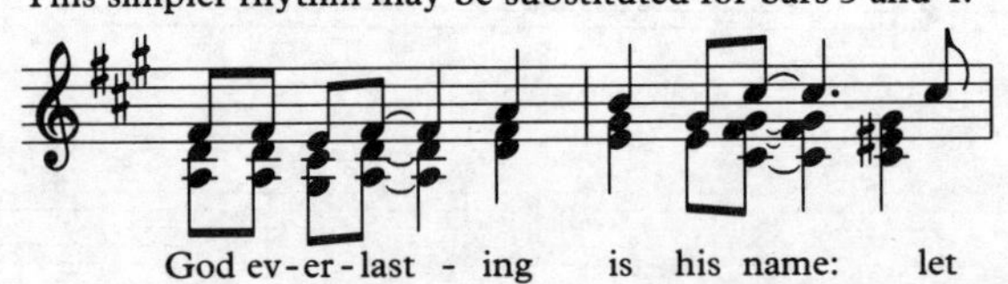
God ev-er-last - ing is his name: let

4 When once the time had fully come
Christ did not scorn the Virgin's womb;
our Lord the sting of death defied
and flung the gate of heaven wide!

5 He shed his blood to pay sin's price,
the full and perfect sacrifice:
as Saviour, reigns eternally;
as Judge of all, presides on high.

6 Lord God, protect us all from sin,
our hearts to love and goodness win;
that we yet firm in faith, shall stay
unshaken in the last great day.

Alternative tune: Old 100th, *Psalms for Today* 156D

Glory to God in the highest 157B(i)

Words: from *Gloria in excelsis*
in *The Alternative Service Book 1980*
International Consultation on English Texts
Music: Paul Herrington

Triumphantly
C9
B♭
Csus2
C
C
f
1 Glo - ry to
B♭
Csus2
C/E
E♭
F
C
God in the high - est: and peace to his peo - ple on earth.
B♭
Csus2
C/E
2 Lord God hea - ven - ly King: al -
E♭
F
C
Smooth
E♭
F
mf
- migh - ty God and Fa - ther, 3 we wor - ship you we

Alternative setting: *Psalms for Today* 157B

C
E♭
Fmaj7
C
give you thanks: we praise you for your glo -
Steadier
Am
Em
F
C
Am
Am/G
p
mp
- ry. 4 Lord Je - sus Christ on - ly Son of the Fa - ther: Lord God
Fmaj7
Esus
E
Am
G
F
p
Lamb of God, 5 you take a - way the sin of the
poco accel.
a tempo
C
Fmaj7
F6
Esus
E
C
mf
world: have mer - cy on us; 6 you are
G
Dm
Am
Am/G
F
Dm7
seat - ed at the right hand of the Fa - ther: re -

C/G
Gsus
C/G
G
C
B♭
f
-ceive our prayer. 7 For you a - lone are the
C
C/E
E♭
F
C
C/E
Ho - ly One: you a - lone are the Lord,
E♭
F
C
C/E
Am
8 you a - lone are the Most High Je - sus
Em
F
C
C/E
Dm7/F Am/E Dm7
C/G
G
Christ with the Ho - ly Spi - rit: in the glo - ry of God the
rit.
C
C/E
E♭
Dm7
C
ff
Fa - ther. A - men.

157B(ii) Glory to God in the highest

Words: from *Gloria in excelsis*
in *The Alternative Service Book 1980*
International Consultation on English Texts
Music: Chris Rolinson
arranged David Peacock

Majestically

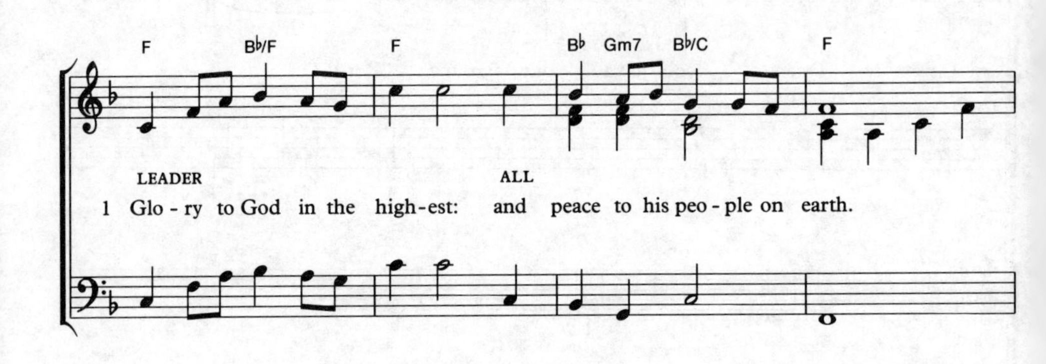

F
B♭/F
F
B♭
Gm7
B♭/C
F
LEADER
ALL
1 Glo - ry to God in the high-est: and peace to his peo - ple on earth.

C/F
B♭/F
F
B♭/F
F
B♭/D
B♭/C
2 Lord God hea-ven-ly King: al - migh-ty God_ and

F
B♭/F
F
B♭/D
B♭/C
Fa-ther, 3 we wor-ship you_ we give you thanks: we praise you for_ your

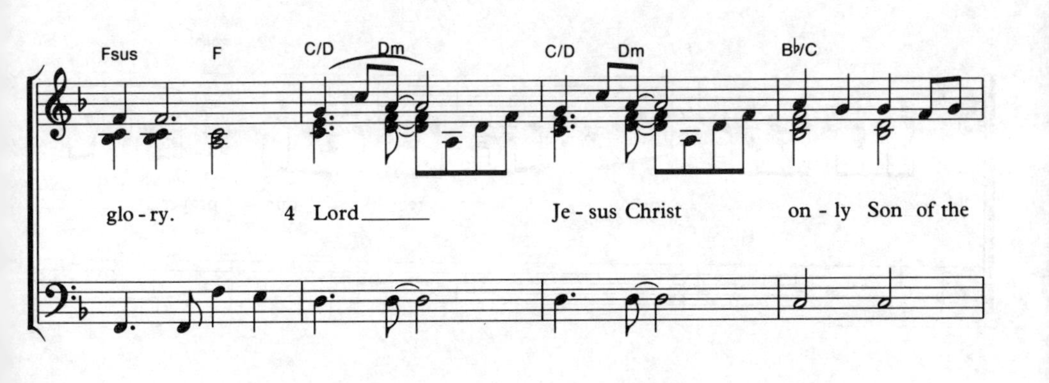
Fsus F C/D Dm C/D Dm B♭/C
glo - ry. 4 Lord Je - sus Christ on - ly Son of the

C/D Dm C/D Dm B♭/C
Fa - ther: Lord God Lamb of God, 5 you take a - way the

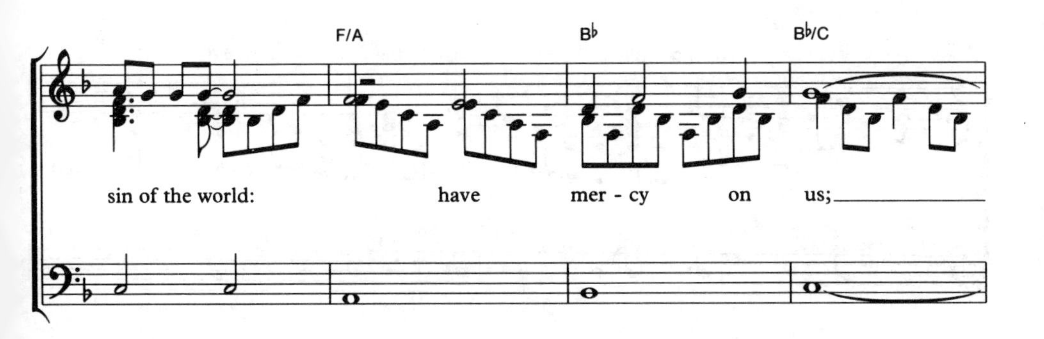
F/A B♭ B♭/C
sin of the world: have mer - cy on us;

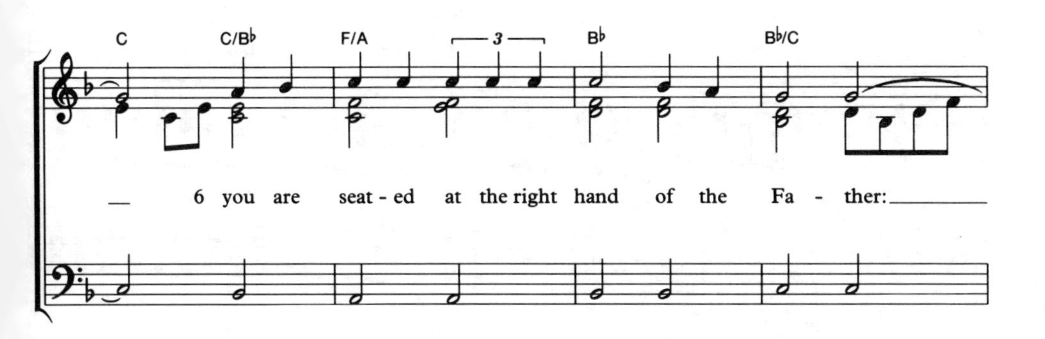
C C/B♭ F/A 3 B♭ B♭/C
6 you are seat - ed at the right hand of the Fa - ther:

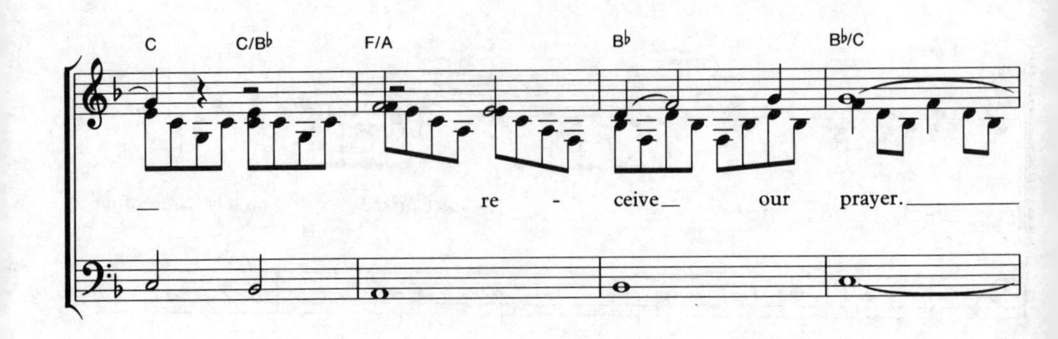
C
C/B♭
F/A
B♭
B♭/C
re - ceive our prayer.

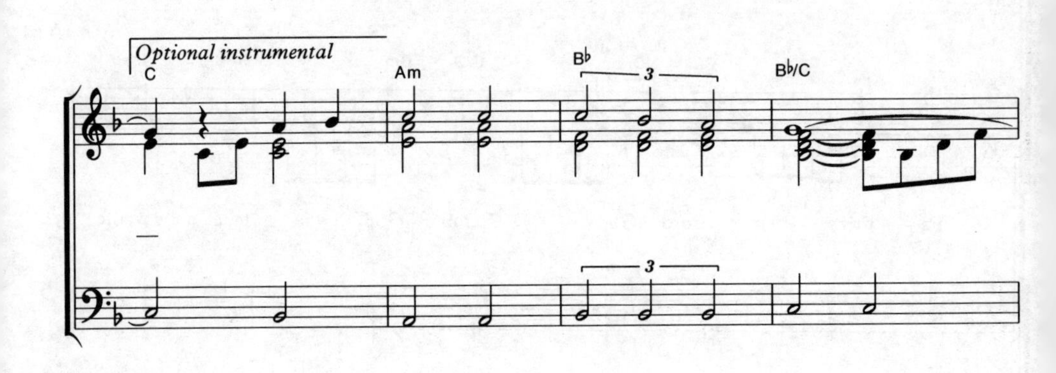
Optional instrumental
C
Am
B♭
3
B♭/C
3

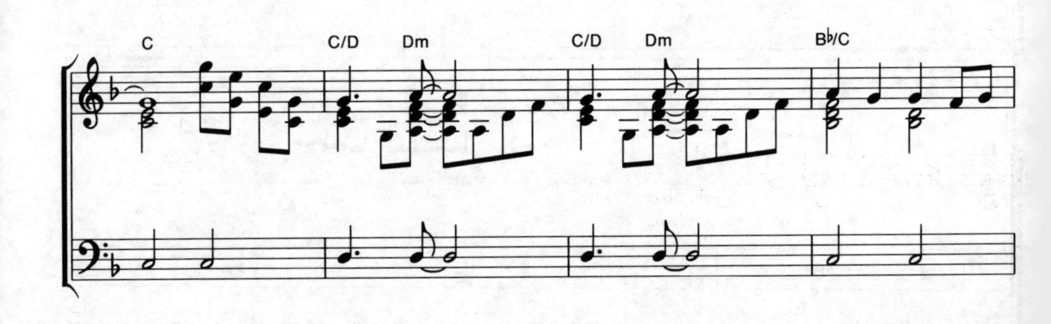
C
C/D
Dm
C/D
Dm
B♭/C

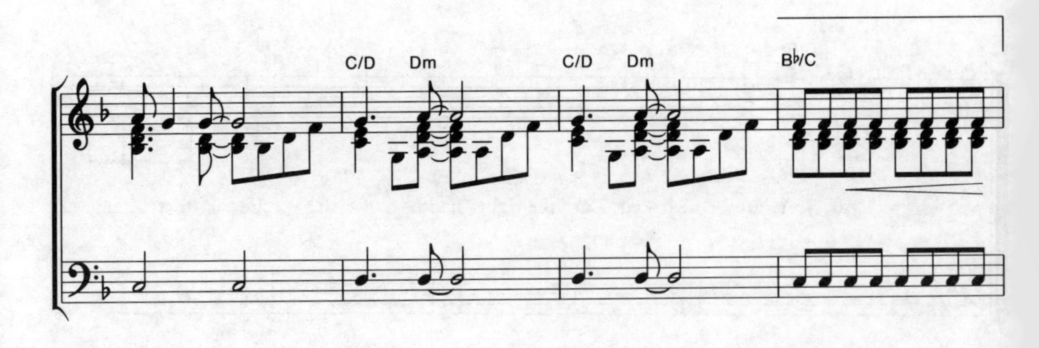
C/D
Dm
C/D
Dm
B♭/C

C F B♭/F 3 F B♭/F 3
7 For you a - lone are the Ho - ly One: you a - lone are the
F C/E Cm/E♭ 3 B♭/D B♭m/D♭ F/C G7/B
Lord, 8 you a - lone are the Most High Je - sus
C/B♭ F/A B♭ F/A B♭
Christ with the Ho - ly Spi - rit:
F/A B♭ G7/B F/C Dm7 Gm7 B♭/C
in the glo - ry of God the Fa -
F E♭ B♭/C C F
- ther. A - - - men.

157C Glory in the highest

Land of hope and glory

Words: from *Gloria in excelsis*
Christopher Idle
Music: E Elgar (1857–1934)
arranged Noël Tredinnick

Capo 3(G)
B♭ (G) F7/C (D7) Gm/D (Em) B♭/D (G) E♭ (C) B♭/F (G)
1 Glo - ry in the high - est to the God of heaven!
2 Je - sus Christ is ri - sen, God the Fa - ther's Son!
3 Christ the world's true Sav - iour, high and ho - ly One,
C7/G (A7) F (D) B♭ (G) C7/B♭ (A7) F/A (D) Dm (Bm)
Peace to all your peo - ple through the earth be given!
With the Ho - ly Spi - rit you are Lord a - lone!
seat - ed now and reign - ing from your Fa - ther's throne:
Gm (Em) C7 (A7) F (D) F7 (D7) B♭ (G) F7/C (D7)
Migh - ty God and
Lamb once killed for
Lord and God, we

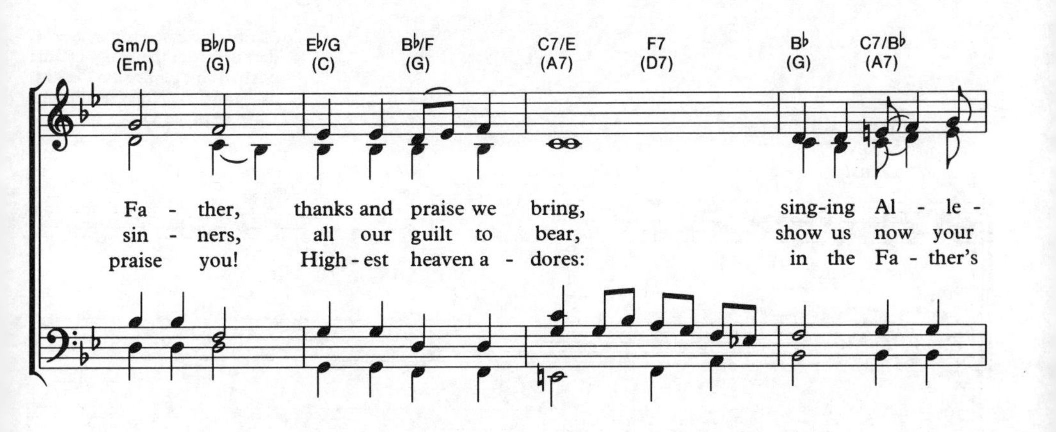
Gm/D (Em) B♭/D (G) E♭/G (C) B♭/F (G) C7/E (A7) F7 (D7) B♭ (G) C7/B♭ (A7)
Fa - ther, thanks and praise we bring, sing-ing Al - le -
sin - ners, all our guilt to bear, show us now your
praise you! High - est heaven a - dores: in the Fa - ther's

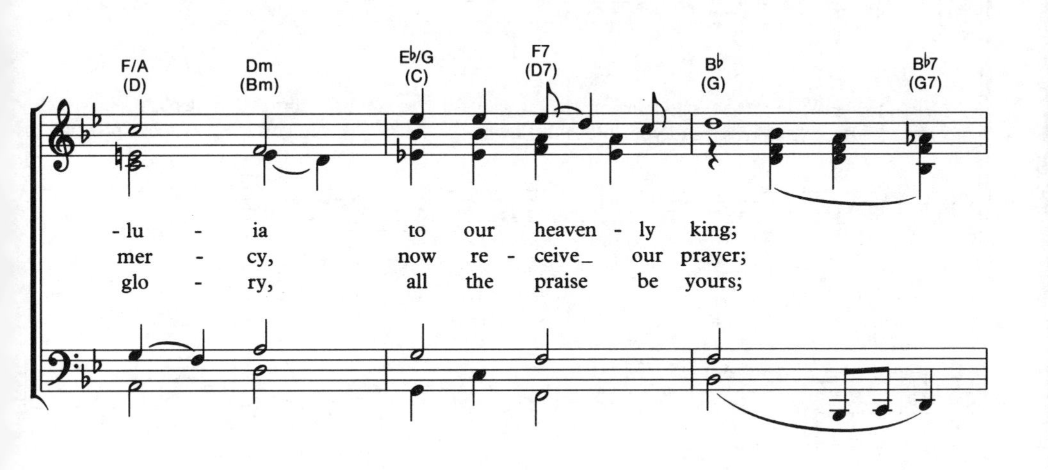
F/A (D) Dm (Bm) E♭/G (C) F7 (D7) B♭ (G) B♭7 (G7)
- lu - ia to our heaven - ly king;
mer - cy, now re - ceive_ our prayer;
glo - ry, all the praise be yours;

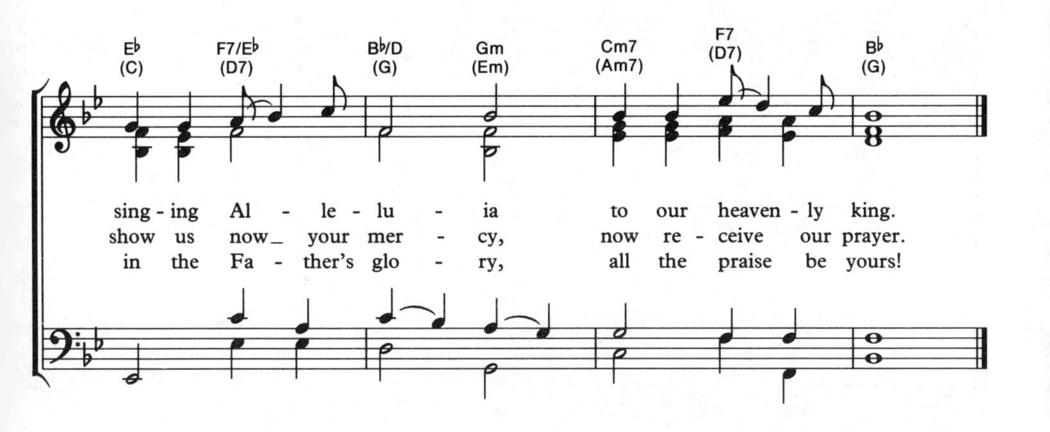
E♭ (C) F7/E♭ (D7) B♭/D (G) Gm (Em) Cm7 (Am7) F7 (D7) B♭ (G)
sing - ing Al - le - lu - ia to our heaven - ly king.
show us now_ your mer - cy, now re - ceive our prayer.
in the Fa - ther's glo - ry, all the praise be yours!

158D Jesus saviour of the world

Words: from *Saviour of the world*
derived from the Daily Office
of the Joint Liturgical Group
Music: Chris Rolinson
arranged David Peacock
Worshipfully
Capo 3(C)
LEADER
1 Je - sus sav-iour of the world come to us in your mer - cy:
2 By your cross and your life laid down you set your peo-ple free:
MEN
we look to you to save and help us,
WOMEN
we look to you to save and help us.
ALL
3 When they were rea - dy to

Gm7
(Em7)
A♭maj7
(Fmaj7)
Fm7
(Dm7)
E♭/B♭
(C)
B♭
(G)
A♭
(F)
B♭/A♭
(G)
per - ish you saved your dis - ci - ples: we look to you to
Gm7
(Em7)
Cm7
(Am7)
A♭
(F)
B♭/A♭
(G)
Gm7
(Em7)
Cm7
(Am7)
Fm7
(Dm7)
come to our help. 4 In the great-ness of your
Gm7
(Em7)
A♭maj7
(Fmaj7)
Fm7
(Dm7)
E♭/B♭
(C)
B♭
(G)
A♭
(F)
B♭/A♭
(G)
mer - cy loose us from our chains: for-give the sins of
Gm7
(Em7)
Cm7
(Am7)
A♭
(F)
B♭/A♭
(G)
Gm7
(Am7)
Cm7
(Am7)
A♭
(F)
all your peo - ple.

Ab/Bb
Bb
(G)
Eb
(C)
Cm
(Am)
Eb
(C)
LEADER
5 Make your-self known as our sav - iour and migh - ty de -

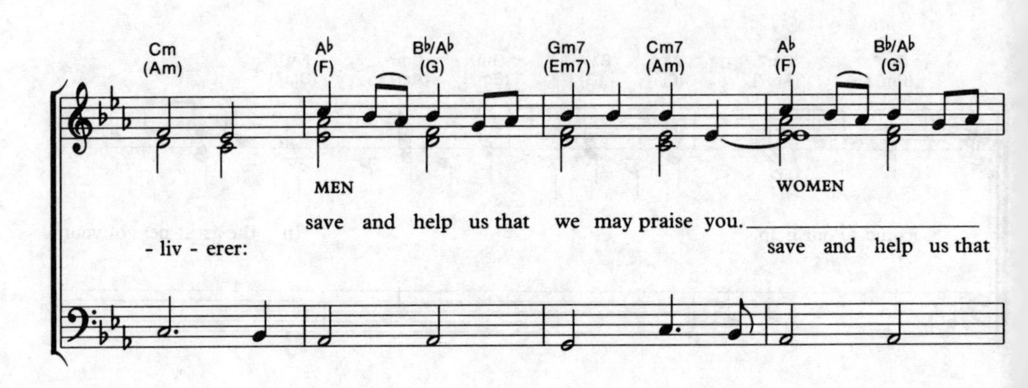
Cm
(Am)
Ab
(F)
Bb/Ab
(G)
Gm7
(Em7)
Cm7
(Am)
Ab
(F)
Bb/Ab
(G)
MEN
WOMEN
save and help us that we may praise you.
- liv - erer:
save and help us that

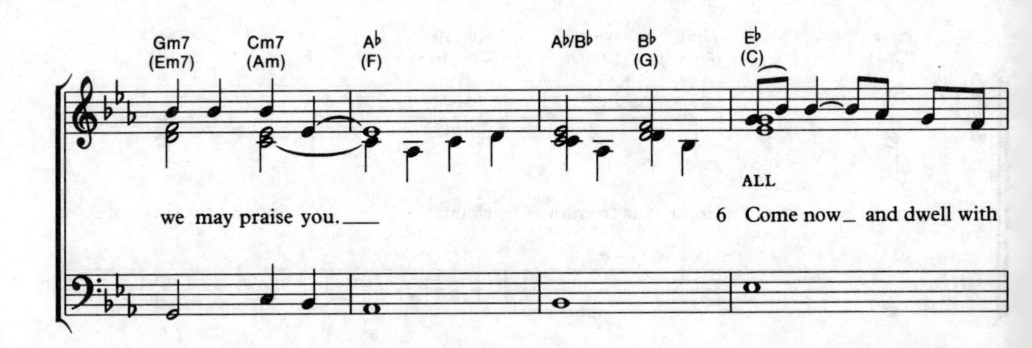
Gm7
(Em7)
Cm7
(Am)
Ab
(F)
Ab/Bb
Bb
(G)
Eb
(C)
ALL
we may praise you.
6 Come now and dwell with

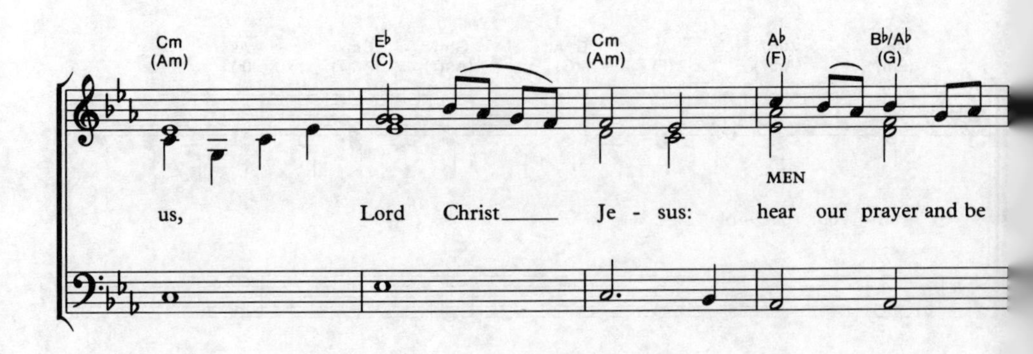
Cm
(Am)
Eb
(C)
Cm
(Am)
Ab
(F)
Bb/Ab
(G)
MEN
us, Lord Christ Je - sus: hear our prayer and be

Gm7 (Em7) Cm7 (Am) Ab (F) Bb/Ab (G) Gm7 (Em7) Cm7 (Am)
with us al - ways,
WOMEN
hear our prayer and be with us al - ways.
Ab (F) Bb/Ab (G) Gm7 (Em7) Cm7 (Am7) Ab (F) Bb/Ab (G) Gm7 (Em) Cm7 (Am7)
MEN
7 And when you come in your glo-ry:
ALL
make us to be one with you
Ab (F) Bb/Ab (G) Gm7 (Em7) Cm (Am) Abmaj7 (Fmaj7) Gm7 (Em7) Fm7 (Dm7)
and to share the life of your king - dom, your
Abmaj7 (Fmaj7) Gm7 (Em7) Fm7 (Dm7) Abmaj7 (Fmaj7) Gm7 (Em7) Fm7 (Dm7) Ab/Bb (F) Eb (C)
king - dom, your king - dom.

159c O gladdening light, O grace

Words: from *Phos hilaron*
Robert Bridges (1844–1930)
in this version Word & Music
Music: Chris Rolinson
arranged David Peacock
Boldly
D D/F♯ Em7 A7 F♯m7 Bm7
1 O gladden-ing light, O grace of God the Fa - ther's
2 As day fades in - to night we see the eve - ning
3 To you of right be - longs the praise of all our
Em7 A7 A♯dim Bm A/C♯ C
face, the e - ter - nal splen - dour
light, our hymn of love out -
songs, O Son of God, life -
G/B Em7 G/A A G/A A D D/F♯
wear - ing: ce - les - tial, ho - ly,
- pour - ing; Fa - ther of might un -
- giv - er; you, there-fore, Lord most
Em7 A7 F♯m7 Bm7 Em7 A7
blessed, our sav - iour Je - sus Christ,
- known, you, his in - car - nate Son,
high the world shall glo - ri - fy

Alternative tune: Nunc dimittis, *Psalms for Today* 159c

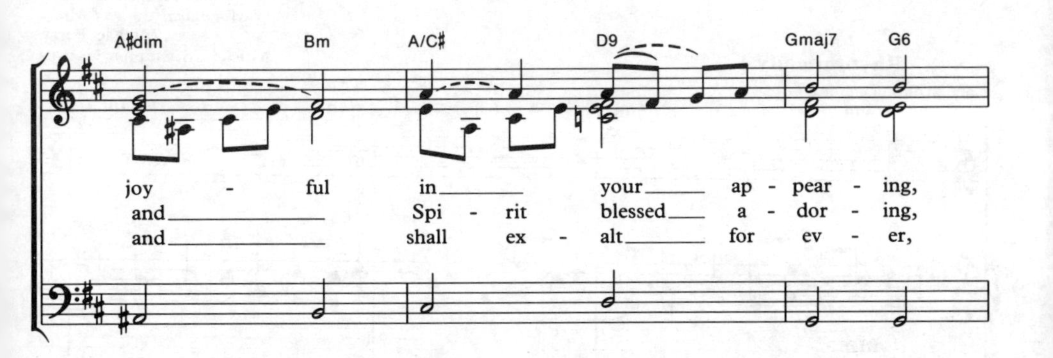
A♯dim Bm A/C♯ D9 Gmaj7 G6
joy - ful in your ap - pear - ing,
and Spi - rit blessed a - dor - ing,
and shall ex - alt for ev - er,

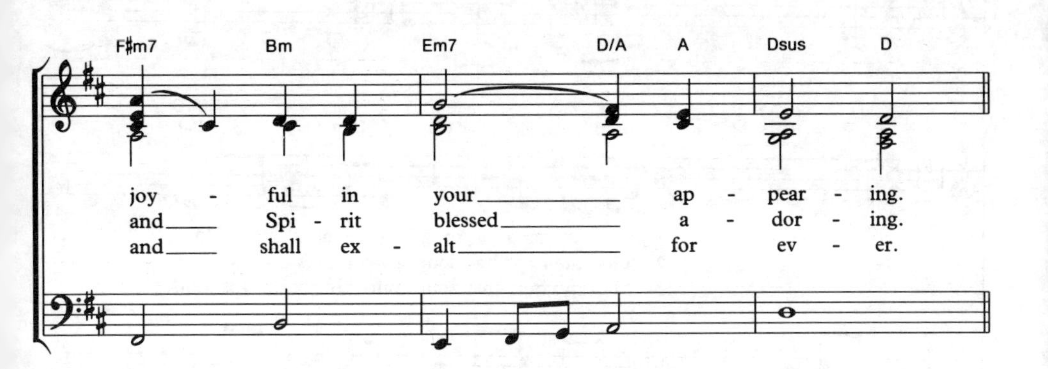
F♯m7 Bm Em7 D/A A Dsus D
joy - ful in your ap - pear - ing.
and Spi - rit blessed a - dor - ing.
and shall ex - alt for ev - er.

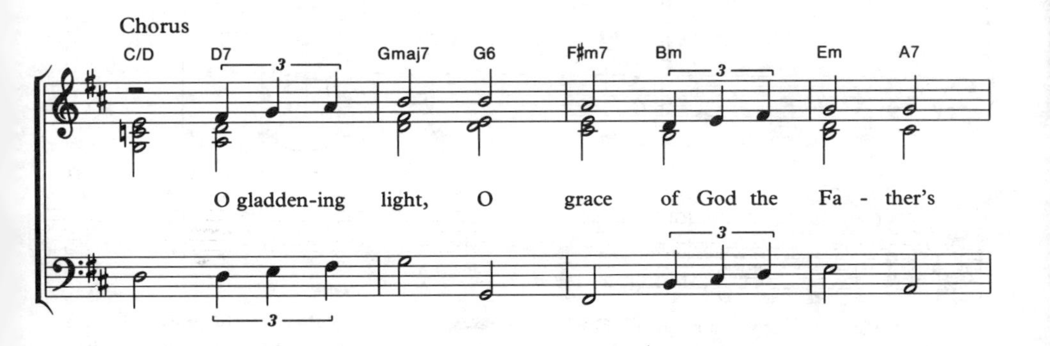
Chorus
C/D D7 Gmaj7 G6 F♯m7 Bm Em A7
O gladden-ing light, O grace of God the Fa - ther's

D G/A A D F♯m7 Em7 D/A A D
face, our sav - iour Je - sus Christ.

160D Mary sang a song

Words: from Luke 1,
Magnificat/Song of Mary
Michael Perry
Music: Christopher Norton

Rhythmically
Capo 3(Am)
Cm (Am) Bb/C (G) Cm (Am) Bb/C (G) Cm (Am) Bb/C (G) Cm (Am)
mp
Bb/C (G) Cm (Am) Bb/C (G) Cm (Am) Bb/C (G)
1 Ma - ry sang a song, a song of love,
2 'God the Lord has done great things for me,
3 'To the hum-ble soul our God is kind,
mf
Cm (Am) Bb/C (G) Cm (Am) Bb/C (G) Ab (F) Bb/Ab (G) Ab (F)
mag - ni - fied the migh - ty Lord a - bove;
looked up - on my life's hu - mi - li - ty;
to the proud he brings un - ease of mind.
me - lo - dies of praise his name
hap - py they shall call me from
Who up - lifts the poor, pulls down

B♭/A♭
(G)
Gsus
(Esus)
F/A
(D)
G/B
(E)
— ex - tol from the ve - ry depths of Ma - ry's soul:
— this day – mer - ci - ful is he whom we o - bey.
— the strong? God a - lone has power to right the wrong!
1.2.
last time
Cm7
(Am7)
F(no 3rd)
(D)
C/G(no 3rd)
(A)
Cm7
(Am7)
C(no 3rd)
(A)

4 'He who has been Israel's strength and stay
fills the hungry, sends the rich away;
God has shown his promise firm and sure,
faithful to his people evermore.'

5 This was Mary's song as we recall,
mother to the saviour of us all:
magnify his name and sing his praise,
worship and adore him, all your days!

161B Bless the Lord

Words: from *Bless the Lord* derived from the Daily Office of the Joint Liturgical Group
Music: Chris Rolinson
arranged David Peacock

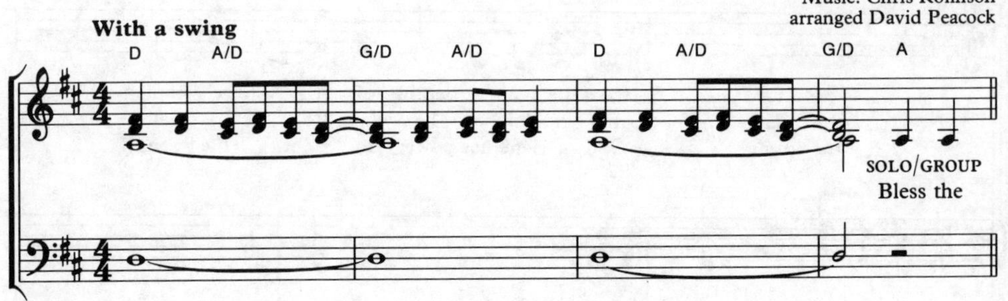

With a swing
D A/D G/D A/D D A/D G/D A
SOLO/GROUP
Bless the

D G/A D D/F♯
Lord the God of our fa - thers:
sits be - tween the che - ru - bim:
ALL
sing his

Em7 D/A G/A D
praise and ex - alt him for ev - er.
SOLO/GROUP
Bless his
Bless him

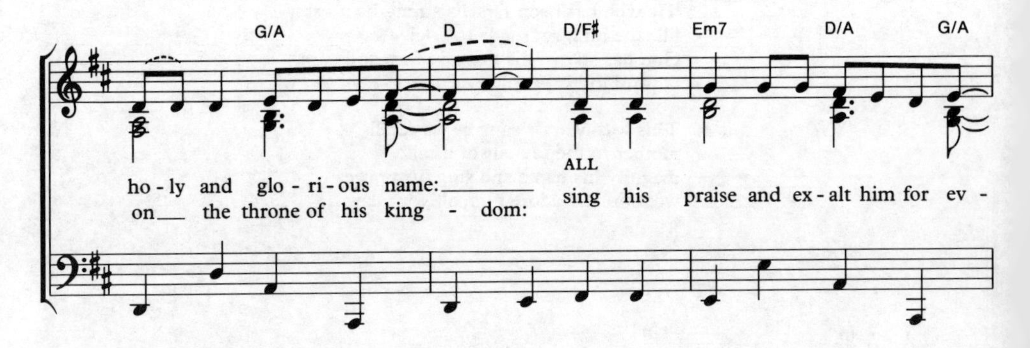

G/A D D/F♯ Em7 D/A G/A
ho - ly and glo - ri - ous name:
on the throne of his king - dom:
ALL
sing his praise and ex - alt him for ev -

Alternative setting: *Psalms for Today* 161B

D D/F♯ G D/F♯
SOLO/GROUP
- er. Bless him in his ho - ly and glo - ri - ous tem -
Bless him in the heights of hea -
2nd time to Coda
Em7 D/F♯ G D/F♯ Em7 D/F♯
ALL
- ple: sing his praise and ex - alt him for ev - er.
- ven:
SOLO/GROUP
Bless
Bless the
G A Bm Em7 D/A G/A
him who be - holds the depths:
ALL
sing his praise and ex - alt him for ev -
D
SOLO/GROUP
- er. Bless him who
CODA
G A Bm
Fa-ther, the Son and the Ho - ly
B♭ Em7 D/A G/A D
Spi - rit:
ALL
sing his praise and ex-alt him for ev - er.

162C Lord now you let your servant

Song of Simeon
Words: from Luke 2, The Song of Simeon/Nunc dimittis in The Alternative Service Book 1980
International Consultation on English Texts
Music: Andrew Maries
arranged David Peacock
Gentle and flowing
Capo 1(G)
F♯m (Em)
F♯m7 (Em7)
B/F♯ (A)
Bm/F♯ (Am)
p legato
con ped.
C♯m7/F♯ (Bm7)
Lord now you let your servant
My own eyes have seen the sal -
go in peace, your
- va - tion,
1.

F♯m
(Em)
E/F♯
(D)
F♯m
(Em)
C♯m
(Bm)
word has been ful - filled.
2.
C♯m/E
(Bm)
D
(C)
C♯m
(Bm)
Bm7
(Am7)
cresc.
which you have pre - pared in the sight of ev - ery
E
(D)
A
(G)
F♯m
(Em)
Bm
(Am)
F♯m
(Em)
f
peo - ple; a light to re - veal you to the
E
(D)
rit.
D
(C)
C♯m
(Bm)
Bm7
(Am7)
mp
na - tions: and the glo - ry of your
C♯m7
(Bm7)
F♯m
(Em)
E/F♯
(D)
Bm/F♯
(Am)
C♯m7
(Bm)
peo - ple Is - ra - el.

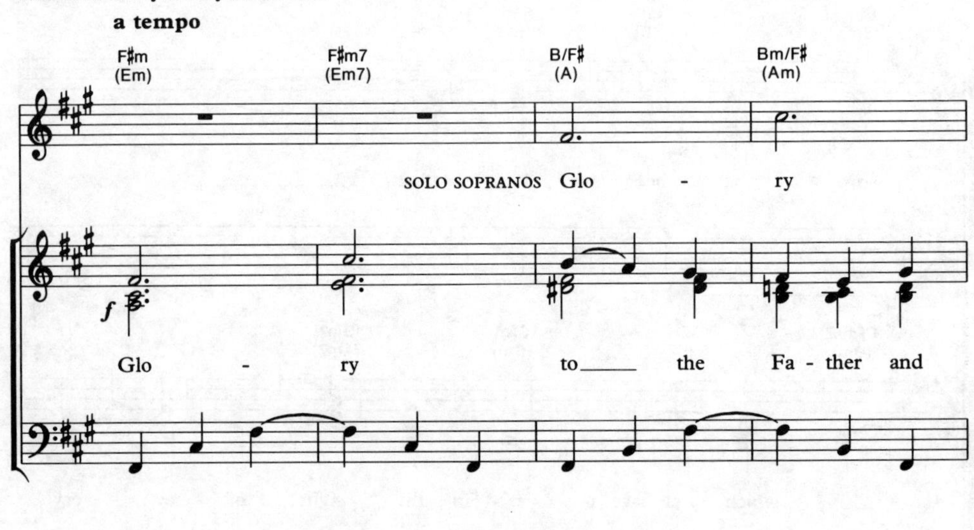
a tempo
F♯m
(Em)
F♯m7
(Em7)
B/F♯
(A)
Bm/F♯
(Am)
SOLO SOPRANOS Glo - ry
Glo - ry to the Fa - ther and

F♯m
(Em)
C♯m7/F♯
(Bm7)
F♯m
(Em)
C♯m7/F♯
(Bm7)
to the Fa - ther and to the
to the Son: and

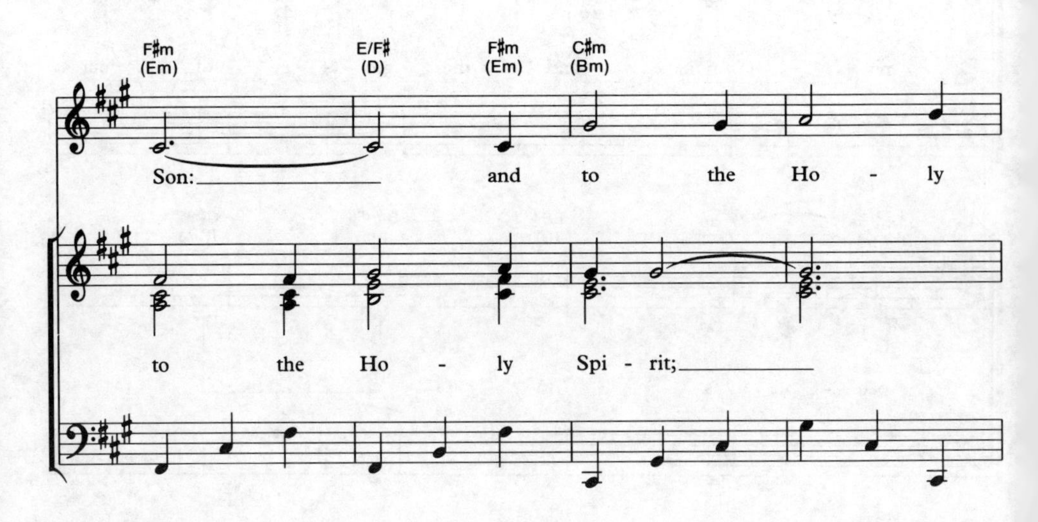
F♯m
(Em)
E/F♯
(D)
F♯m
(Em)
C♯m
(Bm)
Son: and to the Ho - ly
to the Ho - ly Spi - rit;

F♯m
(Em)
F♯m7
(Em7)
B/F♯
(A)
Bm/F♯
(Am)
Spi - rit;
as
it
as
it
was
in
the
be - gin - ning,
is
rit.
F♯m
(Em)
C♯m7/F♯
(Bm7)
F♯m
(Em)
C♯m7
(Bm7)
was
and
shall
be,
now:
and
shall
be
for
ev - er.
slowly
D
(C)
C♯m7
(Bm7)
F♯m
(Em)
pp
A - men, a - men.
pp
A - men, a - men.

162E Jesus, hope of every nation

Eversley

From Luke 2, *The Song of Simeon/Nunc dimittis*
Words and music: Michael Perry
Music arranged David Peacock

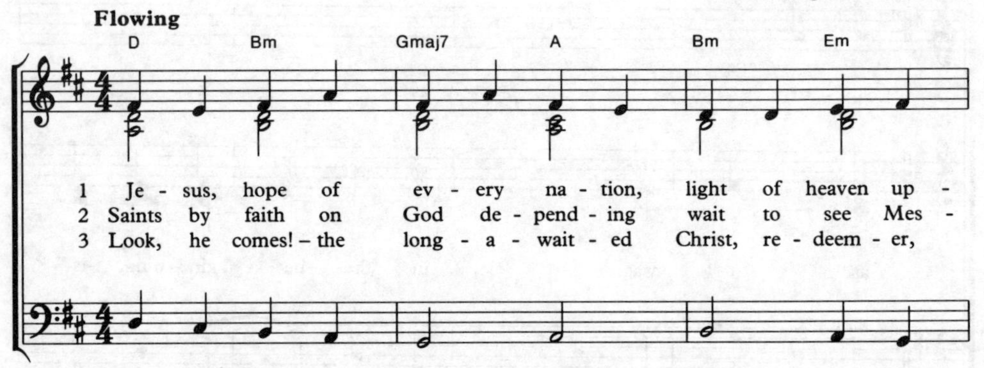

Flowing
D Bm Gmaj7 A Bm Em
1 Je - sus, hope of ev - ery na - tion, light of heaven up -
2 Saints by faith on God de - pend - ing wait to see Mes -
3 Look, he comes! – the long - a - wait - ed Christ, re - deem - er,

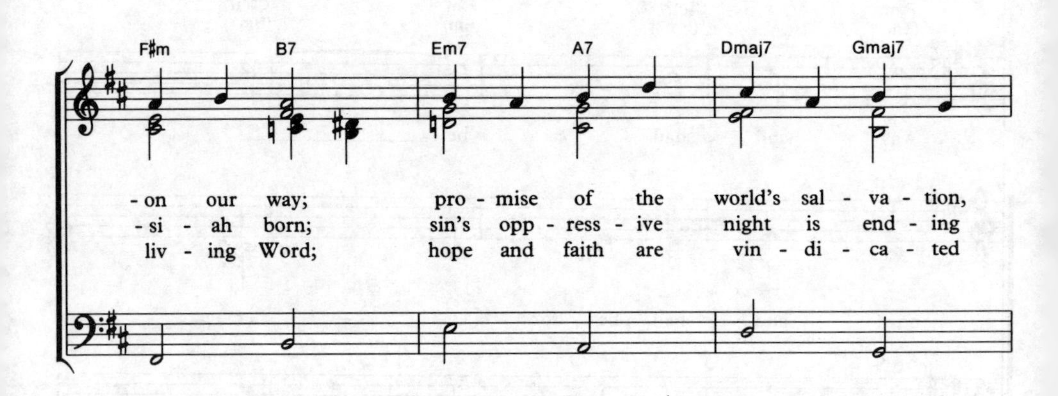

F♯m B7 Em7 A7 Dmaj7 Gmaj7
- on our way; pro - mise of the world's sal - va - tion,
- si - ah born; sin's opp - ress - ive night is end - ing
liv - ing Word; hope and faith are vin - di - ca - ted

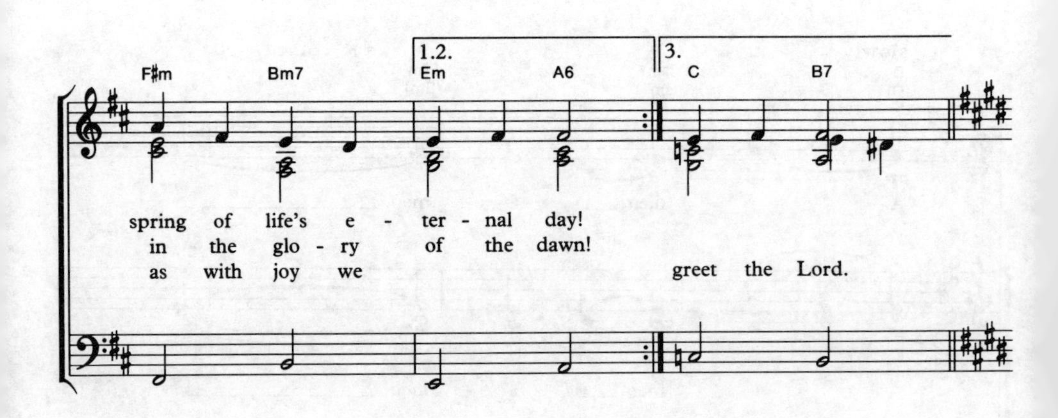

1.2. 3.
F♯m Bm7 Em A6 C B7
spring of life's e - ter - nal day!
in the glo - ry of the dawn!
as with joy we greet the Lord.

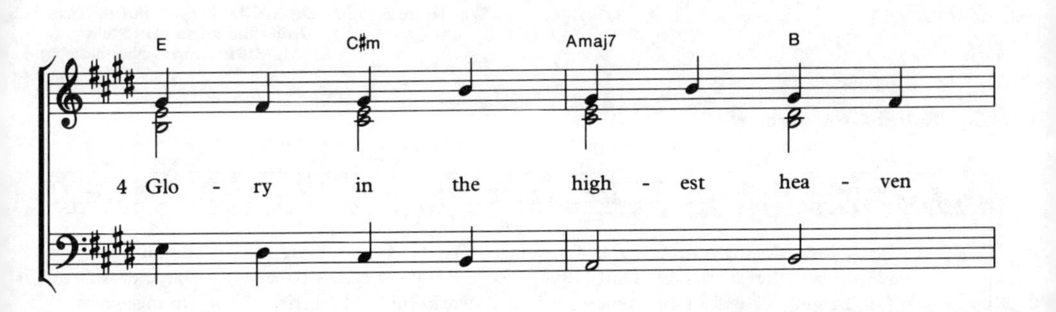
E C♯m Amaj7 B
4 Glo - ry in the high - est hea - ven

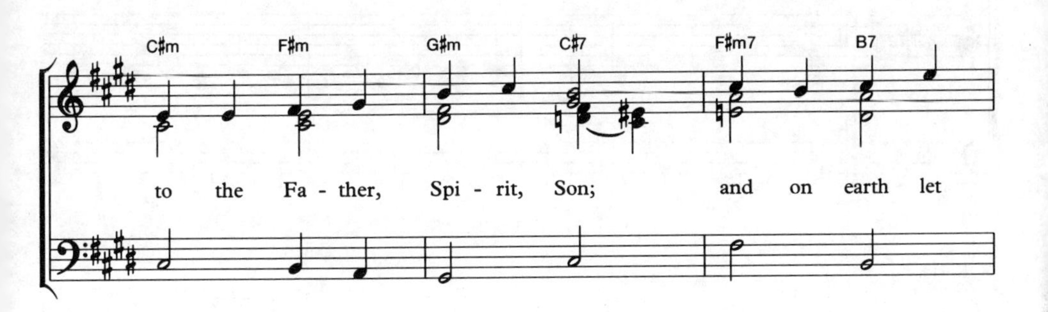
C♯m F♯m G♯m C♯7 F♯m7 B7
to the Fa - ther, Spi - rit, Son; and on earth let

Emaj7 Amaj7 G♯m7 C♯m7 F♯m/B B E
praise be gi - ven to our God, the Three - in - One!

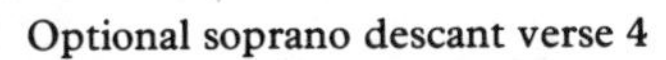
Optional soprano descant verse 4

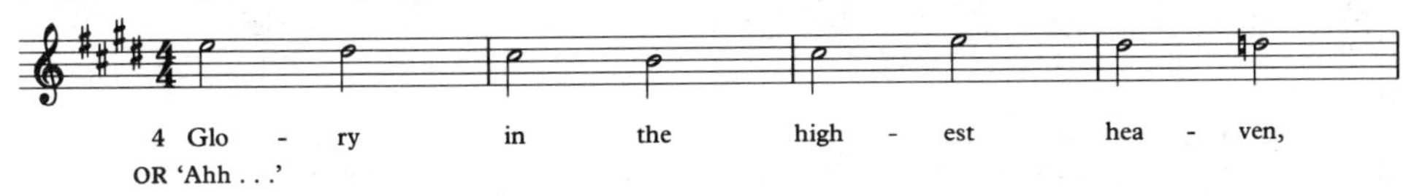
4 Glo - ry in the high - est hea - ven,
OR ‘Ahh . . .’

praise be gi - ven to our God, the Three - in - One!

163B(i) Before the heaven and earth

Words: from Philippians 2 *The Song of Christ's Glory*
Brian Black and Word & Music
Music: Christopher Norton

Calmly, but strong
Csus2 C Em7/B Am9 Am7 C7/G C7 Fsus2 F F/E B7/D♯
1 Be - fore the heaven and earth were made by God's de - cree, the Son of
(2) in the form of God and rich be - yond com - pare, he did not
(3) heights of heaven he came to this world full of sin, to meet with
mp
Em A7/C♯ Dm Eaug Dm7/F F/G G7
1–5.
Csus2 C F/G G7
6.
C
God all - glo - rious dwelt in God's e - ter - ni - ty. 2 Though Lord.
think to grasp his prize; nor did he lin - ger there. 3 From
hun - ger, ha - tred, hell – our life, our love to win. 4 The

4 The Son became true Man
and took a servant's role;
with lowliness and selfless love
he came, to make us whole.

5 Obedient to his death –
that death upon a cross,
no son had ever shown such love,
nor father known such loss.

6 To him enthroned on high,
by angel hosts adored,
all knees shall bow, and tongues confess
that Jesus Christ is Lord.

Before the heaven and earth 163B(ii)

Munden

Words: from Philippians 2, *The Song of Christ's Glory*
Brian Black and Word & Music
Music: David Peacock

Flowing
C
Bm
E7
Am7
1 Be - fore the heaven and earth were made by God's de -
2 Though in the form of God and rich be - yond com -
3 From heights of heaven he came to this world full of
F♯dim
B7
1–5.
Em
A7
Dm
G
C
D7
G
- cree, the Son of God all - glo-rious dwelt in God's e - ter - ni - ty.
- pare, he did not think to grasp his prize; nor did he lin - ger there.
sin, to meet with hun - ger, ha - tred, hell – our life, our love to win.
6.
Em
D7
G
Am
D9
D7
G
bow, and tongues con - fess that Je - sus Christ is Lord.

4 The Son became true Man
and took a servant's role;
with lowliness and selfless love
he came, to make us whole.

5 Obedient to his death –
that death upon a cross,
no son had ever shown such love,
nor father known such loss.

6 To him enthroned on high,
by angel hosts adored,
all knees shall bow, and tongues confess
that Jesus Christ is Lord.

163C Christ Jesus was in the form of God

Words: from Philippians 2, *Song of Christ's Glory*
Liturgy of the Church of South Africa
Music: Chris Rolinson
arranged David Peacock

Sensitively with feeling

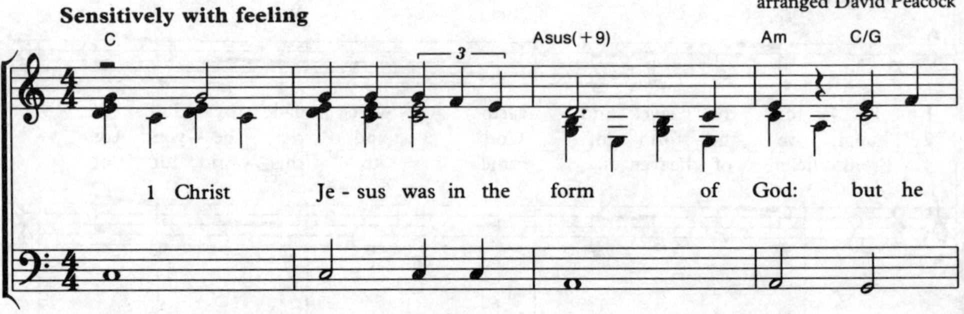

C
Asus(+9)
Am
C/G
1 Christ Je - sus was in the form of God: but he

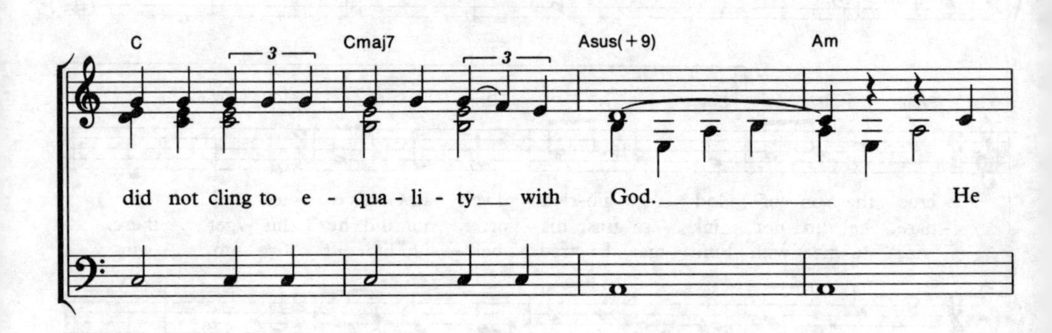

C
Cmaj7
Asus(+9)
Am
did not cling to e - qua - li - ty with God. He

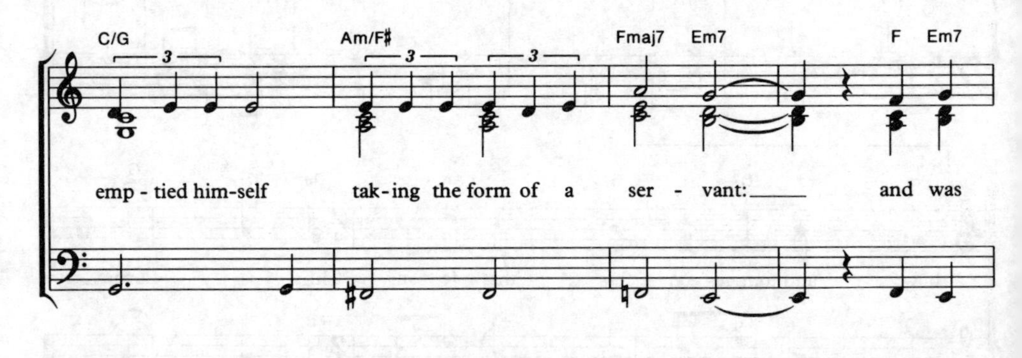

C/G
Am/F♯
Fmaj7
Em7
F
Em7
emp - tied him-self tak - ing the form of a ser - vant: and was

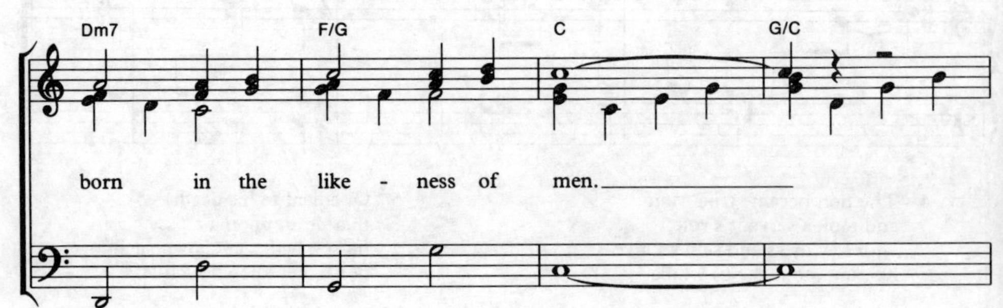

Dm7
F/G
C
G/C
born in the like - ness of men.

Alternative setting: *Psalms for Today* 163C

F/C
Esus
E7/G♯
Am
Em
Be-ing found in hu-man form he
Am
Em
Dm7
C/G
G
hum - bled him - self: and be - came ob-ed - ient un - to death ev - en
Dm7
F/G
G
C
3
death on a cross. 2 There-fore God has high-ly ex -
Asus(+9)
Am
C/G
C
Cmaj7
3
- alt - ed him: and be - stowed on him the name a - bove ev - ery
Asus(+9)
Am
C/G
Am/F♯
3
name, that at the name of Je - sus ev - er - y

163C Christ Jesus was in the form of God

Fmaj7
Em7
Dm7
F
Em
Dm7
F
knee should bow: in heaven and on earth and
F/G
Gsus
G
C
Esus
E7/G♯
un - der the earth;
Am
Em
Am
Em
and ev-ery tongue con - fess that Je - sus Christ is Lord: to the
Dm7
G
Dm7
Gsus
G
glo - ry of God the Fa - ther.
C
Asus(+9)
Am
C/G
3
3 Glo - ry to the Fa - ther and

C
Cmaj7
3
Asus(+9)
Am
to the Son: and to the Ho - ly Spi - rit; as it
C/G
Am/F♯
Fmaj7
Em7
F
Em
was in the be - gin - ning is now and
Dm
Em7
F
F/G
Am
Cmaj7/G
shall be for ev - er. A - - - -
Fmaj7
F6
C/E
Dm
F/G
- men. A - - - -
C
G/C
F/C
F/G
C
- men.

163E Down from the height

Slane

Words: from Philippians 2, *Song of Christ's Glory*
Michael Perry
Music: Irish traditional melody
arranged John Barnard

E A F♯m7 B C♯m E A6 E
1 Down from the height of his glo - ry he came,
2 All through those days his re - solve was the same –
3 Now God has grant - ed him hon - our and fame,
F♯m7 B A6 G♯m7 C♯m7 F♯m7 G♯m A B
will - ing - ly leav - ing his right - ful do - main:
Je - sus the ser - vant, the shar - er of pain:
tak - en him up to the high - est to reign:
C♯m/B F♯m E G♯m C♯m7 A G♯m/B A B
Je - sus was born in the im - age of man;
per - fect o - be - dience, the path of dis - dain,
'Je - sus is Lord!' ev - ery voice shall main - tain,
C♯m G♯m E A C♯m Emaj7/B A6 A A6 E
love was his mo - tive and mer - cy his aim.
down to a death of de - ri - sion and shame.
all of cre - a - tion shall bow to his name.

Glory and honour 164C

Words: from Revelation 4 and 5, *Glory and honour*
derived from the Daily Office
of the Joint Liturgical Group
Music: Chris Rolinson
arranged David Peacock

Not too fast but with bounce

D A Bm7 G9 A7 D A Bm7

G9 A7 D A Bm Bm/A G A/G

Glo - ry and hon - our and power_ are yours by right, O

F♯m7 Bm7 G A/G F♯m7 Bm7

Lord our God:_ for you cre - a - ted all__ things, and

Em7 D/A A Dsus D G/A

by your will they have_ their be - ing.________ Glo - ry and

D A Bm Bm/A G A/G

hon - our and power_ are yours by right, O

Alternative setting: *Psalms for Today* 164C

F♯m7
Bm7
G
A/G
F♯m7
Bm7
Lamb who was slain; for by your blood you ran - somed us for
Em7
G/A
A
A♯dim
Bm
God: from ev - ery race and lan-guage, from
A/C♯
D
G
ev - ery peo - ple and na - tion: to make us a
F♯m7
Bm
Bm/A
king - dom of priests to
optional repeat from 𝄋
G
F♯m7
Em
Asus
A
stand and serve be - fore our God.

D A Bm Bm/A G A/G
To_ him who sits on the throne and to the
F♯m7 Bm7 G A/G F♯m7 Bm7
Lamb, be praise and hon - our, glo - ry and might, for
Em7 D/A A7 Dsus D
ev - er and ev - er and ev - er.
C G/A D
A - - - men,
C G/A D
a - - - - men.

164D Glory and honour and power

Words: from Revelation 4 and 5, *Glory and honour* derived from the Daily Office of the Joint Liturgical Group
Music: Norman Warren

Brightly and rhythmically

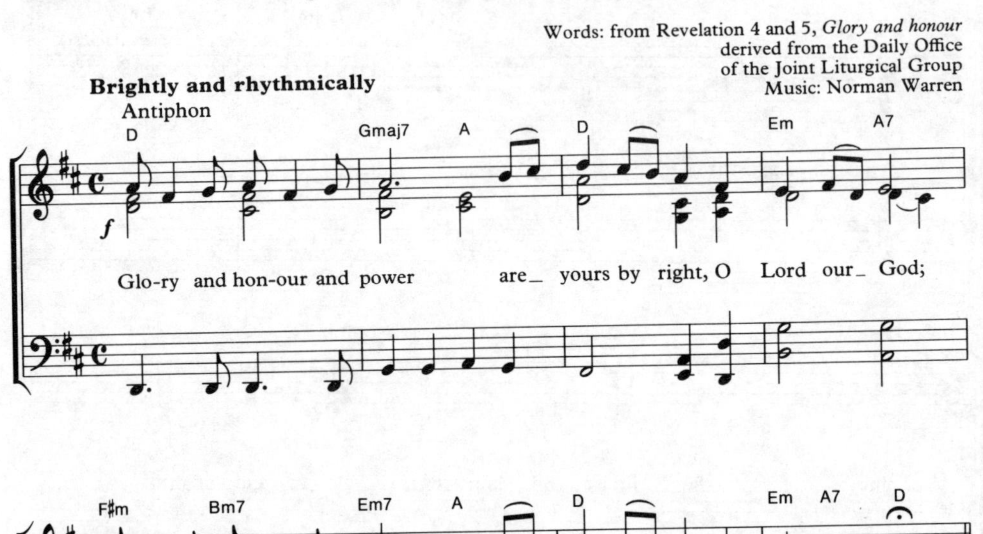
Antiphon
D
Gmaj7
A
D
Em
A7
f
Glo-ry and hon-our and power are_ yours by right, O Lord our_ God;

F♯m
Bm7
Em7
A
D
Em
A7
D
glo-ry and hon-our and power are_ yours by right, O Lamb that was slain:

1.
B♭
E♭
B♭
Dm
Gm
D/F♯
mf
For you cre - a - ted_ all things, and by your will they

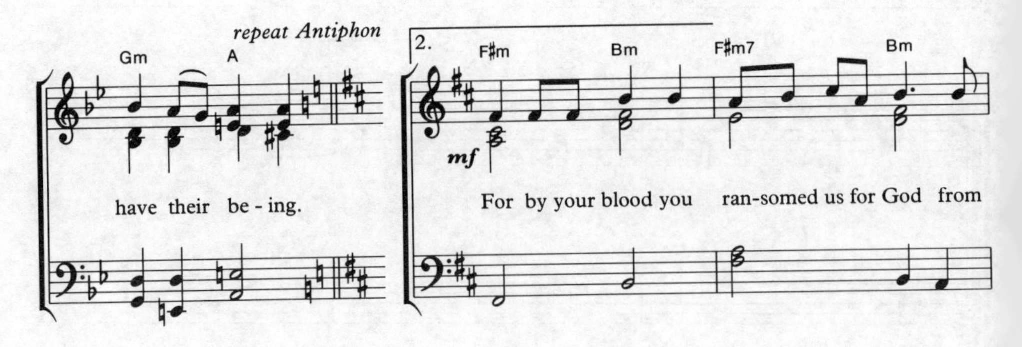
repeat Antiphon
Gm
A
have their be - ing.
2.
F♯m
Bm
F♯m7
Bm
mf
For by your blood you ran-somed us for God from

repeat Antiphon
G
D
Bm
F♯
A7
ev - ery race and lan - guage, from ev - ery peo - ple and na - tion:

3.
B♭
E♭
B♭
Dm
Gm
D/F♯
mf
to make us a king - dom of priests; to stand and serve be -

repeat Antiphon
Gm
A
4.
F♯m
Bm
F♯m7
Bm
f
- fore our_ God.
To him who sits on the throne and to the Lamb, be

repeat Antiphon
G
D
Bm7
F♯7
D/A
G/A
Asus
A7
praise and_ hon-our, glo - ry and might for ev - er and for_ ev - er!
allargando

164E Come and see the shining hope

Marching through Georgia

Words: from Revelation 4 and 5, *Glory and honour*
Christopher Idle
Music: American traditional melody
arranged David Wilson and David Peacock

G C G
1 Come and see the shin - ing hope that Christ's a - post - le saw;
2 All the gifts you send us, Lord, are faith - ful, good and true;
3 Po - wer and sal - va - tion all be - long to God on high!
C G/B Asus A Dsus D7
on the earth, con - fus - ion but in heaven an o - pen door,
ho - li - ness and right - eous - ness are shown in all you do:
So the migh - ty mul - ti - tudes of hea - ven make their cry,
G G7 C G Am7 B7/F♯ E7
where the liv - ing crea - tures praise the Lamb for ev - er - more:
who can see your great - est Gift and fail to wor - ship you?
sing - ing Al - le - lu - ia! where the ech - oes ne - ver die:
Am D7 Gsus G
Love has the vic - tory for ev - er!

Chorus
G/B
C
G
A - men, he comes! to bring his own re - ward! A -
Bm
Asus/E
A7
Dsus
D
- men, praise God! for jus - tice now re - stored;
G
G7
C/G
Am/F♯
Em7
Am/C
B
E7
king - doms of the world be - come the king - dom of the Lord:
Am7
D7
Gsus
G
Love has the vic - tory for ev - er!

164F Glory, glory, glory to the Lord

Words: from Revelation 4 and 5, *Glory and honour*
Michael Perry
Music: Unknown
arranged with descant Norman Warren

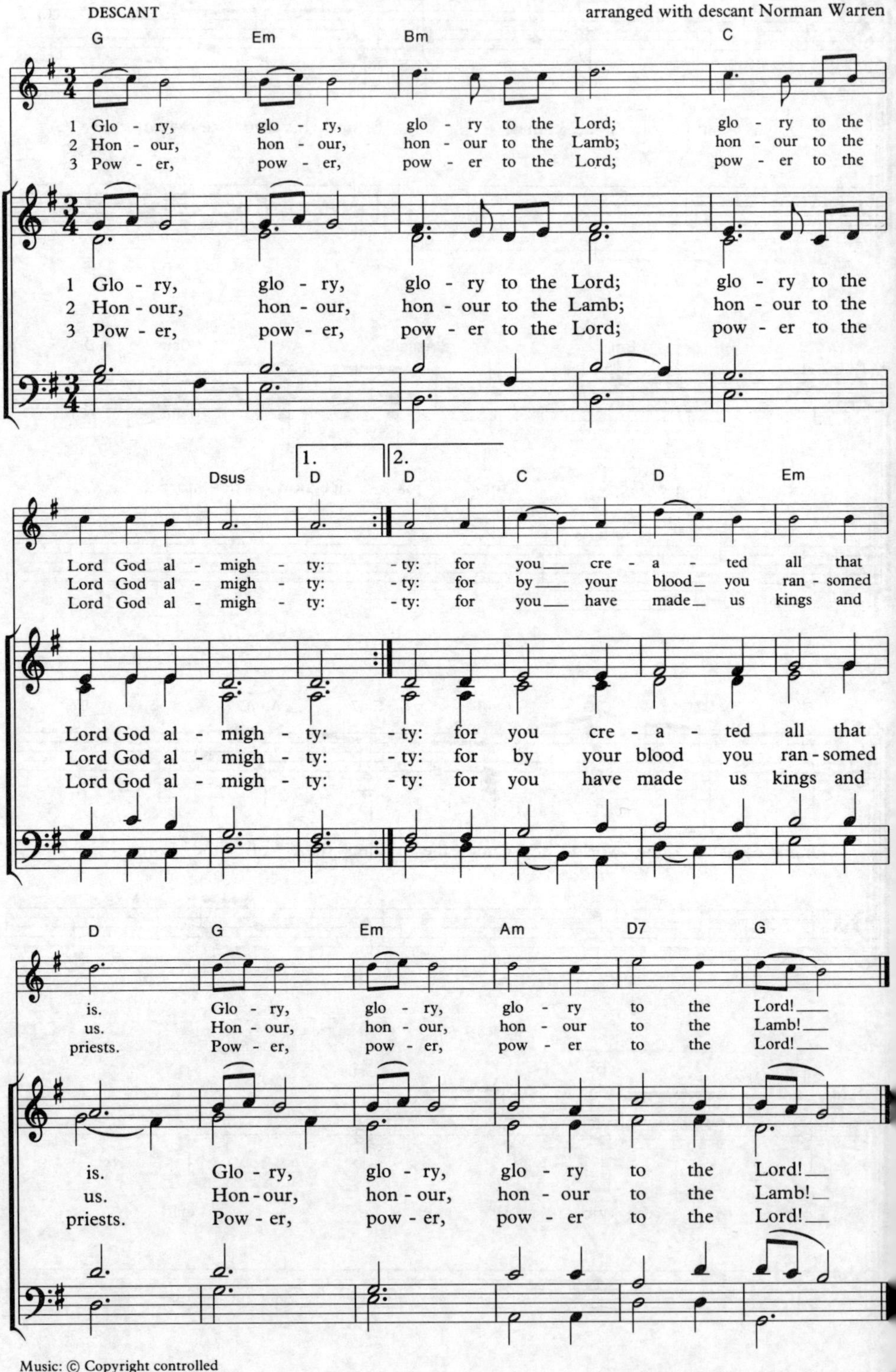

DESCANT

1 Glory, glory, glory to the Lord; glory to the Lord God almighty: (1.) -ty: (2.) -ty: for you created all that is. Glory, glory, glory to the Lord!

2 Honour, honour, honour to the Lamb; honour to the Lord God almighty: (1.) -ty: (2.) -ty: for by your blood you ransomed us. Honour, honour, honour to the Lamb!

3 Power, power, power to the Lord; power to the Lord God almighty: (1.) -ty: (2.) -ty: for you have made us kings and priests. Power, power, power to the Lord!

Glory to the Father

Words: from *Gloria*
Music: Geoff Twigg

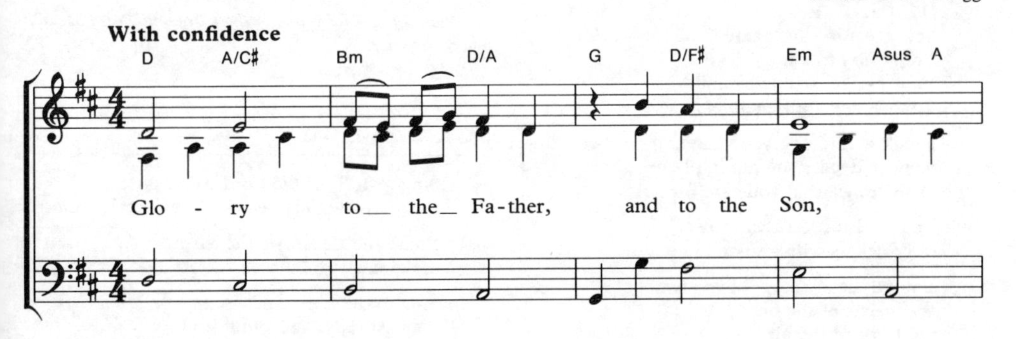
With confidence
D A/C♯ Bm D/A G D/F♯ Em Asus A
Glo - ry to the Fa-ther, and to the Son,

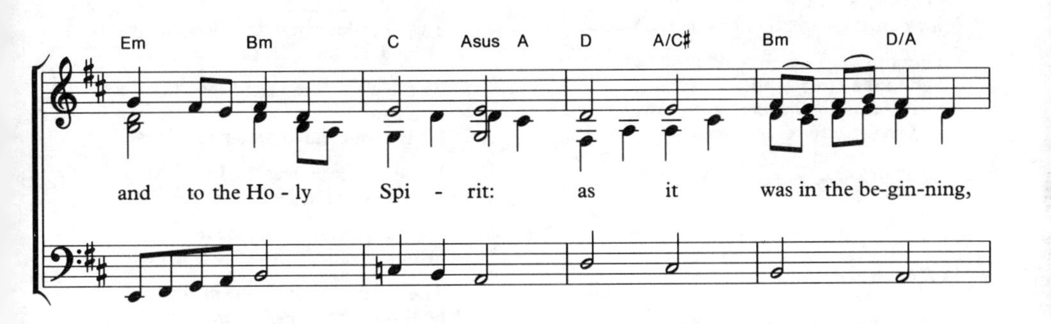
Em Bm C Asus A D A/C♯ Bm D/A
and to the Ho - ly Spi - rit: as it was in the be-gin-ning,

G D/F♯ Em7 D D/F♯ G F♯m7 Em7 Asus A
is now, and shall be for ev - er. A - - - - -

to repeat
D A/C♯ G D/A G/B A/C♯
- men.
to end
D A/C♯ G A G/B A/C♯ D
- men.

8L Psalm 8.1–9

O Lord, our Lord:
how great is your name in all the world!
A **Your glory fills the skies.**
B **Your praise is sung by children.**
C **You silence your enemies.**

I look at the sky your hands have made, the moon and stars you put in place:
ALL **Who are we that you care for us?**

You made us less than gods:
ALL **to crown us with glory and honour.**

You put us in charge of creation:
A **the beasts of the field.**
B **the birds of the air.**
C **the fish of the sea.**

O Lord, our Lord:
ALL **how great is your name in all the world!**

Glory to the Father, and to the Son,
and to the Holy Spirit:
as it was in the beginning, is now,
and shall be for ever. Amen.

The congregation may divide at A, B *and* C.

24L Psalm 24.1–10

The earth is the Lord's, and everything in it:
the world, and all who live here.

He founded it upon the seas:
and established it upon the waters.

E Who has the right to go up the Lord's hill;
who may enter his holy temple?
Those who have clean hands
and a pure heart,
who do not worship idols
or swear by what is false.

They receive blessing continually from the Lord:
and righteousness
from the God of their salvation.

Such are the people who seek for God:
who enter the presence of the God of Jacob.

D Fling wide the gates, open the ancient doors:
that the king of glory may come in.

E Who is the king of glory?
The Lord, strong and mighty,
the Lord mighty in battle.

D Fling wide the gates, open the ancient doors:
that the king of glory may come in.

E Who is he, this king of glory?
The Lord almighty,
he is the king of glory.

Glory to the Father, and to the Son,
and to the Holy Spirit:
as it was in the beginning, is now,
and shall be for ever. Amen.

E – *enquirer,* D – *director, or these lines may also be said by the minister.*

33L Psalm 33.1–22

Sing joyfully to the Lord, you righteous:
it is right that his people should praise him.

Praise the Lord with the harp:
A **make music to him on the strings.**

Sing to the Lord a new song:
B **play skilfully, and shout for joy.**

For the word of the Lord is right and true:
ALL **and all his work is faithfulness.**

The Lord loves righteousness and justice:
A **his endless love fills the earth.**

By the word of the Lord the skies were formed:
B **his breath created moon and stars.**

Let all the earth fear the Lord:
ALL **the people of the world revere him.**

For he spoke, and it came to be:
A **he commanded, and all was made.**

The Lord holds back the nations:
B **he thwarts their evil intent.**

God's purposes are sure:
ALL **his plans endure for ever.**

Happy is the nation whose God is the Lord:
A **happy the people he makes his own.**

The eyes of the Lord are on those who fear him:
B **who trust in his unfailing love.**

We wait in hope for the Lord:
A **he is our help and shield.**

In him our hearts rejoice:
B **we trust his holy name.**

May your constant love be with us, Lord:
ALL **as we put our hope in you. Amen.**

The congregation – and ministers – may divide at A *and* B.

36L Psalm 36.5–9

Your love, O Lord, reaches the heavens:
A **your faithfulness extends to the skies.**

Your righteousness is towering like the mountains:
B **your justice is like the great deep.**

How precious is your love, O God:
A **we find shelter beneath your wings!**

We feast on the food you provide:
B **we drink from the river of your goodness:**

For with you is the fountain of life:
ALL **in your light we see light. Amen.**

The congregation – and ministers – may divide at A *and* B.

40L(i) Psalm 40.1–3

I waited patiently for the Lord:
he turned and heard my cry.

He pulled me out of the slimy pit:
out of the mud and mire.

He set my feet upon a rock:
and made my step secure.

He put a new song in my mouth:
a hymn of praise to God.

Many will see it and fear;
and put their trust in the Lord. Amen.

40L(ii) Psalm 40.4–16

Happy are those who trust in God:
who do not worship idols.

Sacrifice and offering you do not desire:
A **but you want my ears to be open.**

So I said, 'Lord I come:
B **obedient to your word.'**

I delight to do your will, O God:
A **and keep your teaching in my heart.**

I'll tell the world your saving news:
B **you know my lips will not be sealed.**

I have not hid your righteousness:
A **but speak of all your salvation, Lord.**

I do not hide your faithful love:
B **but share your mercy with them all.**

May all who come to you be glad; may all who know your saving power for ever say:
ALL **How great is the Lord! Amen.**

The congregation – and ministers – may divide at A *and* B.

46L Psalm 46.1–11

God is our refuge and strength:
an ever-present help in trouble.

Therefore we will not fear:
A **though the earth should shake,**
B **though the mountains fall into the sea,**
A **though the waters surge and foam,**
B **though the mountains shake and roar.**

The Lord almighty is with us:
ALL **the God of Jacob is our fortress.**

There is a river whose streams make glad the city of God: the holy place where the Most High dwells.
A **God is within her, she will not fall:**
B **God will help her at break of day.**

Nations are in uproar, kingdoms fall:
A **God lifts his voice –**
B **the earth melts away.**

The Lord Almighty is with us:
ALL **the God of Jacob is our fortress.**

Come and see what God has done:
ALL **his devastation on the earth!**

He stops the wars throughout the world:
A **he breaks the bow and shatters the spear –**
B **he sets the shield on fire.**

V Be still, and know that I am God: I will be exalted over the nations, I will be exalted over the earth.

The Lord Almighty is with us:
ALL **the God of Jacob is our fortress. Amen.**

The congregation may divide at A *and* B*;* V *can be a distant voice, or said by the minister.*

47L Psalm 47.1–9

Clap your hands, all you nations:
shout to God with cries of joy.

How awesome is the Lord most high:
A **the King who rules the whole wide earth!**

God has ascended to his throne:
B **with shouts of joy and sound of trumpets.**

Sing praises to our God, sing praises:
A **sing praises to our King, sing praises.**

For God is King of all the earth:
B **sing to him a psalm of praise.**

God is seated on his throne:
A **he rules the nations of the world.**

The leaders of the nations come:
B **as subjects of our holy God.**

The lords of earth belong to God:
ALL **he reigns supreme. Amen.**

The congregation may divide at A *and* B.

51L Psalm 51.6–12, and Psalm 143.6–10

O Lord, I spread my hands out to you:
A **I thirst for you like dry ground.**

Teach me to do your will, for you are my God:
B **let your good Spirit lead me in safety.**

You require sincerity and truth in me:
A **fill my mind with your wisdom.**

Create in me a pure heart, O God:
B **renew a faithful spirit in me.**

Do not cast me from your presence:
A **or take your Holy Spirit from me.**

Give me again the joy of your salvation:
B **and make me willing to obey.**

Glory to the Father, and to the Son,
and to the Holy Spirit:
as it was in the beginning, is now,
and shall be for ever. Amen.

The congregation may divide at A *and* B, *in which case the* Gloria *should be used. Psalms 51 and 143 have been grouped together to provide for an occasion when the person and work of the Holy Spirit is being considered.*

65L Psalm 65.1–13

O God, it is right for us to praise you, because you answer our prayers:

You care for the land and water it:
A **and make it rich and fertile.**

You fill the running streams with water:
B **and irrigate the land.**

You soften the ground with showers:
A **and make the young crops grow.**

You crown the year with goodness:
B **and give us a plentiful harvest.**

The pastures are filled with flocks:
A **the hillsides are clothed with joy.**

The fields are covered with grain:
ALL **they shout for joy and sing.**

Glory to the Father, and to the Son,
and to the Holy Spirit:
as it was in the beginning, is now,
and shall be for ever. Amen.

The congregation may divide at A *and* B.

66L Psalm 66.1–20

Praise your God with shouts of joy:
all the earth, sing praise to him.

Sing the glory of his name:
A **offer him your highest praise.**

Say to him: How great you are:
B **wonderful the things you do!**

All your enemies bow down:
C **all the earth sings praise to you.**

Come and see what God has done:
A **causing mortal men to fear –**
B **for he turned the sea to land,**
C **let his people safely through.**

We rejoice at what he does –
A **ruling through eternity,**
B **watching over all the world,**
C **keeping every rebel down.**

Praise our God, you nations, praise:
A **let the sound of praise be heard!**
B **God sustains our very lives:**
C **keeps our feet upon the way.**

Once, you tested us, O God –
A **silver purified by fire –**

Let us fall into a trap,
B **placed hard burdens on our backs –**

Sent us through the flame and flood:
C **now you bring us safely home.**

I will come to worship you:
A **bring to you my offering,**
B **give you what I said I would,**
C **when the troubles threatened me.**

All who love and honour God:
A **come and listen, while I tell**
B **what great things he did for me**
C **when I cried to him for help,**
A **when I praised him with my songs.**
B **When my heart was free from sin,**
C **then he listened to my prayer.**

Praise the Lord who heard my cry:
ALL **God has shown his love to me! Amen.**

The congregation may divide at A, B *and* C.

67L Psalm 67.1–7

May God be gracious to us and bless us:
A **and make his face to shine upon us.**

Let your ways be known upon earth:
B **your saving grace to every nation.**

Let the peoples praise you, O God:
ALL **let the peoples praise you.**

Let the nations be glad:
A **and sing aloud for joy.**

Because you judge the peoples justly:
B **and guide the nations of the earth.**

Let the peoples praise you, O God:
ALL **let all the peoples praise you.**

Then the land will yield its harvest:
A **and God, our God, will bless us.**

God will bless us:
B **and people will fear him**
ALL **to the ends of the earth. Amen.**

Glory to the Father, and to the Son,
and to the Holy Spirit:
as it was in the beginning, is now,
and shall be for ever. Amen.

The congregation may divide at A *and* B.

80L Psalm 80.1–19

A Hear us, O Shepherd of Israel, leader of your flock.

B Hear us from your throne above the cherubim.

C Shine forth, awaken your strength, and come to save us.
Bring us back, O God, and save us,
make your face to shine upon us.

A O Lord God almighty, how long will you be angry with your people's prayers?

B You have given us sorrow to eat and tears to drink.

C You have made us a source of contention to our neighbours, and our enemies insult us.
Bring us back, O God, and save us,
make your face to shine upon us.

A Return to us, O God Almighty, look down from heaven and see.

B Look on this vine that you planted with your own hand, this child you raised for yourself.

C Let your hand rest upon the people you have chosen, then we will not turn away from you; revive us, and we shall praise your name.
Bring us back, O God, and save us,
make your face to shine upon us.

Glory to the Father, and to the Son,
and to the Holy Spirit:
as it was in the beginning, is now,
and shall be for ever. Amen.

Ministers/leaders may divide at A, B *and* C.

93L Psalm 93.1–5

The Lord reigns, robed in majesty:
A **he arms himself with power.**

The earth is firmly set in place:
B **it never can be moved.**

Your throne was founded long ago:
A **before all time began.**

The oceans raise their voice, O Lord:
B **and lift their roaring waves.**

The Lord is mightier than the sea:
A **he rules supreme on high.**

His laws stand firm through endless days:
B **his praise for evermore.**
ALL **Amen.**

Glory to the Father, and to the Son,
and to the Holy Spirit:
as it was in the beginning, is now,
and shall be for ever. Amen.

The congregation may divide at A *and* B.

95L Psalm 95.1–7

M Come, let's joyfully praise our God, acclaiming the Rock of our salvation.

N Come before him with thanksgiving, and greet him with melody.

A **Our God is a great God –**
B **a king above all other gods.**

A **The depths of the earth are in his hands –**
B **the mountain peaks belong to him.**

A **The sea is his – he made it!**
B **His own hands prepared the land.**

M Come, bow down to worship him;
N kneel before the Lord who made us.

A&B **We are his people,**
the sheep of his flock.

M&N You shall know his power today –
N if you listen to his voice.

Glory to the Father, and to the Son,
and to the Holy Spirit:
as it was in the beginning, is now,
and shall be for ever. Amen.

The congregation may divide at A *and* B, *the ministers at* M *and* N.

96L Psalm 96.1–13

Sing to the Lord a new song:
A **sing to the Lord, all the earth.**

Sing to the Lord, praise his name:
B **proclaim his salvation each day.**

Declare his glory among the nations:
A **his marvellous deeds among the peoples.**

Great is the Lord, and worthy of praise:
B **honour him above all gods.**

Splendour and majesty surround him:
A **power and beauty fill his temple.**

Praise the Lord all people on earth:
B **praise his glory and might.**

Give him the glory due to his name:
A **bring an offering into his temple.**

Worship the Lord in his beauty and holiness:
B **tremble before him all the earth.**

Say to the nations:
ALL **The Lord is king!**

Let the heavens rejoice and the earth be glad:
A **let all creation sing for joy.**

For God shall come to judge the world:
B **and rule the people with his truth.**
ALL **Amen.**

The congregation may divide at A *and* B.

97L Psalm 97.1–12

The Lord is king:
the Lord is king!

Let the whole wide earth rejoice:
A **let the islands all be glad.**

Thunder-clouds encircle him:
B **truth and justice are his throne.**

Fire shall go before the Lord:
C **burning up his enemies.**

Lightning strikes the darkened world:
A **all the people see and fear.**

Mountains melt before our God:
B **he is Lord of all the earth.**

Skies proclaim his righteousness:
C **nations see his glory now.**

Idol-worshippers are shamed:
A **gods bow down before the Lord.**

Let Jerusalem rejoice:
B **in your faithful judgements, Lord!**

Sovereign of the universe:
C **mightier still than all the gods!**

Yet you help your saints, O Lord:
A **saving them from wicked men.**

Light will shine upon the good:
B **gladness fill the righteous heart.**

Now recall what God has done:
C **thank him,**
B **praise him,**
ALL **and rejoice!**

Glory to the Father, and to the Son,
and to the Holy Spirit:
as it was in the beginning, is now,
and shall be for ever. Amen.

The congregation may divide at A, B *and* C.

98L Psalm 98.1–9

Sing to the Lord a new song:
for he has done marvellous things.

His right hand and his holy arm:
have brought a great triumph to us.

A **He lets his salvation be known:**
B **his righteousness seen by the world.**
A **To us he continues his love:**
B **his glory is witnessed by all.**

Shout for joy to the Lord, all the earth:
ALL **and burst into jubilant song.**

A **Make music to God with the harp:**
B **with songs and the sound of your praise.**
A **With trumpets and blast of the horn:**
B **sing praises to God as your king.**

Let rivers and streams clap their hands:
ALL **the mountains together sing praise.**

The Lord comes to judge the whole earth:
in righteousness God rules the world. Amen.

The congregation may divide at A *and* B.

99L Psalm 99.1–9

The Lord reigns:
A **let the nations tremble!**

He sits enthroned on high:
B **let the earth shake!**

Great is the Lord our God:
ALL **exalted over all the world.**

Let the nations praise his awesome name, and say:
A **God is holy!**

Praise the Lord our God, and worship at his feet:
B **God is holy!**

Exalt the Lord our God, and worship on his holy mountain:
ALL **The Lord our God is holy!**

Glory to the Father, and to the Son,
and to the Holy Spirit:
as it was in the beginning, is now,
and shall be for ever. Amen.

The congregation may divide at A *and* B.

100L Psalm 100.1–5

Rejoice in the Lord, all the earth:
worship the Lord with gladness.

Remember the Lord is our God:
A **we are his flock and he made us.**

Come to his temple with praise:
B **enter his gates with thanksgiving.**

The love of the Lord will not fail:
God will be faithful for ever. Amen.

The congregation may divide at A *and* B.

103L Psalm 103.1–22

Praise the Lord, my soul:
A **all my being, praise his holy name!**

Praise the Lord, my soul:
B **and do not forget how generous he is.**

A **He forgives all my sins:**
B **and heals all my diseases.**
A **He keeps me from the grave:**
B **and blesses me with love and mercy.**

The Lord is gracious and compassionate:
A **slow to become angry,**
B **and full of constant love.**

He does not keep on rebuking:
A **he is not angry for ever.**

He does not punish us as we deserve:
B **or repay us for our wrongs.**

As far as the east is from the west:
A **so far does he remove our sins from us.**

As kind as a Father to his children:
B **so kind is the Lord to those who honour him.**

Praise the Lord, all his creation:
ALL **praise the Lord, my soul! Amen.**

The congregation may divide at A *and* B.

104L Psalm 104.1–4, 29–30

O Lord our God, you are very great:
you are clothed with splendour and majesty.

You make winds your messengers:
A **and flashes of fire your servants.**

How many are your works:
B **the earth is full of your creatures!**

When you hide your face, they are afraid:
A **when you take away their breath, they die.**

When you send your Spirit they are created:
B **and you renew the face of the earth.**

Glory to the Father, and to the Son,
and to the Holy Spirit:
as it was in the beginning, is now,
and shall be for ever. Amen.

The congregation may divide at A *and* B, *in which case the* Gloria *should be used.*

105L Psalm 105.1–45

Give thanks to the Lord, praise his name:
A **tell the nations what he has done.**

Sing to him, sing praise to him:
B **tell of all his wonderful deeds.**

Glory in his holy name:
C **let all who worship him rejoice.**

Go to the Lord for help:
A **and worship him for ever.**

Remember the wonders he does:
B **the miracles he performs.**

He is the Lord our God:
C **he judges the whole wide earth.**

He keeps his word and covenant:
A **for a thousand generations.**

The covenant he made with Abraham:
B **the oath he swore to Israel.**

He brought them out of Egypt:
C **and none of them was lost.**

He gave a cloud for covering:
A **a pillar of fire by night.**

He gave them bread from heaven:
B **and water from the rock.**

He brought his people out rejoicing:
C **his chosen ones with shouts of joy.**

ALL **Praise the Lord!**

Glory to the Father, and to the Son,
and to the Holy Spirit:
as it was in the beginning, is now,
and shall be for ever. Amen.

The congregation – and ministers/leaders – may divide at A, B *and* C.

107L Psalm 107.1–31

Give thanks to the Lord, for he is good:
his love endures for ever.

Repeat these words in praise to the Lord:
all those he has redeemed.

Some sailed the ocean in ships:
A **they earned their way on the seas.**

They saw what the Lord can do:
B **his wonderful deeds in the deep.**

For he spoke and stirred up a storm:
A **and lifted high the waves.**

Their ships were thrown in the air:
B **and plunged into the depths.**

Their courage melted away:
A **they reeled like drunken men.**

They came to the end of themselves:
B **and cried to the Lord in their trouble.**

He brought them out of distress:
A **and stilled the raging storm.**

They were glad because of the calm:
B **he brought them safely to harbour.**

Let them give thanks to the Lord:
ALL **for his unfailing love.**

Glory to the Father, and to the Son,
and to the Holy Spirit:
as it was in the beginning, is now,
and shall be for ever. Amen.

The congregation may divide at A *and* B.

111L Psalm 111.1–10

Praise the Lord:
praise the Lord!

With my whole heart I will thank the Lord: in the company of his people. Great are the works of the Lord:
A **those who wonder, seek them.**

Glorious and majestic are his deeds:
B **his goodness lasts for ever.**

He reminds us of his works of grace:
A **he is merciful and kind.**

He sustains those who fear him:
B **he keeps his covenant always.**

All he does is right and just:
A **all his words are faithful.**

They will last for ever and ever:
B **and be kept in faith and truth.**

He provided redemption for his people, and made an eternal covenant with them:
ALL **holy and awesome is his name!**

The fear of the Lord is the beginning of wisdom; he gives understanding to those who obey:
ALL **to God belongs eternal praise!**

Glory to the Father, and to the Son,
and to the Holy Spirit:
as it was in the beginning, is now,
and shall be for ever. Amen.

The congregation may divide at A *and* B.

113L Psalm 113.1–9

A Praise the Lord:
praise the Lord!

B You servants of the Lord, praise his name:
let the name of the Lord be praised,
both now and for evermore!

A From the rising of the sun to the place where it sets:
the name of the Lord be praised!

B The Lord is exalted above the earth:
his glory over the heavens.

A Who is like the Lord our God?
He is throned in the heights above –

B Yet he bends down:
yet he stoops to look at our world.

A He raises the poor from the dust:
and lifts the needy from their sorrow.

B He honours the childless wife in her home:
he makes her happy, the mother of children.

BOTH Praise the Lord:
Amen.

The ministers/leaders may divide at A *and* B.

116L Psalm 116.1–19

I love the Lord because he heard my voice:
A **the Lord in mercy listened to my prayers.**

Because the Lord has turned his ear to me:
B **I'll call on him as long as I shall live.**

The cords of death entangled me around:
C **the horrors of the grave came over me.**

But then I called upon the Lord my God:
A **I said to him: 'O Lord, I beg you, save!'**

The Lord our God is merciful and good:
B **the Lord protects the simple-hearted ones.**

The Lord saved me from death and stopped my tears:
C **he saved me from defeat and picked me up.**

And so I walk before him all my days:
A **and live to love and praise his holy name.**

What shall I give the Lord for all his grace?
B **I'll take his saving cup, and pay my vows.**

Within the congregation of his saints:
C **I'll offer him my sacrifice of praise.**

Praise the Lord:
ALL **Amen, amen!**

The congregation may divide at A, B *and* C.

117L Psalm 117.1–2

Praise the Lord, all you nations:
A **praise him, all you people!**

Great is his love towards us:
B **his faithfulness shall last for ever.**

Praise the Lord:
Amen.

The congregation may divide at A *and* B.

118L Psalm 118.1–29

M Give thanks to the Lord, for he is good:
his love endures for ever.

M All those who fear the Lord shall say:
His love endures for ever.

W Open for me the gates of the Temple; I will go in and give thanks to the Lord.

M This is the gate of the Lord, only the righteous can come in.

W I will give thanks because you heard me; you have become my salvation.

C The stone which the builders rejected as worthless turned out to be the most important of all
ALL **The Lord has done this – what a wonderful sight it is!**

W This is the day of the Lord's victory – let us be happy, let us celebrate:
ALL **O Lord save us – O Lord, grant us success.**

M May God bless the one who comes in the name of the Lord:
ALL **The Lord is God – he has been good to us!**

C From the Temple of the Lord, we bless you.

D With branches in your hands, start the procession and march round the altar:

W You are my God and I will give you thanks:
ALL **You are my God, and I will exalt you.**

M Give thanks to the Lord, for he is good:
His love endures for ever. Amen.

M – *minister,* W – *worshipper – from doorway, then moving through congregation,* C – *choir/chorus,* D – *director – in matter-of-fact tone.*

122L Psalm 122.1–8

I was glad when they said to me:
let us go to the house of the Lord!

Pray for the peace of Jerusalem:
A **may those who love our land be blessed.**

May there be peace in your homes:
B **and safety for our families.**

For the sake of those we love we say:
ALL **Let there be peace! Amen.**

Glory to the Father, and to the Son,
and to the Holy Spirit:
as it was in the beginning, is now,
and shall be for ever. Amen.

The congregation may divide at A *– male voices, and* B *– female voices.*

124L Psalm 124.1–8

If the Lord had not been on our side – now let Israel say:
If the Lord had not been on our side –
A **when enemies attacked us,**
B **when their anger flared against us,**
C **they would have swallowed us alive.**
A **The flood would have engulfed us,**
B **the torrent would have swept over us,**
C **the waters would have drowned us.**

Praise the Lord:
A **who has not given us up to their teeth.**
B **We have escaped like a bird from the snare:**
C **the snare is broken and we are free.**

Our help is in the name of the Lord:
ALL **who made heaven and earth. Amen.**

The congregation may divide at A, B *and* C.

126L Psalm 126.1–6

When the Lord brought us back from slavery:
A **we were like those who dream.**

Our mouths were filled with laughter:
B **our tongues with songs of joy.**

Then those around us said, 'The Lord has done great things for them':
A **The Lord has done great things for us,**
and we are filled with joy.

Those who sow in tears
B **shall reap with songs of joy.**

Glory to the Father, and to the Son,
and to the Holy Spirit:
as it was in the beginning, is now,
and shall be for ever. Amen.

The congregation may divide at A *and* B, *in which case the* Gloria *should be used.*

128L Psalm 128.1–6

The pilgrims' song:
A **Blessed are those who fear the Lord,**
B **who walk in his ways.**

You will eat the fruit of your work; blessings and prosperity will be yours:
A **Blessed are those who fear the Lord,**
B **who walk in his ways.**

Your wife will be like a fruitful vine within your house; your children will be like young olive trees around your table:
A **Blessed are those who fear the Lord,**
B **who walk in his ways.**

May the Lord bless you all the days of your life; may you have prosperity; may you live to see your children's children:
ALL **Peace be with you. Amen.**

The congregation may divide at A *and* B.

134L Psalm 134.1–3

You servants of the Lord,
who stand in his temple at night:
A **praise the Lord!**

Lift your hands in prayer to the Lord:
B **in his sanctuary, praise the Lord!**

May the Lord who made the heaven and earth bless you from Zion:
ALL **Amen!**

Glory to the Father, and to the Son,
and to the Holy Spirit:
as it was in the beginning, is now,
and shall be for ever. Amen.

The congregation may divide at A *and* B, *in which case the* Gloria *should be used.*

136L Psalm 136.1–26

A Give thanks to God, for he is good:
A **his love shall last for ever!**

B Give thanks to him, the God of gods:
B **his love shall last for ever!**

C Give thanks to him, the Lord of lords:
C **his love shall last for ever!**

A For God alone works miracles:
A **his love shall last for ever!**

B The skies were made at his command:
B **his love shall last for ever!**

C He spread the seas upon the earth:
C **his love shall last for ever!**

A He made the stars to shine at night:
A **his love shall last for ever!**

B He made the sun to shine by day:
B **his love shall last for ever!**

C He brought us out from slavery:
C **his love shall last for ever!**

A He leads us onward by his grace:
A **his love shall last for ever!**

B He saves us from our enemies:
B **his love shall last for ever!**

C Give thanks to God, for he is good:
C **his love shall last for ever!**
ALL **Amen!**

The congregation must *divide at* A, B *and* C *saying the whole stanza, OR both ministers* and *congregation should divide.*

143L Psalm 143.6–10, and Psalm 51.6–12

O Lord, I spread my hands out to you:
A **I thirst for you like dry ground.**

Teach me to do your will, for you are my God:
B **let your good Spirit lead me in safety.**

You require sincerity and truth in me:
A **fill my mind with your wisdom.**

Create in me a pure heart, O God:
B **and renew a faithful spirit in me.**

Do not cast me from your presence:
A **or take your Holy Spirit from me.**

Give me again the joy of your salvation:
B **and make me willing to obey.**

Glory to the Father, and to the Son,
and to the Holy Spirit:
as it was in the beginning, is now,
and shall be for ever. Amen.

The congregation may divide at A *and* B, *in which case the* Gloria *should be used. Psalms 143 and 51 have been grouped together to provide for an occasion when the person and work of the Holy Spirit is being considered.*

147L Psalm 147.1–20

O praise the Lord, sing out to God:
such praise is right and good.

The Lord restores Jerusalem:
A **he brings the exiles home.**

He heals all those with broken hearts:
B **he bandages their wounds.**

He counts the number of the stars:
C **he calls them each by name.**

How great and mighty is the Lord:
A **immeasurably wise!**

He raises up the humble ones:
B **and brings the mighty down.**

Sing hymns of triumph to his name:
C **make music to our God!**

He spreads the clouds across the sky:
A **he showers the earth with rain.**

He sends the animals their food:
B **he feeds the hungry birds.**

His true delight is not the strong:
C **but those who trust his love.**

Extol the Lord, Jerusalem:
A **let Zion worship God!**

For God shall keep your people safe:
B **and bring your harvest home.**

He gives commandment to the earth:
C **his will is quickly done.**

He spreads like wool the falling snow:
A **how cold the frosty air!**

He sends the wind, the warming rain:
B **and melts the ice away.**

His laws he gives to Israel:
C **and Judah hears his word.**

He does not favour other lands:
ALL **so, praise the Lord. Amen!**

The congregation may divide at A, B *and* C.

148L Psalm 148.1–14

Praise the Lord!

Praise the Lord from the heavens:
praise him in the heights above.

Praise him, all his angels:
A **praise him, all his heavenly host.**

Praise him, sun and moon:
B **praise him, all you shining stars.**

Let them praise the name of the Lord:
ALL **Praise the Lord!**

Praise the Lord from the earth:
A **praise him, great sea creatures.**

Praise him, storms and clouds:
B **praise him, mountains and hills.**

Praise him, fields and woods:
A **praise him, animals and birds.**

Praise him, rulers and nations:
B **praise him, old and young.**

Let them praise the name of the Lord:
ALL **Praise the Lord! Amen.**

The congregation may divide at A *and* B.

149L Psalm 149.1–9

Praise the Lord:
praise the Lord!

Sing a new song to the Lord:
A **let the people shout his name!**

Praise your maker, Israel:
B **hail your king, Jerusalem.**

Sing and dance to honour him:
A **praise him with the strings and drums.**

God takes pleasure in his saints:
B **crowns the meek with victory.**

Rise, you saints, in triumph now:
A **sing the joyful night away!**

Shout aloud and praise your God!
B **Hold aloft the two-edged sword!**

Let the judgement now begin:
A **kings shall fall and tyrants die.**

Through his people, by his word:
B **God shall have the victory!**

Praise the Lord:
ALL **praise the Lord!**

Glory to the Father, and to the Son,
and to the Holy Spirit:
as it was in the beginning, is now,
and shall be for ever. Amen.

The congregation – and ministers – may divide at A *and* B.

150L 150.1–6

Praise the Lord!

Praise God in his sanctuary:
praise his strength beyond the skies!

Praise him for his acts of power:
A **praise him for his surpassing greatness.**

Praise him with the sounding of the trumpet:
B **praise him with the harp and lyre.**

Praise him with tambourine and dancing:
A **praise him with the strings and flute.**

Praise him with the clash of cymbals:
B **praise him with resounding cymbals.**

Let everything that has breath praise the Lord:
ALL **Praise the Lord! Amen.**

Glory to the Father, and to the Son,
and to the Holy Spirit:
as it was in the beginning, is now,
and shall be for ever. Amen.

The congregation may divide at A *and* B.

Legal Information, Notes and Acknowledgements

Psalms and Liturgical Texts

Those seeking to reprint material in this book which is the property of Jubilate Hymns or associated authors (attributed '/Jubilate Hymns') may write to The Copyright Secretary, Jubilate Hymns Ltd, 61 Chessel Avenue, Southampton SO2 4DY. In the United States of America these copyrights and those of Timothy Dudley-Smith are administered by Hope Publishing Company, Carol Stream, Illinois 60188. Addresses of other copyright-holders can also be supplied.

Jubilate Hymns, Marshall Pickering Communications, Scripture Union, Thankyou Music, Word (UK) Ltd – along with other copyright-holders whose titles they administer (Celebration Services, Maranatha!, Word & Music etc.) have uniform concessions and rates. Details are available from the Copyright Secretary, Jubilate Hymns Ltd.

Most of these publishers also combine to offer a licensing scheme for limited term reproduction. Where this is felt to be an advantage, application should be made to the Christian Music Association at Glyndley Manor, Stone Cross, Pevensey, East Sussex BN24 5BS (0323 440440).

Liturgical (Responsive) Psalms

These texts are the copyright of the Editor, and are available for local reproduction subject to acknowledgement of source in the form 'Reprinted from *Songs from the Psalms* with the permission of Jubilate Hymns Ltd' (or, in the USA, ' . . . of Hope Publishing Company, Carol Stream, Illinois 60188').

Recording and Broadcasting

Jubilate Hymns and associated authors, and Word & Music are members of the Mechanical Copyright Protection and Performing Right Societies.

Acknowledgements

We owe our thanks most particularly to those authors and composers who readily created or adapted their work to meet the need for fluent and congregational texts and music settings of quality and relative simplicity. We mention especially those to whom we turned time and again for help and support: Christopher Norton and Chris Rolinson.

For application of her special expertise to the text of the liturgical (responsive) psalms we thank Rev. Dr. Kathleen Bowe of Cliff College.

For the major task of copyright clearance and assistance in preparing the work for publication we thank Bunty Grundy of Jubilate Hymns. For their encouragement and professionalism we acknowledge the contribution of publishers and typesetters – especially Hodder and Stoughton's Dick Douglas and Kathy Dyke, and Barnes' Michael Mack Smith.

Michael Perry (Editor)
David Peacock (Music Editor)

Chord Chart

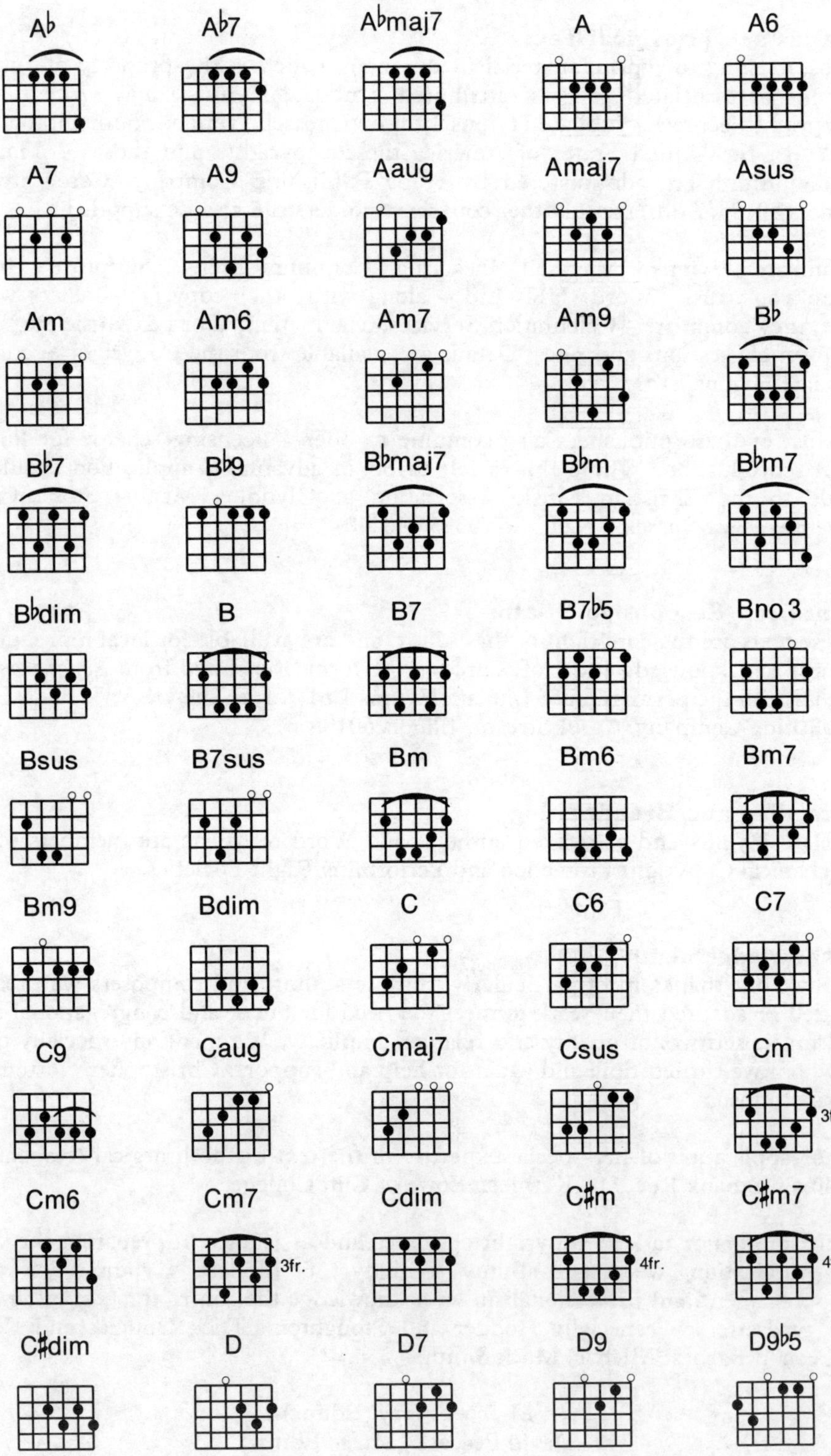

A♭ A♭7 A♭maj7 A A6

A7 A9 Aaug Amaj7 Asus

Am Am6 Am7 Am9 B♭

B♭7 B♭9 B♭maj7 B♭m B♭m7

B♭dim B B7 B7♭5 Bno 3

Bsus B7sus Bm Bm6 Bm7

Bm9 Bdim C C6 C7

C9 Caug Cmaj7 Csus Cm 3fr.

Cm6 Cm7 3fr. Cdim C♯m 4fr. C♯m7 4fr.

C♯dim D D7 D9 D9♭5

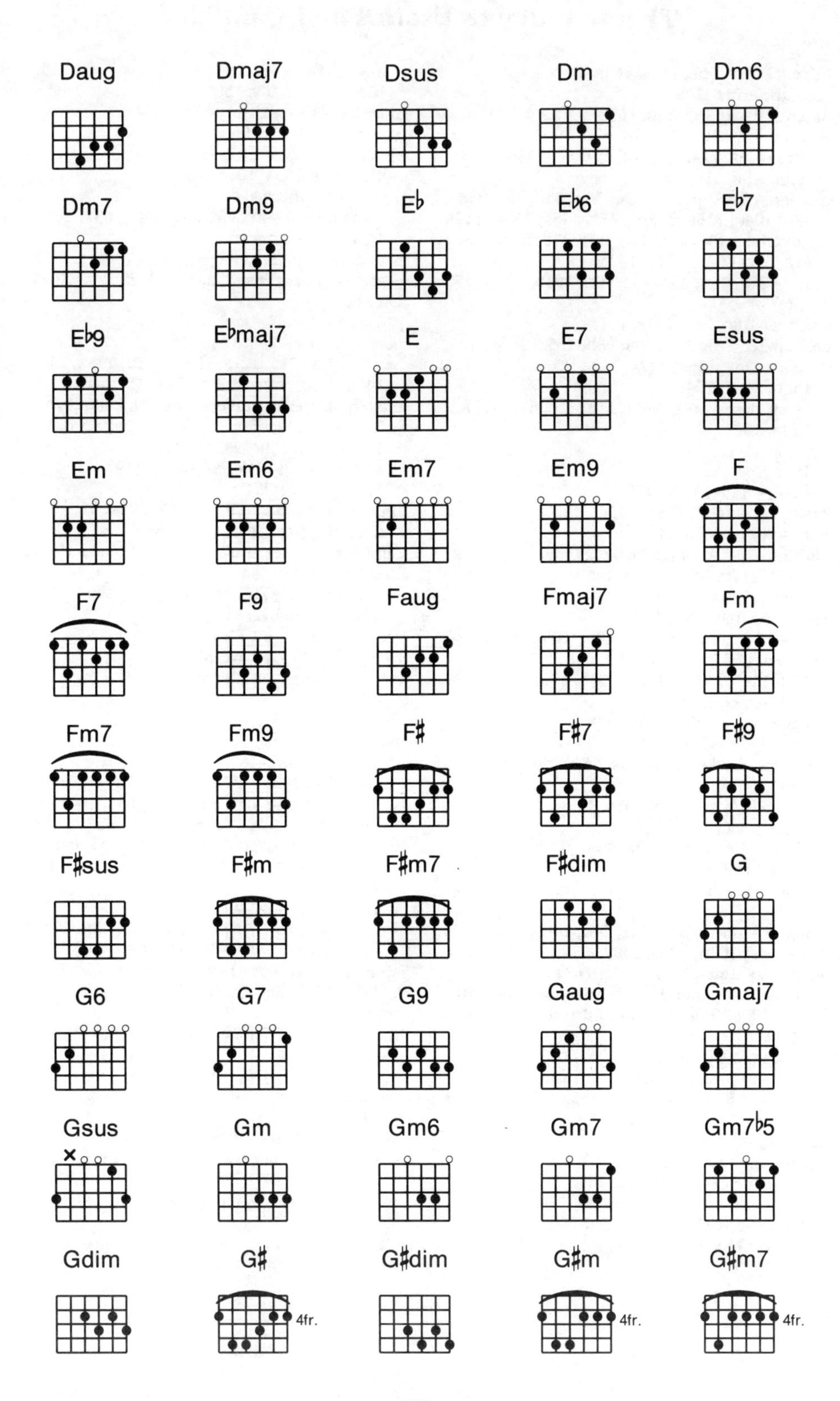
Daug
Dmaj7
Dsus
Dm
Dm6
Dm7
Dm9
E♭
E♭6
E♭7
E♭9
E♭maj7
E
E7
Esus
Em
Em6
Em7
Em9
F
F7
F9
Faug
Fmaj7
Fm
Fm7
Fm9
F♯
F♯7
F♯9
F♯sus
F♯m
F♯m7
F♯dim
G
G6
G7
G9
Gaug
Gmaj7
Gsus
Gm
Gm6
Gm7
Gm7♭5
Gdim
G♯
4fr.
G♯dim
G♯m
4fr.
G♯m7
4fr.

Theme Index to Psalms and Canticles

Index to Settings Suitable for SATB Singing

Index to Psalms with Descants and other Vocal Arrangements

Index to Settings Suitable as Vocal Solos or with Solo Sections

Index to Psalms Suitable for Solo/Group/Choir and Congregation

Although not stated on each setting, this use of items has immediate appeal and facilitates the learning of new psalms.

Index to Psalms Set to Existing Melodies

Psalms Set in Antiphon Style

Rounds and Canons

Index to Settings in Response Style or with Response Sections

Index to Psalms with Instrumental Parts

Index of First Lines